Campbell's
Physiology Notes

Campbell's
Physiology Notes

John Campbell

RN (Adult) RN (Mental Health) DipN BSc MSc PGCPharm Cert Ed CNT NT
Senior Lecturer in Nursing Studies, University of Cumbria, Carlisle Campus.

Lorimer Publications
CARLISLE

© 2009 Lorimer Publications
Revised and reprinted 2011

First published in 2009 by Lorimer Publications, Carlisle, Cumbria, U.K.

A catalogue record for this book is available from the British Library

ISBN 978-0-9553797-2-7

Further copies of this publication and other learning resources can be ordered from: orders@campbellteaching.co.uk
also available from Teaching Aids At Low Cost;

Lesson notes and other free resources may be downloaded from:
www.campbellteaching.co.uk

Printed in Great Britain by Bell and Bain Ltd, Glasgow

Contents

Acknowledgements

This book would not have been possible without the technical support I have generously received from Edward Knapper and Jonathan Forsyth. They have been responsible for the organisation of the diagrams and text. I am also very grateful to my proof readers, they have read the text several times to iron out my many errors in the original writing. These people include Anita Beattie, Ken Lowe, Carol Green, Barbara Bishop, Caroline Dixon, Christine Campbell and Ed Knapper.

I have also enjoyed ongoing support and encouragement from my long term friends and colleagues Cath Boyes and Jean Longrigg. My family, Christine, James and Timothy have been central to all of my writing and I realise it has meant there were often times when I was not there.

Introduction

Welcome to these physiology notes. My name is John Campbell and I work at the University of Cumbria as a Nurse Lecturer. Before entering Nurse Education I gained experience in several fields of nursing including psychiatry, theatres, neuromedicine, tropical medicine and ITU. I still carry out clinical work in various areas.

I am convinced that everyone who works in a clinical environment needs a working knowledge of the normal functioning of the human body. It is only when we understand the normal that the abnormal pathological situation makes any sense. If we can understand how the body goes wrong then it often becomes obvious what needs to be done to treat a disorder. So physiology and pathophysiology can both be used to inform our clinical interventions and provide us with rationales for care. This provides us with more accountability for clinical practice, optimises interventions and makes us more informed and knowledgeable practitioners.

I originally wrote these notes as a revision guide for my students and because they proved useful I decided to expand and publish. The aim is to keep the text concise but to explain the physiology and necessary basic science in a way that is easy to understand and can be learned. Diagrams are an important part of this philosophy. When I first discussed the book with my publisher we thought about getting the diagrams professionally drawn, but rather than producing beautiful pictures we decided that I would draw the diagrams myself, as I draw them for my students. If the diagrams are kept simple in this way they too may be learned. Learning to draw diagrams takes practice but in the end it really helps us to understand the physiology. You may also find it helpful to colour some of the diagrams.

Physiology is a complicated subject and is not easy to learn, the terminology alone is like learning a foreign language. But, if you stick at it and work through the book, both you and your patients will benefit for the rest of your career.

With best wishes,
John Campbell
Carlisle 2011

CHAPTER 1

Cells, Tissues and Bodies

Introduction

Before we get down to some really interesting physiology it may be useful to define a few terms. Physiology is the study of the normal function of a biological system, in this case the human body. Anatomy is the study of normal structure. Inevitably, in order to understand physiology we must also learn some anatomy. Histology is the study of tissues and cytology the study of cells. Biochemistry is the study of the chemistry of living things; most of this chemistry takes place within individual cells. Pathology is the study of abnormal anatomy and pathophysiology means the study of abnormal body function. Histopathology studies abnormalities found in tissues. Psychology studies the normal processes of the mind. Psychiatry is the study of the abnormal mind.

Cells, tissues and organisation

The body is a remarkably complex structure which performs thousands of physiological functions. This means that the structures of the body must be organised in a precise way to carry out these functions. The functional systems of the body, such as the nervous or digestive systems, are themselves made up

BODY
BODY SYSTEMS
ORGANS AND LARGE STRUCTURES
GROUPS OF TISSUES
TISSUES
GROUPS OF CELLS AND STRUCTURAL MATERIAL
INDIVIDUAL CELLS
CELL ORGANELLES
LARGE BIOMOLECULES
SMALL ORGANIC MOLECULES
ATOMS
ELECTRONS, NEUTRONS AND PROTONS

Table 1.1
The body is very highly organised on a number of levels. This table indicates the hierarchy of this organisation, starting with the largest and working down to the smallest.

of organs such as the brain or stomach. Organs in turn are composed of precise arrangements of groups of tissues. A tissue is a group of similar cells, often with associated additional structural material produced and secreted by the tissue cells. Cells which compose a particular tissue are themselves composed of smaller functional units called cell organelles. These organelles can be thought of as the 'organs' of a cell as they perform specialised intracellular functions. Cell organelles are made up of highly structured biomolecules such as proteins, carbohydrates and fats. Large biological molecules are made up of smaller organic compounds. (Organic simply means that the molecule contains some carbon.) The organic molecules are composed of structured arrangements of atoms, which are composed of protons, neutrons and electrons.

Cell organelles

Cells may be considered as the 'units of life'. This means that many of the processes essential for life are carried out inside cells. Cytology is the term used to describe the study of cells. A single cell may be considered to be 'alive'. Some simple organisms such as the amoeba are composed of a single cell. However, in humans billions of cells combine to make up the body. As cells are only 5-10 micrometres (a micrometre is one thousandth of a millimetre) in size they can only be seen with the aid of microscopes. Under a light microscope a cell has a dark staining central region called the nucleus with a clear area surrounding this, referred to as cytoplasm. These components are all surrounded by a cell membrane which encloses the cell.

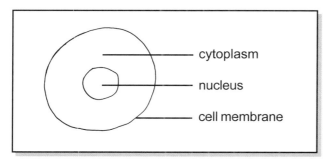

Diagram 1.1
Diagram of a cell as viewed under a light microscope
with a magnification of about 300 times.

However, when cells are examined under the higher power of an electron microscope the organelles may be seen. These are sub units or components of the cell. In the same way that a body is made up of organs a cell is composed of organelles. Organelles are structures within the cytoplasm which perform specific functions. They are the functional units of a cell.

Cell Membrane

This is a very thin membrane which surrounds the outside and marks the boundary of the cell. The cell membrane is composed of a combination of lipids, phosphates and proteins. Because the cell membrane is composed of two layers of phospholipid molecules it is referred to as a phospholipid bilayer. A phospholipid molecule is made up of a combination of phosphate and fatty acids. Cell membranes also contain some cholesterol. The external cell membrane compartmentalises the cell and controls movement of fluid and other substances in and out. This regulatory function means the cell is able to control, to a degree, its own internal environment.

Some of the proteins in the cell membrane are referred to as transmembrane proteins. This means they span the membrane and have ends in the external tissue fluid and internal cytosol. Some of these proteins regulate the passage of substances into and out of a cell. For example, some transmembrane proteins act as tunnels to allow glucose molecules from the tissue fluid into the cytosol. Other membrane bound proteins act as receptors. These specialised receptor protein molecules allow the cell to recognise chemical messages from other cells or from endocrine glands. Once a receptor has detected the presence of a particular chemical messenger this will initiate some physiological change within the cell. As a result cells do not function in isolation but as co-ordinated and disciplined components of the whole body.

Cytosol

Cytosol is the fluid found in the cytoplasm of the cell; it is the intracellular fluid. Cytosol is mostly water with some additional dissolved and suspended molecules, the combination of which is referred to as a colloid. Organelles are suspended within the cytosol and much of the water in the body is located in the cytosol. Many biochemical reactions occur in the cytosol such as the initial processing of glucose in the production of energy and the synthesis of fatty acids.

Cytoskeleton

Microfilaments and microtubules are composed of proteins and extend throughout the cytosol. Collectively these structures form an internal 'skeleton' within a cell referred to as the cytoskeleton. The cytoskeleton provides structural support and strength for a cell and helps to maintain overall shape. Cell movement is also facilitated by the cytoskeleton. This is necessary during the early embryonic development of the body where cells must migrate into the correct positions. Movement is also important for muscle contraction and the movement of white blood cells to combat infection.

Endoplasmic reticulum (ER)

This is an extensive network of flattened interconnected channels and tubules distributed throughout the cytoplasm. Endoplasmic reticulum is itself bounded by membranes. The function of this extensive structure is to move materials around inside the cell, i.e. intracellular translocation. As different organelles within a cell perform different functions, particular substances will be required in specific locations. In this sense the ER is analogous to a road or rail network, delivering raw materials and transporting away finished products. In addition the ER provides support for the overall structure and shape of the cell. The ribosomes are often associated with the endoplasmic reticulum. If an area of ER is associated with ribosomes it is described as rough ER, areas without associated ribosomes are termed smooth.

Ribosomes

These are small dark staining organelles. They are often associated with rough endoplasmic reticulum but free ribosomes may be found anywhere in the cytoplasm. Rough endoplasmic reticulum is described as 'rough' because it is studded with ribosomes. Ribosomes receive genetic instructions from the DNA (deoxyribonucleic acid) in the nucleus of the cell. This information is then transferred to molecules of RNA (ribonucleic acid) which then string together long chains of amino acids to form polypeptides and proteins. Amino acids are subunits of proteins in the same way that bricks are subunits of a wall. Ribosomes are therefore the site of protein synthesis, in essence they are little protein factories. Some of the synthesised proteins are used to form the structures of the individual cell and others are exported from the cell. It is logical that the ribosomes are usually associated with the ER so that they can be supplied with amino acids which are the building blocks of proteins. Synthesized proteins can then be removed to where they are required.

Golgi complex

This is an arrangement of membranes which are responsible for the export of products from a cell. Products from the ER are transported to the Golgi where some further molecular modifications often take place. Once the fat or protein based product is ready, so called secretory vesicles bud off the main Golgi complex and transport the material to the external cell membrane for export. For example, some cells in the digestive system secrete digestive enzymes in this way. Endocrine cells secrete endocrine hormones and liver cells secrete plasma proteins.

Mitochondria

All living cells must be able to produce energy to fuel physiological processes. When a cell is no longer able to produce energy it will quickly die. Mitochondria are usually sausage shaped and have an outer membrane and a highly enfolded inner membrane. This enfolded inner membrane provides a large surface area for the location of enzymes responsible for generation of energy within a cell. These enzymes produce energy by using oxygen to oxidise or 'burn' fuels such as glucose or fatty acids. The energy actually comes from breaking the chemical bonds which hold together the fuel molecule. All of the fuel required for energy production derives from food and all of the oxygen from breathing. Mitochondria are therefore the site of all energy production and are sometimes referred to as the 'power house' of the cell. Cells which use a lot of energy, such as those in muscles, have a lot of mitochondria in their cytoplasm whereas cells which need less energy, such as those which compose the skin, have fewer mitochondria. Cyanide is such a fast acting poison because it halts the process of energy production in mitochondria. Interestingly, mitochondria also contain some DNA. This mitochondrial DNA is only passed on through the maternal line, i.e. from mothers to daughters or from mothers to sons.

Lysosomes

Lysosomes are organelles surrounded by the typical membrane bilayer and contain a variety of digestive enzymes such as lysozyme. They are formed by breaking away from the Golgi apparatus and then dispersing throughout the cytosol. Lysosomes are used in the process of intracellular digestion, i.e. digestion within the cell. Digestive enzymes in the lysosomes break up large complex molecules into smaller ones using the process of hydrolysis. These hydrolysing type of enzyme split large molecules up by adding hydrogen and oxygen. This process of intracellular digestion may digest material from outside the cell. For example, in white blood cells foreign material is ingested by the cell, lysosomes approach the foreign material and spill their digestive enzymes onto it, therefore digesting it. Lysosomes are therefore essential for the process of phagocytosis, a term which literally means 'cell eating'.

In addition to this digestion of extracellular material, lysosomes may also digest intracellular material, i.e. material derived from within the cell itself. As cells need constant maintenance, new components and organelles are constantly being formed meaning old ones need to be removed. Unwanted cellular organelles and biomolecules are digested by lysosomal enzymes in the process of autophagy. Lysosomes may also burst to digest a whole cell which is unwanted by the body in a form of cell suicide called apoptosis.

Peroxisomes

These organelles have a similar appearance to lysosomes but are smaller. Peroxisomes contain enzymes, including hydrogen peroxide, which work by oxidizing toxic substances. If these toxins were not oxidized they would build up to poisonous concentrations within cells. For example, about half the alcohol a person might drink is detoxified by peroxisomes in liver cells.

Nucleus

The nucleus is located at the centre of the cell inside the cytoplasm. There is a separate membrane surrounding the nucleus referred to as the nuclear membrane. Within the nucleus are the chromosomes. All human cells, (at least at some time in their lives) contain 46 of these bodies arranged in 23 pairs. Chromosomes contain the genes which are the genetic information responsible for making and controlling the cell. This is why the nucleus is sometimes referred to as the 'control centre' of the cell.

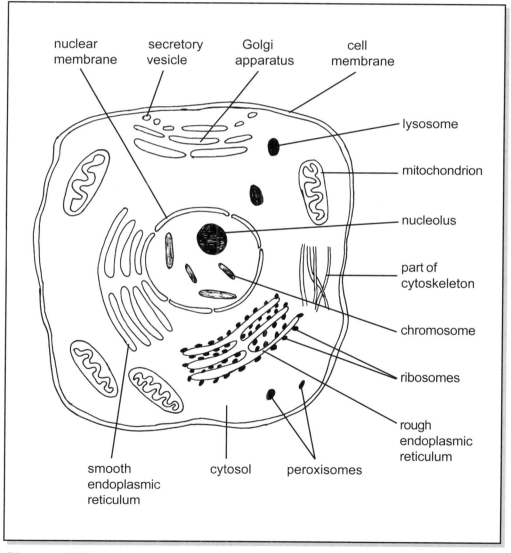

Diagram 1.2
Cell viewed under an electron microscope.

Chromosomes

The term chromosome literally means coloured body. The chromosomes are composed of structural proteins and DNA (Deoxyribonucleic Acid). Genes are part of the chromosomes and are composed of DNA strands. Genes contain the genetic information to create the cell and therefore ultimately to generate the body.

Nucleolus

A nucleolus is a cluster of DNA, RNA and protein within the nucleus. These are the same type of molecules found in the ribosomes. DNA carries the genetic code which is transcribed to form information carrying RNA molecules. This RNA is then used in the synthesis of protein which will form part of the ribosomes. Once formed these ribosomal proteins migrate out into the cytoplasm to form the ribosomes. During periods of increased protein synthesis the nucleoli increase in size. They are also prominent in liver and muscle cells which synthesise large amounts of protein.

Specialised cells

During growth and development cells differentiate into specific types which allows them to perform particular functions. This differentiation is initiated and regulated by genetic instructions from the genes which carry all of the required information. Different cells must have a specialised structure which results in the production of many completely different types of cell. It is this process of cell specialisation which is referred to as differentiation. Specialised cells are required to form the different types of tissue needed to construct the large structures and organs of the body. Different types of cells include nerve cells or neurones, muscle cells, liver cells, blood cells and epithelial cells. Each cell has a structure and function specific to the role that a cell or tissue is required to perform in the body. Groups of similar cells compose tissues. Groups of tissues compose organs and groups of organs compose the systems of the body.

Cell reproduction

All cells are derived from parent cells which underwent a process of cell division. In this process one parent cell grows then divides into two daughter cells. There are only two forms of cell division, referred to as mitosis and meiosis.

Mitosis

Mitosis is often described as 'simple' cell division. During the non-dividing phase of the cell cycle a new, duplicate, set of 46 chromosomes is produced. Each gene is precisely copied to make an exact copy of the original. During mitosis one complete set of chromosomes migrates to each end of the cell. This parent cell then divides into two daughter cells each also containing 46 chromosomes. Because the daughter cells and the parent cell all contain the same number of chromosomes this form of cell division is sometimes referred to as conservation cell division (the number of chromosomes is conserved). The group of descendent cells from a parent cell is described as a cell line.

Mitosis is the type of cell division that occurs when the body grows from a zygote, which is a single fertilised cell, into a baby. It is also the form of cell division which generates new tissue in the process of wound healing. In addition ongoing mitosis maintains the health of most body tissues by replacing old cells with new ones. Because mitosis is the type of cell division that goes on in the body it is sometimes referred to as somatic cell division (soma means body).

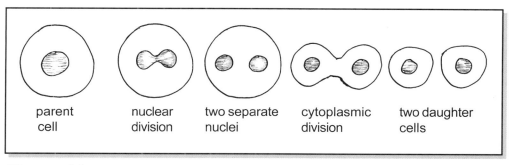

Diagram 1.3
The stages of mitosis in order.

Diagram 1.4
The principle of conservation cell division. A parent cell with 46 chromosomes mitotically divides to produce two daughter cells also with 46 chromosomes. After formation

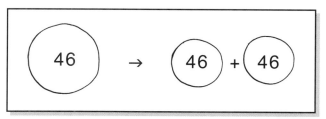

the daughter cells will usually grow until they become the same size as the parent cell.

Meiosis

The other form of cell division is called meiosis and is only used in the production of gametes which are the male sperm and female ova. The function of sperm and ova is to fuse together, forming fertilised cells. Such a fertilised cell is called a zygote. Once formed, a zygote undergoes repeated mitosis to form a new body. If the sperm and ovum each contained 46 chromosomes then the zygote, and hence the new baby, would contain 92 chromosomes. To prevent this increase in chromosome number the sperm and ovum are produced by meiosis which is a reduction cell division. During meiosis the daughter cell (always a sperm or ovum) only receives one from each pair of chromosomes, leaving each sperm or ovum with 23 chromosomes. This means the zygote receives 23 chromosomes from the ovum and 23 from the sperm to give it a full complement of 46. Gametes are produced from germ cells which are only located in the testes and ovaries.

Diagram 1.5
Meiosis; the number of chromosomes is reduced from 46 to 23 per cell.

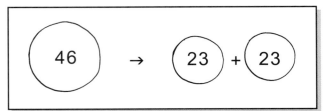

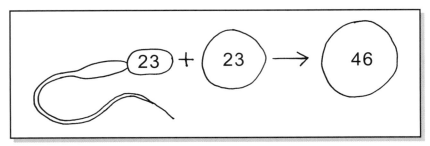

Diagram 1.6
During fertilisation the sperm and the ovum combine to produce a zygote with 46 chromosomes.

Cells and ageing

It seems that many cells have a limited number of times they can divide. Many of these permissible cell divisions take place between the formation of the zygote and the birth of the individual. This means in childhood and adult life only a limited number of further cell divisions are possible. When this number has occurred the cells are not capable of further divisions which results in death of the cell line. If the number of viable cells in a tissue is reduced the result will be that the tissue as a whole deteriorates. As the body is composed of tissue, deterioration in tissues results in the changes in the body we associate with ageing. Ultimately tissues become so non-viable that they fail to perform essential physiological functions, possibly resulting in the death of the individual. For example, the tissues in the wall of a blood vessel may fail resulting in haemorrhage.

As cells age there may also be mistakes in the process of cell division. For example, mutation can occur as a result of a mistake in the production of a new gene or chromosome as a cell divides. The term mutation means a change in a gene or chromosome. This is analogous to copying out a page of writing

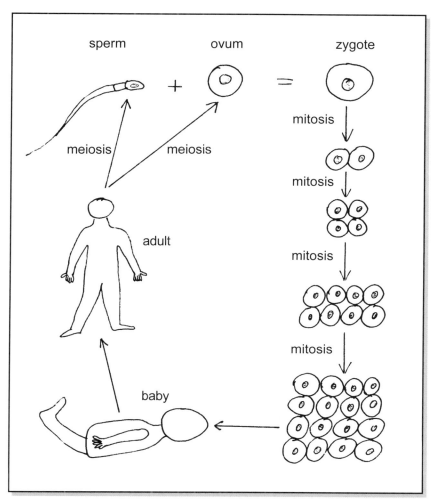

Diagram 1.7
Human life cycle. A male gamete fertilises a female gamete to form a zygote. This divides by the process of mitosis eventually forming a full term baby. After birth there is further mitosis resulting in the growth of the baby, through childhood, into adulthood. The adult then produces gametes, by the process of meiosis, to start the next generation.

and misspelling or missing out some words. The accumulation of these errors in the genetic material of the cell may be one reason why many cancers are more common in older people than in younger people.

Another possible reason why cells age is free radical theory. A free radical is a very reactive form of oxygen which can oxidise and so damage cellular proteins. If free radicals attack the DNA of the genes this may result in age related changes and sometimes mutations which can lead to cancer. While some free radicals are produced as a result of normal metabolic processes, increased numbers may be generated as a result of over eating, exposure to radiation or exposure to polluting chemicals. Some vitamins and other components in fruit and vegetables called flavanoids, inhibit the activity of free radicals and so may slow down cell ageing. This is one reason everyone is advised to eat at least five portions of fruit and vegetables per day.

As people age the rate of mitosis and tissue repair is also reduced as there is a generalised slowing in the rate of metabolic activity. This is one reason why wounds heal much faster in children than in the elderly.

Essential science - the pH scale

To measure how acid or alkaline a solution is the pH scale is used. This is a scale which goes from 1-14. A strong acid such as sulphuric or hydrochloric acid has a pH of 1. Pure water is neutral, it is not acid or alkaline, so it has a pH of 7. A strong alkaline such as sodium hydroxide or ammonium hydroxide has a pH of 14. So the lower the number under 7 the stronger the acid, and the higher the number above 7 the stronger the alkaline.

Cells and enzymes

A cell is essentially a very complex chemical and molecular machine. A wide range of biochemistry is going on in the cell throughout its life span. In order to control the function of the cell it is therefore necessary to control the chemistry of the cell. All intracellular biochemistry is controlled by enzymes. An enzyme is a biochemical catalyst. A catalyst is something which facilitates or speeds up the rate of a chemical reaction without being used up in the reaction itself. The names of enzymes usually end in 'ase', for example, lipase, amylase, creatine kinase and alcohol dehydrogenase.

Each chemical process is catalysed by a specific enzyme. If this enzyme is absent, the particular chemical reaction cannot proceed. Each enzyme is synthesised from the genetic information carried by a specific gene. Enzymes are complex proteins formed into a particular shape; it is because of this complexity that they require specific conditions in order to function. For example, enzymes are specific to a particular range of temperature and pH. A rise in body temperature of one or two degrees is enough to make a person feel very unwell and a rise of six or seven degrees can be life threatening. Even relatively small changes to blood pH are life threatening. If body temperature rises beyond certain levels or there is a change in pH, the physical shape of some enzymes will be altered. As a result they will no longer be able to efficiently catalyse some cell biochemistry; this in turn will lead to interference with the physiology of the cell, and will ultimately lead to cell death.

Metabolism

There are basically two classifications of biochemical reactions taking place within cells. Some reactions build smaller molecules up into bigger ones; these are referred to as anabolic reactions. For example, individual amino acid units can be chemically combined to produce a large protein molecule. Other reactions break larger molecules down into smaller ones, these are catabolic reactions. For example, fatty acids and glucose are broken down in the mitochondria into water and carbon dioxide. Metabolism is a term which describes all of the chemical reactions occurring within the cells, including anabolism and catabolism.

Tissues

The study of tissues is referred to as histology. All of the tissues in the body can be classified under one of four headings. These are the four principal types of tissue: epithelial, connective, muscle, and nervous.

Epithelial tissue

Epithelium describes any tissues which line or cover other structures. The internal and external surfaces of the body are lined with epithelial tissues. Epithelial tissues are composed of fairly tightly packed cells which are arranged on a thin sheet of fibrous tissue referred to as a basement membrane. The two main types of epithelium are simple and stratified.

A simple epithelium is one in which each individual cell is in contact with the basement membrane. This means simple epithelium is only one cell layer thick. There are different forms of simple epithelium which are described according to the shape of the cells. Squamous epithelial cells are flat in shape and so form a very smooth surface. This is important in the lining of blood vessels to allow a smooth flow of blood throughout the circulatory system. If the internal linings were uneven this would lead to turbulent blood flow making clot formation more likely. Cuboidal epithelial cells are cube shaped cells and are found in nephrons and various endocrine glands. Columnar epithelial cells are rectangular or column shaped and line such structures as the gastrointestinal tract. In the respiratory tract the columnar simple epithelium lining the airways has small hair-like structures called cilia. These help to waft mucus from the smaller airways towards the trachea. If cilia are present the lining is referred to as a ciliated epithelium.

A stratified epithelium is one in which some layers of cells are not in contact with the basement membrane so the epithelium consists of various strata (or layers) of cells. Different forms of stratified epithelium again may be made up of different types of cells, for example, stratified squamous epithelium consists of layers of flat shaped cells. In a cuboidal stratified epithelium there are several layers of cuboidal cells. In several stratified tissues the cells start off as cuboidal but become flattened by external pressures as they get nearer the surface.

Diagram 1.8
Four forms of simple epithelium; squamous, cuboidal, columnar and ciliated. Each epithelial layer is one cell thick and is located on a basement membrane.

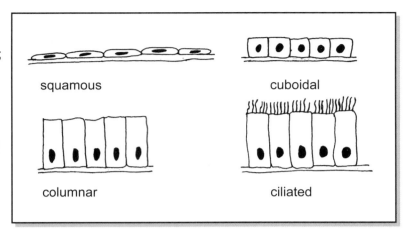

Stratified epithelium is found lining surfaces which are subject to a degree of wear and tear. For example, the mouth is lined with stratified squamous epithelium. This means that during the relative trauma of chewing food, some of the surface cells may be sloughed away from the epithelium without disturbing the overall integrity of the lining. Similar epithelia line the vagina and oesophagus.

Some forms of stratified epithelium are keratinised and stratified. These occur on dry surfaces such as the skin that are subject to wear and tear. Keratin is a protein which is resistant to wear and is waterproof; it also acts as a barrier to the passage of bacteria.

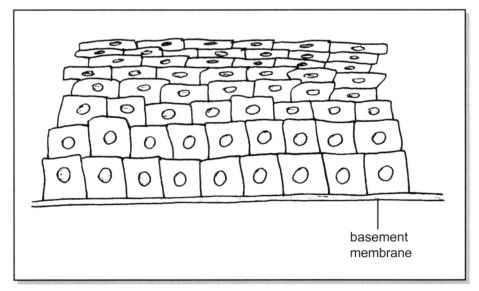

Diagram 1.9
Stratified epithelium; several layers of cells on a basement membrane.

Another form of stratified epithelium is referred to as transitional. This is composed of pear shaped cells and is designed to allow the epithelium to stretch. It is found lining structures which need to alter their size such as the urinary bladder and urethra.

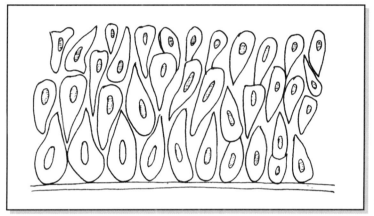

Diagram 1.10
Transitional epithelium.

Connective tissue

There are different types of connective tissues. Usually they contain fewer cells than epithelium but contain more strong and elastic components to give the connective tissues firm structural properties. For example, white fibrous tissue is a strong connector composed of bundles of collagen fibres with a few fibroblasts included in the tissue. Collagen is a protein formed into bundles which have great tensile strength. They are analogous to ropes or cables and give tissue integrity and strength. This is why it is difficult to tear tissues. Fibroblasts are cells which produce the collagen protein.

The spaces between the cells and fibres in connective tissue are filled with ground substance, also sometimes referred to as the matrix. Ground substance is also produced by the fibroblasts and consists of water and glycoproteins. A glycoprotein is a large molecule made from a combination of protein and carbohydrate.

White fibrous tissue composes ligaments and periosteum (ligaments link bone to bone and periosteum surrounds the bones). As ligaments link bones together, it is therefore white fibrous tissue which is largely responsible for holding the body together and keeping the bones in the correct positions relative to each other.

Elastic connective tissue is usually yellowish and stretchy. It is composed mostly of interlinking elastic fibres. Within the tissue are found fibroblasts, these are the cells which produce the elastic fibres. Like collagen, the elastic fibres are made up of a protein, but in elastic fibres the protein is called elastin. Elastin is found in such structures as the walls of blood vessels, lungs, the

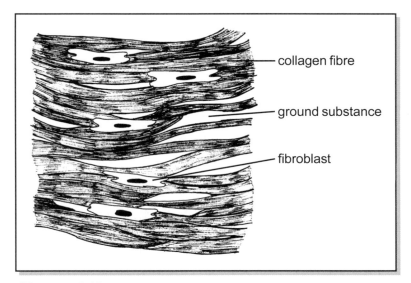

Diagram 1.11
Histology of white fibrous tissue.

epiglottis and the ear lobes. The skin is also elastic due to the presence of elastic fibres. If you pinch up an area of skin and let it go, it quickly returns to its original shape because it is elastic.

In the case of blood vessels the elastic nature of the walls allows expansion when a pulse of blood is flowing through the vessel. However, when there is no pulse of blood the vessel wall will recoil becoming smaller again. This will maintain the blood pressure until the next pulse, smoothing out the blood flow. This effect maintains a more constant blood supply to tissues than an intermittent pulsed supply would provide. In the lungs the elastic nature of the tissue allows expansion during inspiration and aids the process of expiration by recoiling again. The recoiling of the air sacs increases the pressure of the air they contain and helps to 'blow' it out of the lungs.

Loose connective tissue is another common connector and is made up of a combination of elastic and collagen fibres. Again the tissue contains fibroblasts which produce the fibres. Loose connective tissue is found in areas of the body where tensile strength and elasticity are needed together. It is found underneath the skin and between muscle fibres where strength and elasticity are needed in combination. Some texts refer to loose connective tissue as areolar tissue.

Adipose tissue is also classified as a connective tissue and composes the fat of the body. It is found under the skin where it acts as a padding to protect underlying structures. This is one reason it hurts so much when you knock your shin; there is no fat lying over the bone to help protect it from trauma. Subcutaneous fat also gives insulation against the cold. Women store more fat under the skin than men giving their limbs a more rounded appearance. Men store excess fat in the abdomen giving the characteristic 'beer belly' appearance

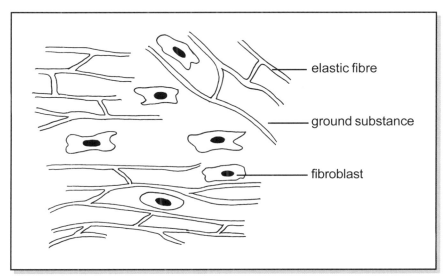

Diagram 1.12
Histology of elastic tissue.

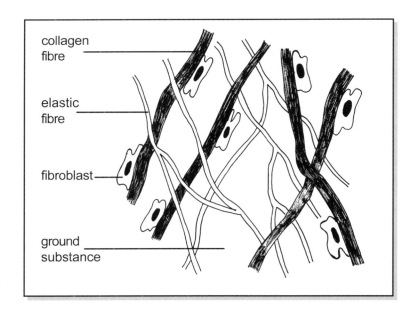

Diagram 1.13
Histology of loose
connective tissue.

in obesity. Adipose tissue is also used to protect organs, for example the kidneys are embedded in a thick layer of fat. As fat is a fuel it also provides an energy reserve. Individual fat cells are called adipocytes and may take up or release fat depending on the food intake and metabolic requirements of the body. Each individual cell stores fat in a large central area called a vacuole. Adipose tissue also contains some collagen based reticular fibres to give it structure and some strength. Reticular or reticulum means to do with a network.

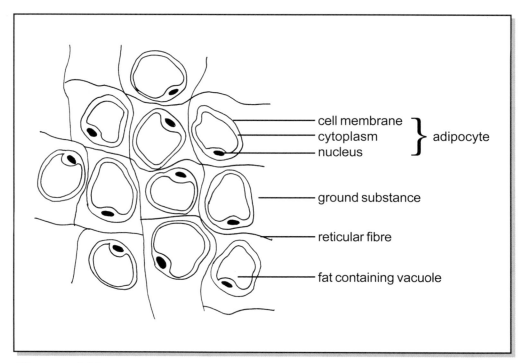

Diagram 1.14
Histology of adipose tissue.

Lymphoid tissue is also classified as a connective tissue. It is composed of a network of connective tissues termed a reticulum. These reticular fibres are very fine and composed mostly of collagen. Within this framework there are large numbers of immunologically active cells such as lymphocytes and monocytes. The main function of the lymphoid tissue is therefore to protect the body against the threat of infection. The lymph nodes, spleen, tonsils and part of the appendix are made out of lymphoid tissue.

Cartilage is a connective tissue which performs such functions as joining the ribs to the sternum and is also found between the vertebrae. Articular cartilage lines joint surfaces to give a smooth, hard, low friction surface between bones. Like other connective tissues cartilage is composed mostly of connective tissue fibres made of collagen. The ground substance is hard but flexible consisting of water, some collagen and some specialised large protein based molecules. The cells in cartilage which produce the collagen and ground substance are also found within the tissue and are called chondrocytes.

Osseous tissue is described as a connective tissue and is another name for bone. Bone is hard in order to give the body a supportive framework. It also protects soft underlying structures such as the heart, lungs and brain. The basic structure of bone is similar to the other forms of connective tissue. It contains tough strong collagen fibres and cells which produce them. The cells responsible for bone production are called osteoblasts. The reason bone is so hard and rigid compared to other tissues is that the ground substance is composed of mineral salts, mostly calcium and phosphates.

Blood is also classified as a connective tissue and is discussed in a separate Chapter.

Muscle tissue

Muscle is another classification of tissue. There are three main types of muscle: skeletal, cardiac, and smooth.

Skeletal muscle is sometimes referred to as striated and is attached to bones via tendons to allow movement of the skeleton. It is also sometimes called voluntary because it is under the control of our will. Skeletal muscles are usually arranged in antagonistic pairs to allow movement in two or more directions. Antagonistic means they are set in opposition to each other in order to bring about opposite movements. So if you want to extend your arm the triceps muscle contracts. However, to flex the arm the biceps muscle contracts. This arrangement is required because muscles can only contract, they cannot actively elongate themselves.

Skeletal muscle cells are unusual in that they contain many nuclei. The muscle cells form long striated structures termed fibres. These muscle fibres are roughly cylindrical and may be 30 cm or more in length. In a skeletal muscle individual muscle fibres run parallel with each other. Using a light microscope the individual muscle fibres are seen to contain alternating light and dark bands. These bands give the muscle fibres a striped or striated appearance. This striation is seen because within the muscle fibres, i.e. inside the muscle cells, are bands of specialised contractile proteins. The striations are composed of the two contractile proteins called actin and myosin. When a muscle contracts the actin and myosin fibres pull into each other and overlap. This has the effect of reducing their length and so the length of the whole muscle fibre. Within the muscle

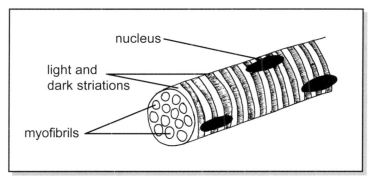

Diagram 1.15 (i)
Skeletal muscle tissue. A single muscle fibre with alternating dark and light bands. There are multiple nuclei.

fibres the contractile proteins are arranged in very small structures referred to as myofibrils; myo is the prefix which refers to muscle. The energy required for the contraction of muscle is produced by mitochondria also located within the muscle cells. Muscle fibres are held together by connective tissue which continues to form tendons at the end of the muscle.

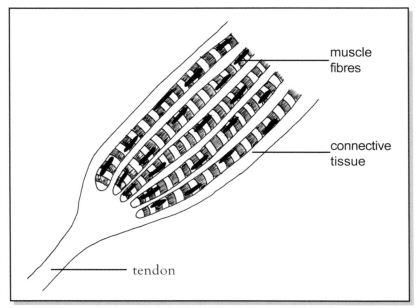

Diagram 1.15 (ii)
A group of muscle fibres grouped together to form a muscle.

Cardiac muscle is only found in the heart and composes the myocardium, which is the middle muscular layer. The myocardium powers the contractions of the heart. Like skeletal muscle it is also somewhat striated in appearance. Because the cardiac muscle is not under direct control of the will it is a form of involuntary muscle. Individual cardiac muscle cells link up with each other to form networks throughout the tissue. These interconnections allow electrical impulses to travel across the tissue. This is important as the muscle is stimulated to contract by an electrical signal. Cardiac muscle is able to rhythmically contract about 70 times per minute for a full lifetime. This may be in excess of 2.8 billion (thousand million) individual contractions.

Smooth muscle is not striated and is found in places like the walls of hollow structures. For example, blood vessels, the stomach, intestine and the bladder. It is usually involuntary, under the control of the autonomic (i.e. automatically controlled) nervous system. Smooth muscle contracts more slowly than striated muscle but it may contract very powerfully, e.g. the myometrium composes the middle layer of the uterus and is composed mostly of smooth muscle. This

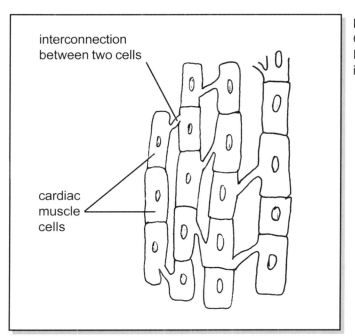

Diagram 1.16
Cardiac muscle tissue.
Individual cells are
interconnected.

interconnection
between two cells

cardiac
muscle
cells

is able to generate a force of contraction sufficient to deliver a baby through the birth canal during birth. Often smooth muscle contractions are sustained and rhythmic in nature. The individual cells are long and tapered at the ends. They are held together by connective tissue. Like striated muscles they contain contractile proteins but these are not arranged in a way which gives rise to a striated appearance.

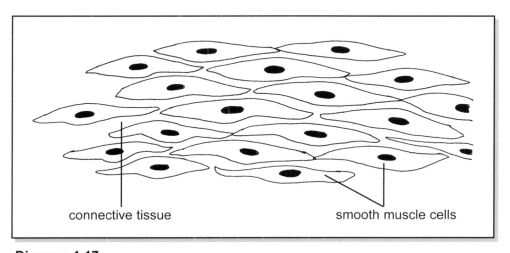

connective tissue   smooth muscle cells

Diagram 1.17
Smooth muscle tissue. Individual tapered muscle cells in a connective tissue.
There are junctions between some of the individual cells.

Nervous tissue

Nervous tissue is composed of neurones or nerve cells. Some neurones carry nerve impulses from the central nervous system to muscles and are termed motor neurones. Motor means to do with movement, for example, a reduced motor function would mean a reduced ability to move. Nerve cells which carry information from sensory receptors into the central nervous system are called sensory neurones. These neurones are therefore essential for touch, taste, smell, sight and hearing. Nerve cells which connect other nerve cells together are sometimes called relay neurones. The nature and function of these cells is discussed more fully in chapter 6.

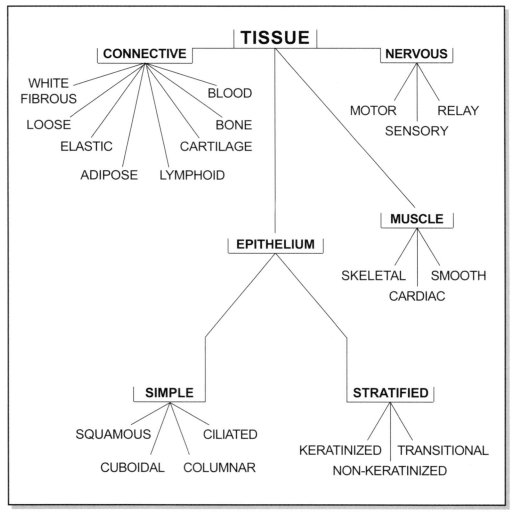

Table 1.2
Classification of body tissues.

Cells, tissues and fluids

In an average adult body there is approximately 42 litres of water, comprising around 60% of body weight. Most water, normally around 28 litres, is found inside the cells which comprise the body. Although in reality this water is located in billions of individual cells it is collectively referred to as the intracellular compartment. The remaining 14 litres of the fluid in the body is located outside the cells so is termed extracellular fluid. Total blood volume in an adult is usually about 5 litres. This is located in the heart and various blood vessels, a space collectively referred to as the vascular compartment. However, only 3 litres of the blood volume is made up of water, the other 2 litres are blood cells. This leaves approximately 11 litres of extracellular fluid which is located in the tissues. This tissue or interstitial fluid is located in the interstitial compartment which in reality is in all of the tissue spaces of the body. This compartmentalisation of body fluids is important for a number of physiological reasons, but we need to cover some science first.

Essential science - diffusion and osmosis

Diffusion

This can be defined as the process whereby liquids or gases of different concentrations mix up with each other, when they are brought into contact, until their concentrations are equal throughout. For example, if you take a glass of clear water and put in a drop of ink, at first you will have an inky area while the rest of the water will still be clear. However, over time, even if you do not stir it up, the whole glass will become inky as the ink molecules mix up with the rest of the water molecules in the glass.

This happens because the water and ink possess some heat energy. In a hot object the molecules are vibrating; in fact the hotter the substance the more vigorously the molecules will be vibrating. This is the difference between a hot and a cold substance. In the hot substance the molecules are vibrating more energetically than in the cold. The result of this molecular movement is that the ink and water molecules vibrate into each other and end up mixing in together until their distribution is equal throughout the particular medium. The hotter the water the more rapidly the process of diffusion will take place. Because diffusion requires the molecules to be able to move relative to each other the process can only take place in fluids (gases and liquids are both defined as fluids). This principle of molecular vibration and heat is referred to as kinetic theory. Kinetic means to do with movement.

Diffusion is a physical process which is essential for numerous physiological processes. For example, the concentration of oxygen in the air sacs of the lungs is higher than in the blood which is pumped to the

---

lungs. Diffusion occurs in an attempt to make the concentration of oxygen equal in the air and in the blood. This results in the movement of oxygen from air into the blood. If this process were to suddenly stop we would all die within a few minutes.

The rate at which diffusion occurs depends on several factors including temperature, size and concentration of the particular molecules, pressure and the area over which diffusion is free to occur.

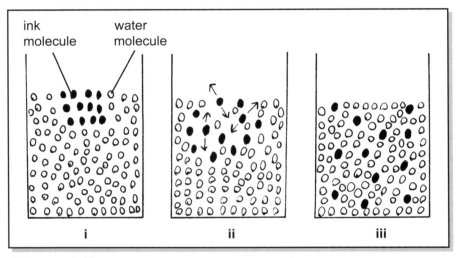

Diagram 1.18
The process of diffusion.
(i)   Ink molecules are introduced into a glass of warm water.
(ii)   Because the ink and water molecules are vibrating there are random collisions resulting in a mixing of the two fluids (only the vibration of 3 ink molecules is illustrated).
(iii)   After a period of time and many random collisions the ink is equally distributed throughout the water.

Osmosis

Diffusion can occur in any fluid with any molecule which is soluble. However osmosis is a special case of diffusion. It is the passage of water across a semi-permeable membrane under the influence of osmotic potential. (The terms osmotic potential and osmotic pressure mean the same thing.) In physiology, osmosis only applies to the movement of water across biological membranes. A semi-permeable membrane will allow the free passage of water molecules but will restrict the movement of other molecules. In theory, if a membrane were fully permeable, it would allow the free passage of all molecules.

A useful way to learn about osmosis is to have a solution of pure water on one side of a semi-permeable membrane with a sugar solution on the other. The membrane will allow the passage of water molecules but will not be permeable to the sugar, because it is only semi-permeable. The process of diffusion will mean that the water will diffuse through the membrane until the concentration of water molecules is equal on both sides. Despite this the sugar molecules will still only be on one side of the membrane. Because the sugar molecules take up space in the sugar solution the result is that there is a net movement of water molecules from the pure water side of the membrane to the sugar solution side of the membrane. It is this movement of water across the membrane which is referred to as osmosis. So water will diffuse from a watery solution to a less watery solution, i.e. osmosis waters things down. The power of a solution to osmotically attract water through a semi-permeable membrane is termed osmolarity.

Osmosis explains why we give saline and not pure water in intravenous infusions. If infusions contained pure water this would reduce the osmolarity of the blood and alter the osmotic balance between the plasma and the cytoplasm of red blood cells. This would mean that water from the diluted plasma would diffuse into the red cells and blow them up with water. This could result in some of the red cells bursting like overfilled balloons - this would lead to many pathological problems.

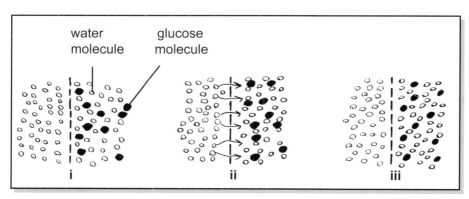

Diagram 1.19
The process of osmosis.
(i)   Pure water and a glucose solution are separated by a semi-permeable membrane.
(ii) The water molecules are able to diffuse through the membrane because they are small. The larger glucose molecules cannot get through.
(iii) After a period of time the number of water molecules on both sides of the membrane will be the same. This means there has been a net movement of water into the sugar solution. In effect the sugar solution has been watered down. (Hint: try counting up the number of water molecules on both sides of the membrane in each diagram.)

Importance of fluid compartmentalisation

If you go out for a long walk on a hot day you could lose a litre or more of fluid as sweat. If you then lose your way home you could lose a further litre. This will mean you become thirsty but you will not die. Sweat is produced from water in the plasma by sweat glands. This means that during your walk, 2 litres of fluid was removed from the 5 litres of blood circulating in the body. If you lose 2 litres of blood in haemorrhage death can be the result; however, at the end of the walk your blood pressure and blood volumes will still be normal. This means that the fluid in the blood has been replaced despite the fact that you did not have access to a drink.

Blood contains large protein molecules called plasma proteins. These molecules give the blood its osmolarity, i.e. they make it osmotic so water will diffuse into it. When water is lost from the blood to produce sweat there is less water left so blood osmolarity increases as the blood becomes more concentrated

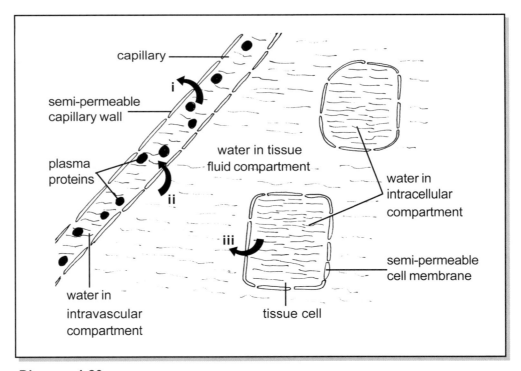

Diagram 1.20
Compartmentalisation and osmotic movement of body fluids.
(i)   When water is lost from the blood the osmolarity of intravascular fluid increases.
(ii) This results in water being osmotically sucked into the blood from the interstitial (or tissue) compartment.
(iii) As the osmolarity of the tissue fluid increases water diffuses out of the intracellular compartment by osmosis into the tissue fluid.

and less watery. The result of this is that water diffuses through the semi-permeable membranes of the capillaries from the tissue fluid by the process of osmosis. This movement of water restores the blood volume to normal. However, if more water is sucked from the tissue fluid into the blood, the tissue fluid will, in turn, also become more osmotic. This will result in water moving from the intracellular compartment through the semi-permeable cell membranes into the interstitial compartment to maintain tissue fluid volumes. Tissue fluid does not contain proteins like plasma but osmolarity is generated by the presence of sodium (remember salt is sodium chloride).

So the compartmentalisation of body fluids means there is a large fluid reserve to maintain blood volumes during periods of water loss when drinks are not available. Blood volumes will only be reduced when dehydration is severe.

Whole body structure and body cavities

Most of the organs of the body are contained in closed cavities. The cranial cavity is located inside the skull and houses the brain. This cavity is continuous

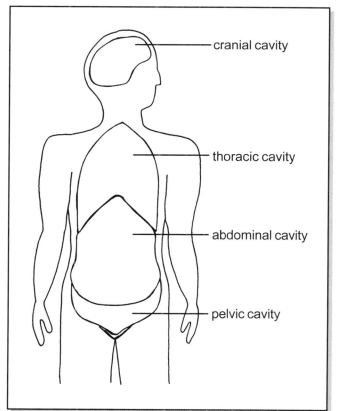

Diagram 1.21
The principal closed body cavities.

with the vertebral cavity; this is inside the vertebral column and contains the spinal cord and some other large nerves. The thoracic cavity is located in the thorax or chest. At the back of the thoracic cavity are the 12 thoracic vertebrae, the rest is surrounded by the ribs. This well protected cavity contains the heart and lungs as well as the main airways and several major blood vessels. The bottom border of the thoracic cavity is marked by a domed sheet of muscle called the diaphragm.

Below the diaphragm is the abdominal cavity. Behind this cavity are the large bones of the lumbar vertebrae, most of the cavity is surrounded by sheets of muscle. An upper area is also protected by the lower ribs. Most of the digestive organs are found in the abdomen, as well as the liver, spleen and kidneys. Surrounding the abdominal cavity is a layer of connective tissue called the peritoneum. Below the peritoneum is the pelvic cavity which is largely surrounded by the bones of the pelvis. The pelvis contains the bladder and reproductive organs. The testes are kept outside the pelvic cavity to keep them cool as sperm prefers temperatures of about 35°C.

CHAPTER 2

Cardiovascular System

Basic structure of the heart

The heart is a hollow organ located in the centre, and extending to the left of, the thoracic cavity. With the sternum and ribs to the front and the thoracic spinal column behind, the heart is well protected from physical trauma. Within the heart there are four chambers. The two upper chambers are termed atria and the lower chambers ventricles. These chambers are simply named according to the side of the heart they are on, so they are the right and left atria, and the right and left ventricles. Valves separate the atria from the ventricles and the ventricles from the aorta and pulmonary artery. The left and right sides of the heart are separated by the cardiac septum. This means that blood from the right side cannot mix with blood from the left side and vice versa.

The wall of the heart is in three layers

The inner layer of the heart is called the endocardium and is composed of smooth squamous epithelium. When an epithelium is lining internal structures it is referred to as an endothelium. This endothelium allows the smooth

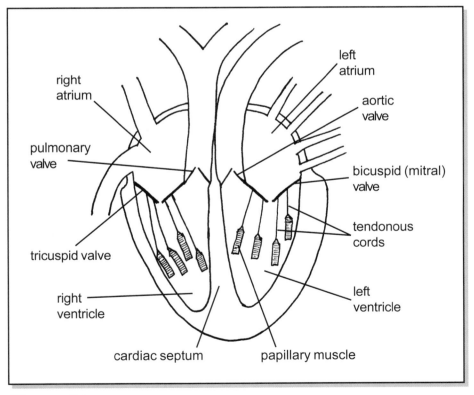

Diagram 2.1
The basic structures of the heart. The muscular wall of the left ventricle is thicker than that of the right ventricle. The walls of the atria are relatively thin.

uninterrupted flow of blood through the heart. Endocardium also covers the heart valves. The importance of the smooth lining provided by the endocardial endothelium is highlighted if it becomes infected, a condition termed endocarditis. Usually caused by a Streptococcus, this condition causes inflammation of the endothelium followed by deposits of the blood clotting protein fibrin, causing the build up of 'vegetation'. If this material is dislodged it will enter the circulatory system as emboli which can lodge in the small arterial supply of any part of the body.

The myocardium is the middle layer of the heart wall and is composed of specialised cardiac heart muscle. All of the energy for the pumping action of the heart is generated by the contraction of the myocardium. This cardiac form of muscle is only found in the heart and is composed of specialised cells called cardiomyocytes. Myocardial muscle is striped or striated in nature but, unlike skeletal muscle, is involuntary. As the myocardium must contract approximately 72 times per minute it uses a lot of nutrients and oxygen.

The outer layer of the heart is termed the pericardium and is composed of two layers. An inner layer is composed of serous membrane which is adherent to the outside of the myocardium. This is referred to as the visceral pericardium or epicardium. The outer pericardial layer is composed of tough fibrous tissue, which is itself lined internally with another layer of serous membrane. A serous membrane is a membrane which secretes serous lubrication fluid, in this case to allow the heart to move within the fibrous pericardial sac with minimal friction between layers. This allows the heart to expand and contract smoothly during a normal cardiac cycle. The fibrous layer is protective and prevents the heart over expanding. If fluid or blood collects under the fibrous pericardium the pressure can squash the heart and may cause death. This condition is termed cardiac tamponade.

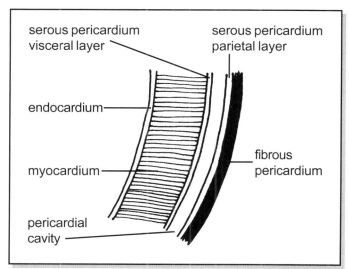

serous pericardium visceral layer

serous pericardium parietal layer

endocardium

myocardium

fibrous pericardium

pericardial cavity

Diagram 2.2
The three layers which compose the wall of the heart, endocardium, myocardium and pericardium.

Heart valves ensure one way flow of blood

Valves are essential to control the direction of blood flow through the heart, opening and closing as a result of pressure changes in the blood. A valve will only allow the blood to flow in one direction.

The atria and ventricles are separated by valves collectively referred to as atrioventricular valves. On the right side, the atrioventricular valve is called the tricuspid valve. This is because it is made up of three separate cusps. The bicuspid valve is between the left atrium and ventricle and is composed of two cusps. Often the bicuspid valve is referred to as the mitral valve as an alternative name. These valves allow the free flow of blood from the atria into the ventricles but close during ventricular contraction to prevent blood passing from the ventricles back into the atria.

Atrioventricular valves are attached to the ventricular wall by strong tendons called chordae tendineae or tendonous cords. These prevent the valves opening upwards, i.e. the wrong way. The tendonous cords are themselves connected to the wall of the heart via specialised muscle bundles called papillary muscles. Papillary muscles contract at the same time as the ventricular wall. As they contract they pull on the tendonous cords which tightly close the valves, preventing any possible regurgitation of blood from the ventricles back into the atria.

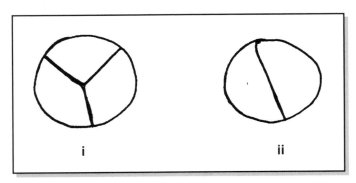

i   ii

Diagram 2.3
(i)   View of the closed tricuspid valve from above.
(ii) View of the closed bicuspid (mitral) valve from above.

Between the left ventricle and the aorta is the aortic valve (in some texts you may see this referred to as the aortic semilunar valve). Between the right ventricle and the pulmonary artery is the pulmonary valve (also sometimes referred to as the pulmonary semilunar valve). When the ventricles are contracting the aortic and pulmonary valves open to allow the free flow of blood into the aorta and pulmonary artery. At the end of ventricular contraction these valves close to prevent blood flowing from the aorta and pulmonary artery back into the ventricles.

Cardiac massage is a technique that can be used when the heart is not able to contract independently. This takes advantage of the valves within the heart only allowing blood to flow in the correct physiological direction through the heart. In cardiac massage the heart is compressed between the thoracic vertebral column and the sternum. As the pressure in the heart increases, blood will open the valves and be forced through the heart and out into the aorta and pulmonary artery. Good cardiac massage will therefore generate a cardiac output which may be detected as a central pulse. This cardiac output will perfuse the vital organs of the body such as the lungs, brain, kidneys and the heart itself. This can be maintained until additional treatments restore a normal cardiac rhythm.

Blood flow through the heart

The heart is the pump which generates the flow of blood through the arterial and capillary systems of the body.

Atrial function

Atria act as receiving chambers for the venous blood which is returning to the heart via the large veins. When the ventricles are not contracting blood returning to the heart, via the large veins, will pass directly through the atria, through the atrioventricular valves and will start filling up the ventricles.

However, when the ventricles are contracting blood returning to the atria will not be able to pass directly into the ventricles. Therefore during ventricular contraction returning blood is stored in the atria. Once the ventricles have completed a contraction, the atrioventricular valves will open and the blood stored in the atria will rapidly pass into the ventricles. One tenth of a second before the onset of the next ventricular contraction, when the ventricles are already about 85% full of blood, the atria contract and complete the filling of the ventricles. This final filling of the ventricles by atrial contraction is termed atrial kick. This effect is very important during exercise, when the volumes of blood returning to the heart are increased. Both atria contract essentially at the same time.

Ventricular function

Ventricles are pumping chambers which pump blood into the arteries. The left ventricle pumps blood into the main artery supplying blood to the body. This large vessel is referred to as the aorta. The right ventricle pumps blood into the main artery supplying blood to the lungs which is called the pulmonary artery (pulmonary always means to do with the lungs). Very shortly after the atria finish contracting, ventricular contraction begins. The ventricles start to contract from the cardiac apex, towards the base. This has the effect of directing blood towards the atrioventricular valves. In addition to contracting inwards the left ventricle shortens, pulling the cardiac apex towards the valves. As the ventricles start to contract, the pressure of the blood they contain increases. This increase in intraventricular pressure has the effect of closing the atrioventricular valves preventing blood from being pumped from the ventricles back into the atria. Both ventricles contract essentially at the same time.

It is interesting to note that ventricular contraction does not completely empty the ventricles. At the start of ventricular contraction (in a resting adult) a ventricle will contain 120mls of blood. During ventricular contraction 70mls of this will be ejected. This leaves 50mls of blood in the ventricle at the end of a contraction.

The cardiac cycle

A cardiac cycle is one complete contraction and relaxation of the heart. It describes the events which take place during one heart beat. The heart contracts at a regular rate from about eight weeks after conception until the death of the individual. Resting heart rate varies with the age of the person from about 140 at birth to around 110 at age two, 80 at age ten to around 70 in adults.

Systole and diastole

Systole refers to contraction of the myocardium. Atrial systole describes contraction of the atrial myocardium and ventricular systole is contraction of the ventricles. Diastole refers to the rest of the time when the myocardium is not contracting and therefore describes the resting phase of each cardiac cycle. In a cardiac cycle ventricular systole immediately follows atrial systole.

During ventricular diastole the ventricles fill with blood prior to the next contraction. There is then a period of systole when the ventricles are actively contracting. During a cardiac cycle ventricular systole takes 0.3 seconds and ventricular diastole about 0.5 seconds. As heart rate increases, for example during exercise, the length of diastole decreases.

Systolic blood pressure is generated as a result of ventricular contraction during ventricular systole. As the left ventricle pumps blood around the whole body, relatively high pressures must be generated. However, as the right ventricle only has to pump blood to the lungs only relatively low pulmonary arterial blood pressures are required. This explains why a typical blood pressure in the systemic circulation is 120/80 mmHg whereas in the pulmonary circulation it is 25/8 mmHg. The first figure represents the blood pressure in the arteries during ventricular systole and is referred to as the systolic pressure. The second figure is the pressure in the arteries when there is no active ventricular contraction during diastole. This second pressure reflects the elasticity of the arterial system and is termed the diastolic pressure. These principles explain why the wall of the left ventricle contains a much greater muscle mass than the right ventricle. The atrial walls are also relatively thin, as they only have to pump blood from an atrium into a ventricle.

Heart sounds

Both atrioventricular valves close at the same time, making a sound referred to as a 'lub'. The closure of the two arterial semilunar valves makes a 'dub'. These are termed the first and second heart sounds, so the normal heart should make a lub dub, lub dub, lub dub. Heart sounds can easily be heard with a stethoscope. Additional sounds may be abnormal and are often caused by disturbances in the smooth flow of blood. An abnormal heart sound, referred to as a 'whoosh', is often heard in septal defects where there is a communication between the right and left sides of the heart (a hole in the heart). The resultant mixing of oxygenated and deoxygenated blood reduces the efficiency of the circulatory system. In this case some oxygenated blood is returned to the lungs and some deoxygenated blood is pumped into the systemic circulation. Such conditions are usually congenital and often require surgical correction.

Blood circulation through the lungs and around the body

The heart is actually two pumps in one; there is a body pump and a lung pump. The left side pumps blood to the body (the systemic circulation) and the right side to the lungs (the pulmonary circulation).

As the left ventricle contracts blood is ejected into the aorta. From the aorta blood passes, via the arterial system, to perfuse all the tissues of the body. As the blood circulates through the capillaries of the body it gives up oxygen to the tissues. Veins then collect the blood and return it towards the heart. The systemic veins drain blood into two large central veins called the superior and inferior vena cava. These two veins drain the top and bottom halves of the body respectively. The superior and inferior vena cava then drain directly into the right atrium.

From the right atrium the blood passes through the tricuspid valve into the right ventricle. When the right ventricle contracts this causes the closure of the tricuspid valve and the opening of the pulmonary valve. This means blood will be pumped into the pulmonary artery, and on to the lungs. Back flow from the pulmonary artery into the right ventricle is prevented by the pulmonary valve. Shortly after leaving the right ventricle, the pulmonary artery divides into two main branches, one to each lung.

Blood is pumped to the lungs to be oxygenated and to excrete (excrete just means to get rid of) carbon dioxide. Haemoglobin in red blood cells absorbs oxygen from the lungs. This oxygenated blood will then return to the left side of the heart via the pulmonary veins. The four pulmonary veins, two from each lung, drain blood into the left atrium. From the left atrium, blood passes through the bicuspid valve into the left ventricle.

The order of the circulation of the blood can therefore be summarised as follows; left ventricle - aortic valve - aorta - body - vena cava - right atrium - tricuspid valve - right ventricle - pulmonary valve - lungs - pulmonary vein - left atrium - bicuspid valve - left ventricle. Both sides of the heart contract together, simultaneously pumping blood to lungs and body.

Arterial blood in the systemic circulation is bright red because it is rich in oxyhaemoglobin which is a bright red pigment. This is because the blood has passed through the lungs and is fully oxygenated. An oxygen saturation probe indicates that arterial blood in a healthy person is usually 98-99% saturated with oxygen. However, in the pulmonary arteries, the blood is on the way to the lungs to be oxygenated, after giving up much of its oxygen to the tissues of the body. This is why blood in the pulmonary arteries is dark red and deoxygenated. Blood in the systemic veins is dark red, compared to blood in the pulmonary veins which is bright red and fully oxygenated.

Circulation of blood through the coronary arteries

The first two arteries to leave the aorta are the right and left coronary arteries. These subdivide and supply blood to all of the smaller coronary arteries which perfuse the myocardium with blood. As this blood perfuses the myocardium it supplies the nutrients and oxygen essential for energy production and contraction. Disease of these arteries is termed coronary artery disease and is the single most common cause of death in most developed countries. This disease occurs when the lumen of the arteries is clogged up with a fatty cholesterol based material called atheroma. Because the atheroma blocks off part of the lumen, less blood is able to get through to the myocardium. This reduction in blood supply is called ischaemia. In addition, the atheroma increases the probability that a blood clot may form in the lumen of the artery, a pathological condition referred to as thrombosis. Clinically these consequences of atheroma may cause angina and myocardial infarction.

The internal electrical conducting system

The cardiac cycle is controlled by specialised conducting tissue in the heart. Inside the right atrium is an area of specialised cardiac muscle tissue termed the sinoatrial (SA) node. Because this controls the pace of the heart it is sometimes called the pacemaker. This area generates the initial electrical impulse which stimulates myocardial contraction. From the SA node an impulse spreads to both atria stimulating their contraction. The impulse travels across the atria via specialised conduction pathways termed the internodal tracts; this is because they are between the SA node and the atrioventricular (AV) node.

The AV node collects an impulse from the atria and passes it on to the bundle of His (or atrioventricular bundle) in the cardiac septum. The AV node is the only pathway the impulses can travel in order to spread from the atria to the ventricles; the rest of the tissue in the plane of the valves is electrically insulating. In the cardiac septum the bundle of His divides into two, forming the right and left bundle branches, which carry the electrical impulse to the right and left ventricles. The result of this arrangement is that an impulse is

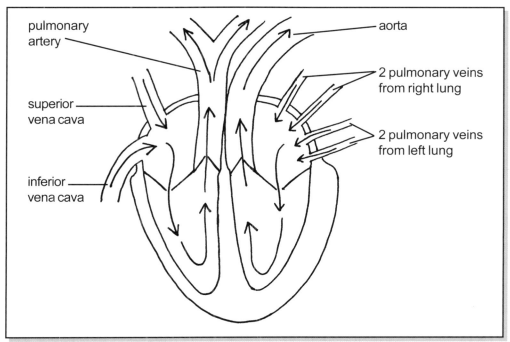

Diagram 2.4
The major blood vessels associated with the heart. Arrows indicate direction of blood flow.

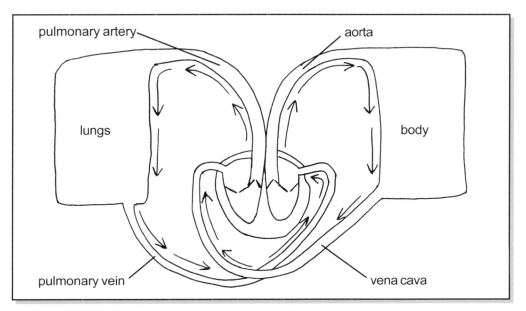

Diagram 2.5
This simplified diagram shows the flow of the blood through the heart and around the body and the lungs. You may find it helpful to colour these diagrams in. The tradition is red for oxygenated blood and blue for deoxygenated.

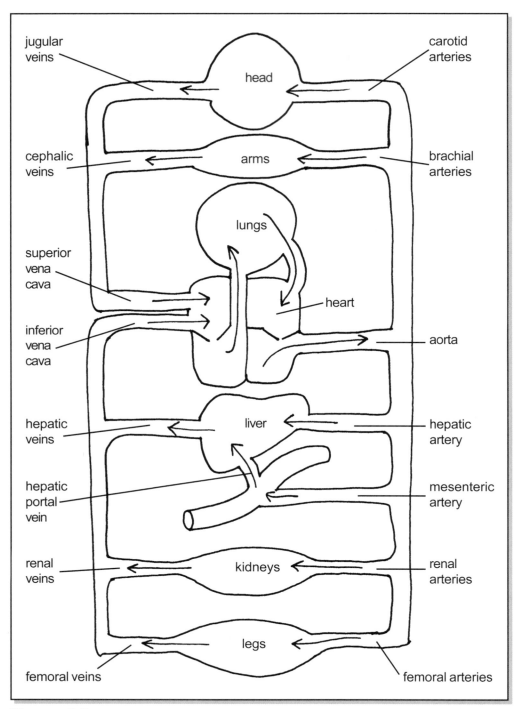

Diagram 2.6
This diagram shows more detail of the flow of blood around the systemic circulation.
Arrows indicate direction of blood flow.

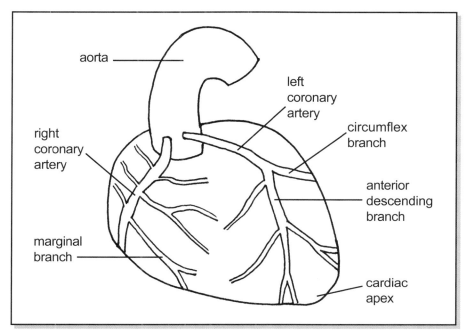

Diagram 2.7
The main coronary arteries as seen from the front. Coronary arteries are relatively thin arteries, partly explaining why they are prone to blockage in coronary arterial disease. The circumflex branch of the left and the right coronary artery carry on around the back of the heart to perfuse the posterior wall with blood.

carried rapidly down through the cardiac septum. Finally the impulse innervates the ventricular myocardial muscle via the small Purkinje fibres (or conduction myofibres). This means that ventricular contraction will start from the cardiac apex and work towards the base, pushing the blood upwards, towards the arterial valves. It is this internal conducting system which is responsible for the initiation and phases of the cardiac cycle.

Unlike other muscles the myocardium internally generates the electrical impulses which lead to muscle contraction. As mentioned, this electrical activity originates from the sinoatrial node. However, outside factors will influence the heart rate and strength of contraction. Adrenaline will increase heart rate, as will stimulation by the sympathetic nervous system. This is why heart rate, and the strength of contractions, will increase during exercise, excitement or as a result of anxiety. Parasympathetic stimulation will slow the heart rate and so reduce cardiac output. When we are relaxed the parasympathetic nervous system will slow the heart rate and reduce the strength of individual contractions. The internal generation of the electrical activity required for cardiac contraction explains why a donated heart will carry on contracting after a heart transplant operation.

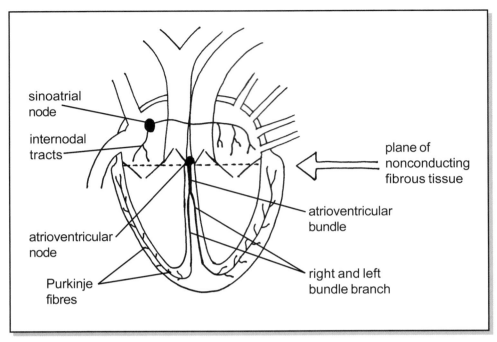

Diagram 2.8
The components of the cardiac internal conducting system. The sinoatrial node generates a new electrical impulse prior to every cardiac cycle. Firstly this impulse causes atrial contraction. As an electrical impulse cannot be transmitted through the non-conducting fibrous tissue of the valvular plane it passes down to the ventricles via the AV node. This same impulse then causes ventricular contraction.

The PQRST as seen using an electrocardiograph

When the myocardium is stimulated by an electrical impulse the myocardial cells will depolarise. This means the electrical polarity across all of the individual cell membranes will reverse. At rest any muscle cell is negatively charged on the inside and positive on the outside. Arrival of an electrical impulse will reverse this resting potential causing the cells to depolarize, becoming positive on the inside and negative on the outside. It is this depolarisation of the myocardial cells which initiates their contraction. The collective electrical activity of the myocardial cells depolarizing, and then repolarizing, may be detected with electrodes on the surface of the body. In health the contraction of the myocardial muscle cells will occur essentially at the same time as the cells depolarize. This means we can directly relate the electrical patterns we can detect on the surface of the body with the contractions of the myocardium. This is the principle of the electrocardiogram (ECG). When this is recorded three characteristic electrical phases can be clearly seen.

Firstly there is a P wave. This is the electrical activity, as detected on the surface of the body, as a result of the depolarization of the atrial myocardium.

Secondly there is the larger QRS complex caused by the depolarization of the larger muscle mass of the ventricular myocardium. This complex is associated with ventricular contraction. Thirdly there is a T wave. This is not associated with any muscular contraction but arises as the ventricular muscle repolarizes to an electrically resting state. Finally, there is a short gap before the next atrial contraction at the start of the next cardiac cycle.

A normal cardiac cycle must have a PQRST phase in that order. In health the occurrence of these phases of the cycle is fairly regular and the rate is usually between 60 and 100 per minute. So a normal rhythm has a PQRST, in the correct order, is regular, with a rate between 60 to 100 cycles per minute. This normal rhythm is called a sinus rhythm because the cardiac rhythm is controlled by the sinoatrial node in the right atrium.

If the phases of the cardiac cycle occur regularly, and in the correct order, at a rate of less than 60 times per minute, the rhythm is termed sinus bradycardia. This is normal in people who are physically fit or who are very relaxed. If the rate is over 100, with a regular PQRST in the right order, this is termed a sinus

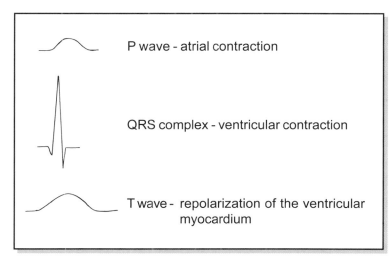

P wave - atrial contraction

QRS complex - ventricular contraction

T wave - repolarization of the ventricular myocardium

Diagram 2.9
The components of the cardiac cycle and the events the electrical activity represents.

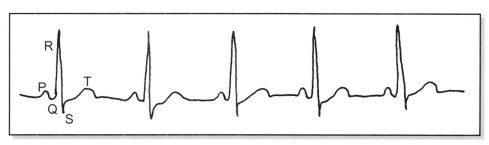

Diagram 2.10
A normal ECG recorded from one of my students.

tachycardia. A sinus tachycardia is of course normal during exercise. The terms P,Q,R,S and T do not stand for anything and have no intrinsic significance what so ever. They are arbitrary names given to specified phases.

Effects of exercise

Exercise increases heart rate, which is the number of times the heart beats per minute. It also increases stroke volume which is the amount of blood pumped out per cardiac contraction. These two factors combine to increase cardiac output, which is defined as the volume of blood pumped out from the left ventricle per minute. To be precise, cardiac output equals heart rate multiplied by stroke volume. At rest a normal stroke volume will be around 70mls. If the heart rate is 72 beats per minute this would give a cardiac output of 70 x 72 which equals a cardiac output of 5040 mls. As an average adult has about 5 litres of blood in total, the cardiac output figure means the entire volume of the blood circulates through both the body and lungs once per minute.

With increasing levels of physical activity cardiac output will progressively rise. This will increase the rate at which blood circulates around the lungs and body tissues and so increase the delivery of oxygen and nutrients to active muscles. During vigorous exercise an average adult might be able to increase their cardiac output to 20 or 25 litres per minute for a period of time. A trained athlete will be able to achieve a cardiac output of 35 or even 40 litres per minute for a short time.

Regular exercise is good

Regular exercise is very good for humans; it lowers the levels of sugar (glucose) in the blood and increases levels of the protective HDL (high density lipoprotein) cholesterol. Exercise will increase metabolic rate and sustained exercise will burn up excess body fat preventing obesity. Although exercise raises blood pressure at the time, it lowers blood pressure overall. It makes the heart muscle stronger and helps to keep the coronary arteries patent. These factors mean regular exercise helps to protect against heart attacks and strokes. Recent findings indicate that regular exercise reduces the risks of developing some forms of cancer. Exercise tones and strengthens many muscles in the body and as exercise applies forces through the bones of the skeleton it will increase bone strength. Exercise in childhood and young adult life will build up bone mass and make osteoporosis less likely in later life. Regular exercise is an effective treatment for depression. If people are immobilised and unable to exercise they may suffer from numerous complications such as blood clots in the veins of the legs and lungs, pressure sores, depression, constipation, pneumonia and atrophy of bones and muscles. This is why everyone should try to exercise for a least half an hour every day unless there is some medical reason not to.

Blood vessels

The main types of blood vessels are: arteries, arterioles, capillaries, venules and veins.

Arteries

An artery is any vessel which carries blood away from the heart. Essentially arteries are tubes which supply an area of tissue with blood. This is vital; if an area is deprived of a regular blood supply the tissues will die because all of the oxygen and nutrients the cells require are transported to them in the blood. Larger arteries divide into smaller arteries so the whole of the body can be perfused with blood.

Arteries have fairly thick walls because the blood they carry is at relatively high pressure. If an artery is cut the blood initially come out in spurts. This form of arterial bleeding represents the pressure changes in the arterial system as the left ventricle contracts and relaxes. Fortunately, most arteries are deep in the body for protection. Because the arteries carry blood directly from the heart, a pulse can be felt every time the heart contracts.

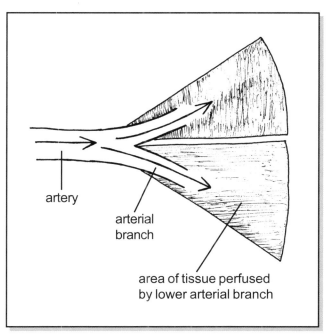

Diagram 2.11
An artery supplying an area of tissue with blood. Often an arterial branch will supply a wedge shaped area of tissue.

artery

arterial branch

area of tissue perfused by lower arterial branch

Arterial walls consist of three layers or coats usually described as an outer, middle and inner tunica (tunica is a word which means coat). Firstly the tunica externa (also called tunica adventitia) is the external or outer layer; this is composed mostly of connective tissues, containing collagen and elastic fibres.

Secondly the tunica media is the middle layer; this contains elastic fibres and smooth muscle. The third inner layer is called the tunica interna (or intima); this is a flat layer of smooth squamous endothelium to allow smooth flow of blood. The hole in the middle of any vessel is referred to as the lumen.

All of the systemic arteries carrying blood to the body branch from the aorta. The carotid arteries can be felt in the neck and supply the head with blood. Blood pressure is usually recorded from the brachial artery supplying the arm. The femoral pulse can be felt in the groin. Behind the knee, the pulse of the popliteal artery can be felt. The most common pulse felt in clinical practice is the radial; this is where the radial artery passes over the radius. However, in many clinical emergency situations it may not be possible to feel the radial pulse, so we should always assess a central pulse, usually the carotid or femoral. Other main arteries include the intercostal arteries to the intercostal muscles, the hepatic artery to the liver, and the renal arteries to the kidneys.

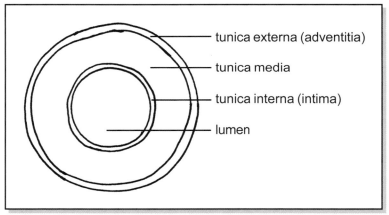

Diagram 2.12
Cross section of an artery to show the three layers and lumen.

Arterioles

Small arteries divide into even smaller arterial vessels called arterioles. These vessels are almost microscopic and carry blood into the microscopic capillaries. Arterioles contain circular smooth muscle fibres in their walls which allow them to dilate and constrict. This vasodilation and vasoconstriction allows for the regulation of the flow of blood through a tissue (vaso means to do with blood vessels). For example, after a heavy meal the arterioles to the gut will dilate, increasing the volumes of blood perfusing the capillaries of the gut wall. During exercise the arterioles supplying the skeletal muscles will dilate to increase their blood supply. When someone is cold the arterioles supplying the skin capillary beds will vasoconstrict to reduce the amount of warm blood near the surface of the skin. Alcohol has the opposite effect and causes peripheral vasodilation; this is why alcohol should not be given to cold people. This ability of the arterioles to alter the diameter of their lumen therefore allows for precise regulation of the volumes of blood perfusing a particular tissue at a particular time.

Arterioles and control of blood pressure

Blood pressure is determined by two factors; the cardiac output and the peripheral resistance. As discussed cardiac output describes the volume of blood discharged into the systemic circulation over one minute. If cardiac output increases, this has the effect of increasing flow rate and so will increase blood pressure. This is analogous to turning a tap where a small turn will result in a small flow of water with low volumes and pressure. However, if the tap is turned up the flow rate and pressure will increase.

The other factor in determining blood pressure is the resistance generated by the arterial system to the cardiac output. Blood pressure is determined by the cardiac output multiplied by the peripheral resistance. It is this peripheral resistance, generated mostly at the level of the arterioles, which is the main factor determining blood pressure. This means that arteriole tone is vital in the regulation of blood pressure. Widespread constriction of the arterioles will narrow the total lumen of the arterial system which in turn will increase resistance to blood flow. The resistance to blood flow offered by the arterioles is termed peripheral resistance. Conversely if the arterioles are dilated, there will be less resistance to blood flow and peripheral resistance will be reduced. If peripheral resistance is increased blood pressure will also be increased. Conversely, if peripheral resistance is lowered, due to vasodilation, blood pressure will be lowered.

The relative tone of the arterioles, and so systemic blood pressure, is regulated via two separate mechanisms. Firstly neuronal reflexes maintain blood pressure on a short term basis. This effect will increase blood pressure over a second or two to meet the current requirements of the body. For example, blood pressure will be increased if we stand up in order to ensure the brain is perfused with blood. This short term vasomotor control is coordinated by a specialised area in the medulla oblongata (part of the brain stem) called the vasomotor centre. The second mechanism is the renin-angiotensin mechanism. This hormonal regulation is the main factor determining long term blood pressure control and is discussed in chapter 10.

Efficient regulation of blood pressure is essential for life. If blood pressure is too low, tissues will not be adequately perfused. For example, if the brain is acutely hypoperfused a person will lose consciousness and faint. If the blood pressure perfusing the kidneys is inadequate they will not be able to generate glomerular filtrate and so will not produce urine. However, chronic high blood pressure will lead to atheroma formation in larger arteries and thickening of the walls in smaller arteries. The walls of blood vessels will be weakened leading to aneurysm and possible haemorrhage. Sustained high blood pressure can also lead to heart failure, renal damage leading to renal failure and retinal damage leading to blindness.

Capillaries

Capillaries are the smallest blood vessels and are microscopic. They receive blood from the arterioles. Capillaries are the only part of the circulatory system where there is exchange of materials from the blood to the tissues or from the tissues to the blood; all other vessel walls are too thick to allow diffusion. Capillaries however, are able to facilitate this exchange because they are only one squamous cell thick. This means the diffusional distance between the blood and the tissue cells is very small, allowing relatively free diffusion. The cells which comprise the capillary walls are called endothelial cells. Exchange of material between the blood and tissue fluid is aided by small gaps which are present between some of the capillary endothelial cells. These gaps are called capillary pores.

Living tissue contains millions of capillaries arranged in beds. A capillary bed refers to a system of capillaries perfusing a particular area of tissue. For example, finger nail beds are pink because of the colour of the blood passing through a capillary bed. If you press on your finger nails the beds turn white.

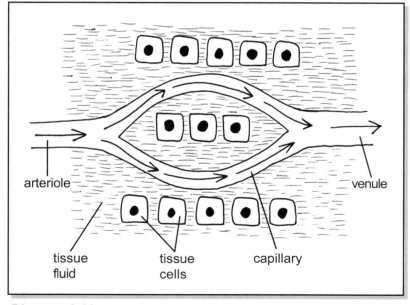

Diagram 2.13
An arteriole divides into a group of capillaries which perfuse some tissue cells.

This is because the pressure of the nail from above has squeezed the blood out of the capillary bed, so the pink colour is lost. Overall the capillaries form a massive surface area between the blood and the tissues. It has been suggested the total area of capillary wall in an adult is 6000 square metres.

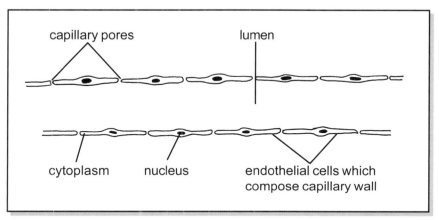

Diagram 2.14
A magnified view of a capillary wall made up of individual endothelial cells.

Tissue fluid formation and reabsorption

As can be seen from diagram 2.13, the cells of a tissue are bathed in tissue fluid. This is essential to keep the cells moist and to prevent them drying out. In addition, tissue fluid is the essential medium for diffusion between the blood and capillaries. Substances diffuse from the blood, through the tissue fluid, before reaching and diffusing into cells. The same is true for substances the cells excrete. These waste products must diffuse into the tissue fluid before they can diffuse through the capillary wall into the blood.

It is the capillaries which are responsible for the formation of the tissue fluid. At the arteriole end of the capillary, because the blood has recently left the arterial system, the blood pressure is still relatively high. Because the pressure in the capillary is greater than in the tissue fluid, water molecules, which are small enough to fit through the capillary pores, are forced out from the capillary blood into the tissue spaces. Larger components of the blood such as cells and plasma proteins, which are big molecules, remain in the capillaries. Once formed, tissue fluid bathes and flows over the individual tissue cells.

At the venous end of a capillary blood pressure is lower because the blood is nearing the lower pressure venous system. Because blood plasma contains large protein molecules, the plasma generates an osmotic potential which tends to draw in water. At the venous end of the capillary, the osmotic potential is greater than the blood pressure which is trying to force water molecules out of the capillary. The net effect of this is that water molecules are osmotically drawn back into the blood at the venous end of the capillary. The overall result of this process of tissue fluid formation and reabsorption is that there is a flow of fresh tissue fluid over the tissue cells, from the arterial to the venous end of the capillary. This flow helps keep tissue cells nourished and oxygenated as well as removing toxic waste products.

When the levels of protein in the blood are very low, such as in severe malnutrition, the plasma is no longer able to generate the osmotic potential required to reabsorb tissue fluid. This is why people with severe protein deficiencies develop oedema (the retention of fluid in the tissues).

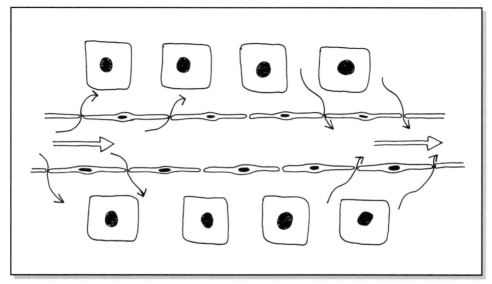

Diagram 2.15
Formation and reabsorption of tissue fluid. Water is exuded from the arterial end of the capillary, washes over the tissue cells and is reabsorbed at the venous end of the capillary. Dark arrows represent tissue fluid movement; white arrows indicate direction of blood flow.

Gaseous exchange between capillary blood and tissue cells

Capillaries are the site of gaseous exchange between the blood and tissues. All living tissues need a constant supply of oxygen to allow mitochondria to produce the energy essential for life. In the systemic circulation, arterial blood arrives from the arterioles containing high concentrations of oxygen. Because the tissues have been using up oxygen, the concentration in tissue cells is relatively low. This means there will be a diffusion gradient, between the high level of oxygen in the blood, and lower level in the tissues. The result of this is that oxygen will diffuse from the blood into the tissue cells.

The same principle of differential concentrations of dissolved gas also determines the movement of carbon dioxide. Ongoing metabolism in the cells produces carbon dioxide, the concentration of which will therefore rise. Arterial blood arrives from the arterioles containing very low concentrations of carbon dioxide. This means there is a concentration gradient from the cells to the blood, resulting in the diffusion of carbon dioxide from tissue cells into the blood. By these mechanisms the cells maintain oxygenation and dispose of waste carbon dioxide.

In addition to gaseous exchange, nutrients that cells require diffuse from the blood to the cells through the capillary walls and tissue fluids. Nutrients include amino acids, fatty acids, glucose, minerals and vitamins. As well as producing waste carbon dioxide, cells produce other chemical wastes as a result of their metabolic processes. These include waste nitrogen containing toxic molecules such as ammonia. If these are allowed to accumulate in the tissues they would eventually poison the cells.

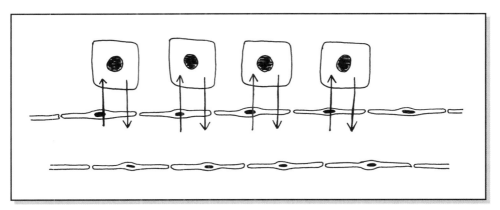

Diagram 2.16
Gaseous exchange between blood and tissues, oxygen diffuses from capillary blood to tissue cells and carbon dioxide from tissue cells to blood.

Veins

A vein may be defined as any vessel which carries blood towards the heart. Veins have the same basic three layered structure as arteries, with a central lumen, tunica interna, media and externa. Because the pressure of blood in the veins is lower than in arteries, the walls are thinner. Unlike arteries veins have valves within their lumen to prevent back flow of blood. Systemic veins carry deoxygenated blood and the pulmonary veins carry oxygenated blood. Because systemic veins carry deoxygenated blood at relatively low pressure, venous bleeding is seen as the oozing of dark red blood. This is opposed to the spurting of bright red blood from a freshly cut artery.

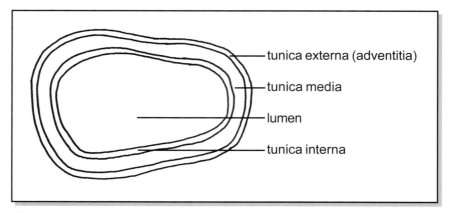

Diagram 2.17
A cross section of a vein.

Deep and superficial venous systems

Veins are often described as existing in two systems; the superficial and the deep venous systems. Superficial veins can be seen and palpated under the skin. These veins are therefore external to the muscles. Deep veins are found deeper in the body, often in muscles. Between the superficial and the deep venous systems are small veins called perforator veins, so called because they perforate the muscle fascia. Venous blood flows from the superficial veins, through the perforator veins, into the deep veins. Once the blood is in the deep venous system it can be rapidly returned to the heart.

If a tourniquet is applied to an arm this will obstruct the normal venous return from the limb. Providing the pressure applied by the tourniquet is less than arterial blood pressure, blood will still be pumped into the arm. This means that blood will accumulate in the arm and the superficial veins will become full and dilated. In clinical practice these superficial veins are very useful for gaining venous access. Once a vein has been cannulated blood samples may be taken or intravenous fluids or drugs given.

Mechanisms facilitating return of venous blood to the heart

Blood flows along the arteries because of the pumping effect of the heart generating a blood pressure. However, once blood has passed through the capillaries, virtually all of this pressure is lost. In veins above the heart, blood can return to the right atrium under the influence of gravity, but for veins below the level of the heart, extra mechanisms of venous return are needed. The mechanisms of venous return are; contraction of adjacent muscles, contraction of adjacent arteries and negative and positive pressures set up in the thorax and abdomen during respiration. All of these mechanisms rely on the action of valves in the veins. These prevent back flow of blood from the centre to the periphery. Any blood trying to flow backwards will have the effect of closing off the valve immediately below. The importance of venous valves is clearly illustrated in varicose veins where there is failure of the valves and pooling of blood dilates the veins.

The most dramatic mechanism of venous return is contraction of adjacent muscles. This works especially well for deep veins which run through muscles. When a muscle contracts, veins within the muscle are squeezed, this has the effect of raising the blood pressure within the lumen of the vein. This will close the valves below the area of increased pressure and force blood upwards, towards the centre of the body. This mechanism works so efficiently in the calf muscles it is referred to as the calf muscle pump. This is why it is important that patients on bed rest keep their ankles moving, this will activate the calf pump, returning blood and preventing pooling of blood in the legs.

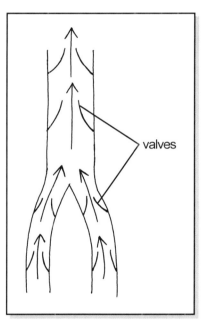

Diagram 2.18
A series of valves in peripheral veins. Blood flowing upwards will automatically open the valves whereas blood flowing backwards will close them. This arrangement means blood can only travel in one direction, from the periphery towards the heart. Arrows indicate the direction of blood flow.

Deep veins, arteries and nerves often run together in the body, usually in areas where they are protected from outside trauma. For example, the main vein and artery in the upper leg lie behind the quadriceps muscle and femur. This means they are protected from most blows or traumas coming from outside. This is why the upper outer aspect of the thigh is a safe site for intramuscular injections; the needle is unlikely to hit a nerve, artery or vein. Because arteries pulsate, they press on adjacent veins and so slightly squeeze them. This will increase the pressure of the blood in the lumen of the vein, so aid venous return. This is a less dramatic mechanism than skeletal muscle contraction but it is constant.

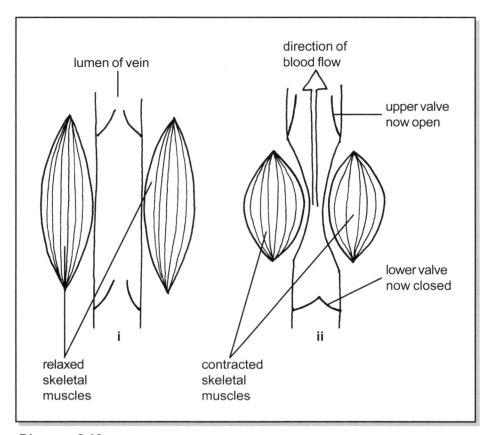

Diagram 2.19
The action of the calf muscle pump, muscle contraction shortens the muscle which squeezes the vein running through.
(i)   A deep vein in a muscle which is relaxed.
(ii)   A deep vein in a muscle which is contracting.

During inspiration the diaphragm moves down. As the diaphragm is between the thorax and the abdomen, downward movement compresses the abdominal contents. Because the inferior vena cava runs through the abdomen, this will be slightly compressed during inspiration. This pressure on the vena cava will increase the pressure of the blood it contains, closing the valves beneath, while pumping blood back into the thoracic cavity. Also during inspiration, because the diaphragm moves down, and the ribs move up and out, the pressure in the thorax is reduced. This reduction in pressure sucks blood into the thoracic vena cava from the abdominal vena cava.

During expiration, because the diaphragm moves up, the pressure in the abdomen is lowered. This allows blood from the leg veins to pass up, into the abdominal vena cava. Expiration also causes pressure changes in the thorax as the diaphragm moves up and the ribs down and inwards. This has the effect of increasing the pressure in the thorax. This will increase the pressure on the thoracic vena cava, increasing the pressure of the blood it contains. This has the effect of squeezing blood from the thoracic vena cava back into the right atrium.

Clinical applications of venous return physiology

The mechanisms of venous return described above are one reason why patients on bed rest should be advised to take regular deep breaths, as well as keeping their ankles moving. If venous return is too sluggish there is the possibility of a blood clot forming in the deep veins, a condition referred to as deep venous thrombosis. This can be very painful, but the real danger is that a part of the blood clot may break off and form an embolus. This will travel with the venous blood back through the right side of the heart and will become jammed in a branch of the pulmonary artery. This condition is referred to as pulmonary embolism and is life threatening.

Some veins you may come across in clinical practice include the jugular in the neck and the subclavian under the clavicle. A venous cannula may be sited in the cephalic vein, over the lateral surface of the radius. The femoral veins drain blood from the legs and the main veins draining blood from the arm are the cephalic and the larger axillary vein. Renal veins carry blood from the kidneys directly to the inferior vena cava. Hepatic veins also directly drain blood from the liver back into the inferior vena cava.

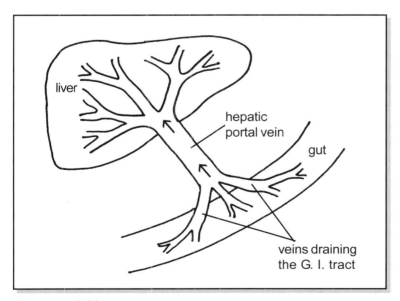

Diagram 2.20
Portal veins; Blood draining from the gastrointestinal tract carries absorbed nutrients and bacterial toxins directly to the liver for biochemical processing. Arrows indicate direction of blood flow.

Portal veins

A portal vein is one which does not drain into a larger vein but ends in capillaries. There is a portal system between the hypothalamus and the anterior pituitary to carry hypothalamic releasing hormones. As blood is passing directly from one area to another it is not diluted in the entire blood volume. This means smaller volumes of hormone may be used to generate the desired physiological effect which increases the efficiency of the process. The other main example of a portal system is the hepatic portal vein. Blood draining from the stomach, small and large intestine is collected together into this single vessel. The result of this is most of the blood drained from the gut passes directly into the liver; only once this blood has circulated through the liver does it enter the inferior vena cava via the hepatic veins. As the blood is carried directly to the liver, absorbed food products may be immediately processed by liver cells, for example, glucose can be stored as glycogen. However, the main reason for the hepatic portal system is to allow the liver to break down bacterial metabolic toxins, generated in the lumen of the gut, before they enter the systemic circulation. If these toxins freely entered systemic blood, there would be a chronic, low grade poisoning of all bodily organs.

CHAPTER 3

Lymphatic System

The lymphatic system

The lymphatic system consists of the lymphatic drainage vessels and other structures which contain lymphatic tissue. Lymphatic tissue is also sometimes referred to as lymphoid tissue.

Lymphatic drainage structures

Lymphatic capillaries drain the tissues

Most of the tissue fluid formed at the arterial end of the capillary is, as we have seen, reabsorbed back into the blood at the venous end of the capillary. However, along with tissue fluid, a few protein molecules also escape from the capillaries into the tissue spaces. If these large osmotic molecules were allowed to remain in the tissue fluid they would increase the osmotic potential, leading to an accumulation of water in the tissue spaces. An excess of fluid in the tissues is abnormal and is termed oedema.

If excess tissue fluid was allowed to accumulate this would cause swelling and would increase the diffusional distance between the blood and tissue cells. This would reduce the speed at which oxygen could be delivered to tissue cells and reduce the rate at which waste products could be removed; both of these effects would reduce tissue viability. The mechanism which removes exuded proteins from the tissue fluid, preventing oedema, is the lymphatic drainage system. Once fluid has passed from the tissue spaces into a lymphatic vessel it is called lymph, or lymphatic fluid.

Unlike blood capillaries the lymphatic capillaries are blind-ended. However, like blood capillaries they are located in the tissue spaces. Lymphatic capillaries are highly permeable and will absorb excess tissue fluid and infecting bacteria, as well as proteins. Endothelial cells which compose the lymphatic capillary walls are separated by pores which allow fluid to enter. The cells also overlap to form valves. This means fluid and other material is able to enter from the tissue spaces but may not escape back out from the lymphatic capillaries. As a lymphatic capillary fills with lymph the pressure in the lumen will close the valves in the wall of the capillary.

Afferent lymphatic vessels transport lymphatic fluid towards lymph nodes

Lymphatic capillaries drain into progressively larger lymphatic vessels. These lymphatic vessels have valves to ensure one way flow of the lymphatic fluid (or lymph) away from the tissues and towards the lymph nodes. In this respect they have a drainage function similar to veins, although lymphatic vessels have more valves and thinner walls. As lymphatic vessels may drain bacteria from a site of tissue infection, it is sometimes possible to see 'tracking' of inflammation along the line of a lymphatic vessel. This is a classical clinical feature and may indicate spread of the infection.

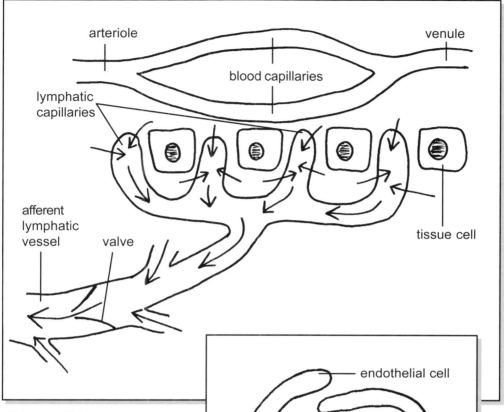

Diagram 3.1
Lymphatic capillaries are located between the cells and blood capillaries of the tissues. Once tissue fluid enters a lymphatic capillary it is referred to as lymphatic fluid. Arrows indicate direction of lymphatic fluid flow from lymphatic capillaries into progressively larger vessels. Valves ensure one way flow from the tissues towards lymph nodes. The vessel is afferent because it is transporting lymphatic fluid towards a lymph node.

Diagram 3.2
Cross section of an individual lymphatic capillary; overlapping cells may 'flap' inwards to allow larger objects, such as bacteria or cancer cells, to drain in with proteins and any excess tissue fluids. The endothelial cells of the lymphatic capillaries act as valves, allowing material in and preventing it from returning to the tissue spaces.

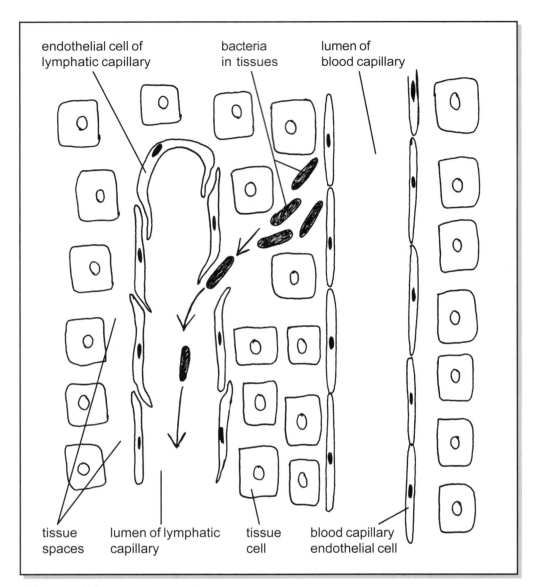

endothelial cell of lymphatic capillary

bacteria in tissues

lumen of blood capillary

tissue spaces

lumen of lymphatic capillary

tissue cell

blood capillary endothelial cell

Diagram 3.3

Fortunately bacteria cannot be absorbed directly through the walls of blood capillaries into the blood. If this did happen bacteria could rapidly multiply and spread all around the body leading to systemic sepsis. However, in this diagram a group of bacteria have entered the tissue spaces through a cut or burn. The increased pressure in the tissue spaces caused by the presence of the bacteria has caused the endothelial cells of the lymphatic capillary to part slightly allowing the bacteria to enter the lumen. Once in the lymphatic lumen they will not be able to leave as any increased pressure within the lymphatic capillary will close the gaps between the endothelial cells. In this way the cells of the lymphatic capillary function rather like a one way cat flap, allowing bacteria in but not out. Once in the lymphatic capillary the bacteria will be washed along in the flow of lymph towards a lymph node where they will be destroyed.

Lymph nodes filter lymphatic fluid

These nodes are found throughout the body but are more common at particular sites such as the axilla and groin. There are also numerous internal lymph nodes in the thorax and abdomen. Lymph nodes are surrounded by a capsule composed of dense connective tissue. The capsule folds inwards forming trabeculae, which create spaces within the node referred to as sinuses. Throughout the node there is a network of reticular fibres (reticulum is latin for net). These fibres form a three dimensional network throughout the node. Several afferent lymphatic vessels drain into a lymph node. The lymphatic fluid then percolates through the node, and because of the reticulum bacteria or cancer cells get trapped.

Lymph nodes are packed with white blood cells. Macrophages are able to phagocytose bacteria trapped in the reticular fibres. There are also numerous lymphocytes. T cells are able to recognise viruses and bacteria, and instruct B cells to produce antibodies. In addition infection will trigger mitosis in B cells to produce many more B cells and plasma cells. These specialist defence cells are capable of synthesising large amounts of a specific antibody to combat an infection.

These immunological functions mean the lymph nodes are able to trap and kill micro-organisms which are drained from infected tissue. They also function as an early warning system for tissue infections. Infection may be recognised and an immune response commenced before any infection reaches the blood. Lymph nodes are able to do this because they are physiologically situated between the tissues and blood. Lymphatic fluid may only return to the blood once it has passed through a lymph node. When challenged by infection the lymph nodes swell, largely due to the proliferation of white blood cells. The correct term for this swelling is lymphadenopathy, but they are usually referred to as 'swollen glands'. Scientifically lymph nodes are not glands because they do not produce an endocrine or exocrine product.

In addition to filtering out foreign organisms, lymph nodes are able to filter cancer cells preventing or slowing the spread of a cancer around the body. One of the characteristics of cancer cells is that they no longer adhere to surrounding cells effectively. This means they may break away from their original location and be absorbed by the lymphatic capillaries. From the lymphatic capillaries the cancer cells will drain into the afferent lymphatic vessels and then into lymph nodes. Lymph nodes will filter out cancer cells, retaining them in the node. Within a lymph node cytotoxic T lymphocytes and NK (natural killer) lymphocyte cells are then activated against the malignant cells. This will delay the spread of malignant cells to other locations around the body. However, if cancer cells continue to reproduce in the lymph nodes they will eventually spread around the body in the process of metastasis.

If a lymphatic vessel is blocked, or several lymph nodes are surgically removed, this can lead to areas of localised oedema as there is obstruction of normal lymphatic drainage.

Efferent lymphatic vessels transport lymphatic fluid away from lymph nodes

The vessels carrying lymphatic fluid away from the lymph nodes are referred to as efferent. As the lymphatic fluid has been filtered through the lymph nodes it should be consistently sterile. Efferent lymphatic vessels join together to form larger drainage vessels called trunks. Trunks from the right side of the thorax, right arm and right side of the head and neck join to form the right lymphatic duct which drains its contents directly into the right subclavian vein, which is located just under the clavicle.

Lymphatic trunks from both legs, abdomen, left side of the head, neck, thorax, and left arm all drain into the left lymphatic duct. This is the main lymphatic duct in the body, and drains its fluid into the left subclavian vein. Two to three litres of fluid are drained back into the venous blood per day via the two lymphatic ducts. Therefore there is a complete circulation of lymphatic fluid from the tissue spaces back into the venous blood.

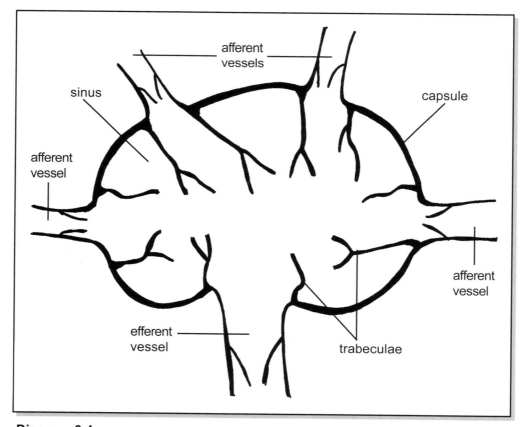

Diagram 3.4
A lymph node. Lymphatic fluid enters via afferent vessels and leaves via efferent vessels.

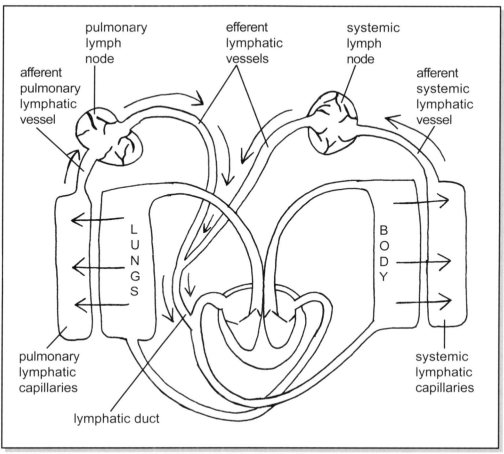

Diagram 3.5
Circulation of lymphatic fluid from the pulmonary and systemic lymphatic capillaries back into the systemic venous circulation. Arrows indicate direction of flow of lymphatic fluid.

Other lymphatic tissues

Lymphatic tissue is composed of fine reticular fibres which combine to form a connective tissue. These fine fibres often form a three dimensional framework like scaffolding, which can act as a support for other tissues and cells. The reticular fibres in lymphatic tissues support dense masses of white blood cells particularly macrophages and lymphocytes. In addition to lymph nodes this lymphatic tissue is found in several other structures.

Spleen holds a reserve of red and white blood cells

The spleen is an organ located in the upper left area of the abdomen, just under the left costal margin (just below the ribs). It is the single largest mass of lymphoid tissue in the body. In a similar way to lymph nodes filtering lymph, the spleen filters blood to ensure it remains sterile. There are two types of tissue in the spleen referred to as red and white pulp.

White pulp is composed of lymphatic tissue and is full of lymphocytes and macrophages. These cells will kill any bacteria which have entered the blood. In addition if micro-organisms are detected, they will trigger proliferation of defensive white cells. The sheer numbers of white cells in the spleen means that infections can often be eliminated before they have time to be established. This vital defensive role of the spleen is illustrated in people who have had their spleen removed (usually after a traumatic rupture). These people are no longer able to rapidly respond to a bacterial or viral challenge, and are at risk of sudden, overwhelming infection. Many take regular prophylactic antibiotics against this life threatening possibility.

Red pulp carries out various functions related to red blood cells. It contains blood filled spaces called sinusoids. Just as the white pulp acts as a reservoir of white cells the red pulp holds a reserve of red cells. If there is haemorrhage, the spleen can contract and transfer blood from the sinusoids into the systemic circulation. In addition to this liquid blood, packed red blood cells from the red pulp may enter the systemic circulation if they are required. The result of this is that after a loss of blood the numbers of red blood cells in the circulatory system can be rapidly restored. This restores the oxygen carrying capacity of the blood and so allows the person to be able to fight or run effectively shortly after losing some blood, increasing the probability of survival after an injury. This explains why people are able to return to work shortly after donating a unit of blood.

Various white blood cells including macrophages, lymphocytes and granulocytes are also found in the red pulp. Macrophages in the red pulp phagocytose old and defective red blood cells making the spleen the main site of red cell breakdown, a process referred to as haemolysis. As the spleen is a highly vascular organ it may bleed massively if it is ruptured by abdominal trauma. This may happen as a consequence of external forces caused by such events as road traffic accidents, violence or falls. Sometimes the blood vessels to the spleen need to be tied off and the spleen removed to prevent life threatening haemorrhage.

T lymphocytes mature in the thymus gland

The thymus is located in the chest, posterior to the sternum. As well as the endocrine functions discussed in chapter 7, the thymus is involved in the maturation of T lymphocytes. Immature, undifferentiated T cells divide in bone marrow and migrate to the thymus gland. Here they develop and differentiate into mature, immunocompetent T lymphocytes. Some of the T cells released from the thymus remain in the blood, but many travel to other areas of lymphoid tissue, such as the lymph nodes or spleen where they remain. Most of the activity of the thymus in differentiation and maturation of T cells takes place in the few months before and after birth, although there is some ongoing activity in childhood. If the thymus gland is removed in adult life the function of the T lymphocytes is not seriously impaired.

The tonsils

These are collections of lymphoid tissue associated with the upper airway. They are located at either side of the throat and are visible through an open mouth. This is a logical site for lymphoid tissue with reserves of leucocytes, as the airway is frequently exposed to bacteria and viruses in inhaled air. Tonsils are located under the moist epithelial lining of the pharynx and their function is to filter tissue fluid. This means they will filter any bacteria which have infected the epithelium and the tissue fluid beneath. Tonsils can become loaded with bacteria and severe tonsillitis may develop (itis always means inflammation of). In the past tonsils were surgically removed for repeated tonsillitis; however, it is now recognised that tonsillitis is a sign that they are performing their immunological function. There are actually three collections of lymphatic tissue referred to as tonsils. These are in the nasopharynx, at the base of the tongue and in the lateral walls of the oropharynx at the back of the mouth. It is the tonsils in the oropharynx that people usually mean when referring to 'tonsils'. Their correct name is the palatine tonsils.

Diffuse lymphatic tissue

This form of lymphatic tissue is not surrounded by a capsule. In comparison, the spleen, lymph nodes and thymus are all compartmentalised by their own capsule. The appendix, attached to the caecum of the large intestine, contains a lot of diffuse lymphatic tissue. In the small intestine there are about 30 areas or patches of lymphoid tissue located in the connective tissues of the ileum. These are referred to as aggregated lymphatic follicles (formally called Peyer's patches). While small areas of diffuse lymphatic tissue can be safely removed, (such as in appendicectomy), collectively this lymphatic tissue is necessary to protect specific areas of the body. In addition to these specific areas small amounts of lymphatic tissue are found in almost every organ of the body. It is also necessary for there to be enough lymphatic tissue to protect the whole body against systemic infection.

CHAPTER 4

Blood

Components of Blood

Blood consists of two basic constituents. The first is the fluid component, referred to as plasma. Within the plasma floats the second component, the blood cells. Blood volume is normally made up of about 55% plasma and 45% cells. If an anticoagulant, such as heparin, is added to a sample of blood, which is then centrifuged, all of the cells will be forced to the bottom of the tube while the plasma remains floating on top.

Diagram 4.1
Sample of anticoagulated, centrifuged blood to show the cellular and plasma components. Most of the cells are red but there is a thin layer of white cells just below the plasma.

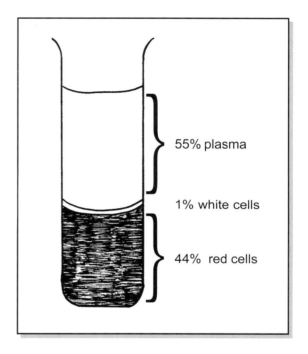

55% plasma

1% white cells

44% red cells

Blood volumes vary with body size

Blood volumes will clearly vary depending on the size of the person. At six months of age a baby will typically have a total of about 500 mls of blood. This will rise to a litre at two years of age. A ten year old may have about 2 litres and a twelve year old a little over 3 litres. This has clear implications for the significance of blood loss in children; most adults can lose 500 mls of blood without any problems but in children this volume of loss could be fatal. Average sized adults have a total of 5 litres of blood, with larger individuals having correspondingly more.

Plasma

Plasma is a yellowish fluid which is about 91% water. This keeps the blood fluid, allowing it to circulate around the body. The rest of the plasma is made up of various substances in solution and suspension; these include plasma proteins, nutrients, dissolved gases and waste products.

Plasma proteins

Proteins are organic molecules made up of precise sequences of amino acids which are chemically bound together. There are three main plasma proteins; albumin, globulin and fibrinogen. Proteins are very large molecules and their presence is vital to generate plasma osmotic potential. Without this osmotic property the blood would be unable to reabsorb tissue fluid into the venous ends of the capillaries. Albumin is the most common plasma protein and also generates most of the osmotic potential of plasma. The globulin proteins include the immunoglobulins, also called antibodies, which allow the body to fight off infections. Without these immune proteins we would probably die from the next viral or bacterial infection we pick up. Other globulin proteins act as carrier molecules which transport some hormones and minerals around the body. Fibrinogen is a plasma protein which is essential for the process of normal blood clotting.

As fats are not soluble in water they are transported around the body bound to plasma proteins. These combinations of fat and protein are termed lipoproteins and are soluble in water.

Nutrients and waste products

Plasma carries absorbed nutrients from the gut to all of the tissues of the body which need them. These include glucose, amino acids and vitamins. It also transports waste substances such as ammonia from the tissues to the liver, where this poisonous waste is converted into urea, which is much less toxic. Once formed, the urea is transported in solution from the liver to the kidneys for excretion.

Other plasma components and functions

Plasma is a carrying vehicle for a range of dissolved salts in ionic form. These include sodium, chloride, bicarbonate, potassium, phosphate, magnesium and calcium. Plasma also carries some dissolved gases such as carbon dioxide, nitrogen and some oxygen. Most of the carbon dioxide transported by the blood is carried by the plasma. Plasma also transports endocrine hormones from glands to their target tissues.

Collectively the blood is important in transferring heat around the body, helping to regulate body temperature. Heat from warm, metabolically active areas, such as the muscles and liver must be transported away to prevent localised overheating. This warm blood can then be used to warm cooler areas such as the feet.

Blood is slightly alkaline. Arterial blood has a pH of 7.35-7.45, but venous blood is slightly more acidic with a normal pH of 7.35. This difference is caused by the increased volumes of carbon dioxide carried in the venous blood, some of which is carried as carbonic acid.

Blood cells

There are two main forms of blood cells; red cells and white cells. Red cells are correctly termed erythrocytes and white cells leucocytes.

Red blood cells are erythrocytes

The function of the erythrocytes is to carry oxygen from lungs to tissues and carbon dioxide from tissues to lungs. The percentage of blood which is composed of red cells is termed the haematocrit; this may be lowered in some forms of anaemia. Red cells are biconcave discs. This shape provides a large surface area for gaseous exchange and also gives the cell flexibility. Some capillaries are so small the red cells have to squeeze through by deforming their shape. Red cells are about 7 micrometres in diameter (i.e. 7 one thousandths of a millimetre). Every cubic millimetre (mm^3) of blood contains about 5 million red blood cells.

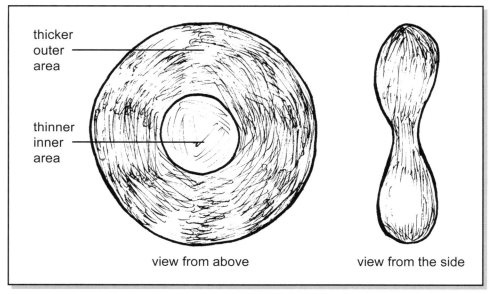

thicker outer area

thinner inner area

view from above   view from the side

Diagram 4.2
Views of a red cell from above and the side. From above the outer, thicker area of the cell appears to be darker red than the thinner, inner central area. The lighter area in the centre of the erythrocyte (area of central pallor) representing the thinner middle, is one third or less of the total diameter.

Blood is red because of the presence of the red cells. Erythrocytes are red because they contain a large pigmented protein molecule called haemoglobin. It is haemoglobin which actually carries the oxygen. A single haemoglobin molecule can form a loose bond with four oxygen molecules. Although the haemoglobin molecule is large it is based on four atoms of iron. If there is no iron, haemoglobin cannot be synthesised. This is why iron deficiency will cause anaemia. Vitamin B_{12} and folic acid are also essential for normal maturation of red blood cells in the bone marrow. This means deficiency of these essential nutrients will also lead to anaemia. Anaemia means a reduced oxygen carrying capacity of the blood. Mature red blood cells in the circulating blood are unique as they have no nucleus which allows more space for carrying haemoglobin but also limits the life span of red cells to about 17 weeks.

In the lungs, dark red, deoxygenated haemoglobin will combine with oxygen to form bright red oxyhaemoglobin. In the systemic capillaries the reverse will happen; oxyhaemoglobin will give up oxygen molecules and revert to deoxyhaemoglobin. It is this colour change which accounts for the bright red blood seen in arterial haemorrhage as opposed to the dark red blood seen in venous bleeding.

The process of oxygen transfer may be summarised as follows:

IN THE LUNGS
Haemoglobin + oxygen → oxyhaemoglobin

IN THE TISSUES
Oxyhaemoglobin → haemoglobin + oxygen

Erythrocytes are formed from blood stem cells in the red bone marrow, a process which is called erythropoiesis. A stem cell is any cell which is capable of differentiation into other cell types. Red bone marrow is found in the ends of long bones and in flat bones such as the sternum and pelvis. The regulation of erythropoiesis is discussed in the chapter on the endocrine system.

At the end of their life span, old red cells are phagocytosed by large cells called macrophages. This takes place mostly in the spleen, but also in the liver and bone marrow. Protein from the old red cells is broken down into amino acids and the iron is transported back to the bone marrow to be recycled. The coloured pigment from the haemoglobin is converted into a bile pigment called bilirubin, which is taken up by the liver and excreted into the small intestine in bile.

White blood cells are leucocytes

Leucocytes basically protect the body against disease and infection. These include resistance to bacteria, viruses, fungi, protozoa, worms and some toxins. Some leucocytes will also attack and kill some cancer cells. They also unfortunately 'defend' the body against transplanted organs. This is because white cells are able to distinguish between 'self' and 'non-self' material, and will attack anything they perceive to be non-self. White cells are much less numerous than red cells. Each cubic millimetre of blood contains about 7000 leucocytes.

There are two main forms of white cells which are described according to the appearance of their cytoplasm. Some white cells have cytoplasm which appears granular, so this group are classified as granulocytes. Other white cells have cytoplasm which appears clear, with no obvious granules; these are called agranulocytes (a or an means without, so these cells are without granules). There are three types of granulocytes; neutrophils, eosinophils and basophils (note all of the names of granulocytes end in phil). There are only two main forms of agranulocytes, lymphocytes and monocytes. However, thrombocytes (platelets) are normally included in this group.

Neutrophils

Neutrophils are the most common form of leucocyte, normally composing 60-70% of the white cells in the blood. Most of the granules in the cytoplasm are fairly small and may be difficult to see under a light microscope. Granules in the cytoplasm contain lysozyme and a variety of other enzymes capable of digesting bacteria and other material during phagocytosis. The nucleus of a neutrophil has two to five lobes which are connected by fine threads. This is why neutrophils are sometimes referred to as polymorphonuclear leucocytes. (Poly means many and morph relates to shape).

During an infection the number of neutrophils will increase significantly to help the body fight the causative microorganism. This increase in number is called a neutrophil leucocytosis. As well as killing bacteria, neutrophils will kill fungi. In addition they will phagocytose dead or damaged body cells. When body cells die or are killed, e.g. after injury, it is important that they are phagocytosed to remove them. If left in a tissue, necrotic (dead) cells form an excellent habitat and food supply for infecting bacteria. Neutrophils migrate out of inflamed blood vessels into areas where there is injury or infection to perform these immune functions.

Eosinophils

These cells are often slightly larger than neutrophils at about 13-15 micrometres. The cytoplasmic granules in eosinophils are larger than those found in neutrophils. Normally about 2-4% of the leucocytes in blood are eosinophils. The nucleus usually has two lobes, again joined by a thin thread. Eosinophils help the body fight infections of protozoa and larger parasites such as worms. If a parasite enters the body eosinophils attach themselves to the surface of the parasite using adhesion molecules. They then deposit digestive enzymes and other toxic molecules from their granules onto the parasite. This toxic assault will weaken or kill the parasite, reducing the damage it is able to inflict on the body tissues.

Eosinophils are attracted to areas where allergic reactions are occurring, such as the bronchioles in people with asthma. Once in the area they are able to chemically neutralise and detoxify some of the inflammation causing substances, such as histamines which are involved in the generation of allergic responses. This is why eosinophil numbers increase in parasitic infections and allergic disorders. Many eosinophils migrate out of the blood to protect the tissues against potential infection, often where a body surface is exposed to the external environment. They are found associated with mucous membranes in the digestive and respiratory systems as well as the female reproductive tract.

Basophils

These cells are uncommon in the blood and only compose approximately 0.5% of leucocytes. The nucleus is irregular and lobed, but is often hard to see through the large, abundant granules in the cytoplasm. These granules contain histamine, heparin and bradykinin. The physiological role of basophils in the blood is unclear; however, it is well known that heparin prevents blood coagulation. Most basophils enter the tissues where they remain localised. In the tissues they are called mast cells and their main function is to facilitate an inflammatory reaction in response to any insult of the tissue. If a tissue is damaged mast cells will release inflammatory mediators such as histamine and bradykinin. These mediators generate the characteristic heat, pain, redness and swelling of the inflammatory response.

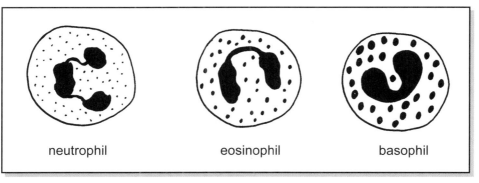

Diagram 4.3
The granulocytic leucocytes are neutrophils, eosinophils and basophils.

Lymphocytes

These are the most common form of agranulocytes, normally comprising about 20-25% of circulating leucocytes. Lymphocytes may be classified as large or small. Large lymphocytes are the natural killer or NK cells and are able to kill body cells infected with viruses.

Most of the lymphocytes are classified as small; they are about the same size as the red cells. The nucleus is large and spherical. Large numbers of lymphocytes can be found in lymphatic tissue, such as in the spleen, lymph nodes, tonsils and appendix. There are two main forms of small lymphocyte, these are called B and T. B lymphocytes mature in bone marrow and T lymphocytes mature in the thymus gland. The function of the B lymphocyte cell lines is the production of antibodies. An antibody is an immune protein, produced in response to the presence of a specific antigen. An antigen is something the immune system recognises as foreign such as a measles virus.

There are three forms of T lymphocyte. These are called T helper cells, T cytotoxic cells and T suppressor cells. T helper cells 'help' B cells to produce antibodies. B cells will only produce antibodies when stimulated to do so by T helpers. Human immunodeficiency virus (HIV) attacks and kills T helper cells. This means they are unable to stimulate antibody production. Without the antibodies, immunodeficiency results which can lead to acquired immunodeficiency syndrome (AIDS).

When B cells have produced enough antibodies to deal with a particular infection, T suppressor cells inhibit B cell lines, and antibody production will be reduced. T cytotoxic cells have a range of defensive functions. They are able to detect and kill cells which are infected with viral particles. Although this strategy kills a body cell, it also kills the viruses in the cell, and so prevents them infecting further cells. Cytotoxic T cells are also able to detect and kill some cancer cells. It may be that malignant cells arise comparatively frequently, but are destroyed before they can divide to form a tumour. T cytotoxic cells will also directly attack foreign material such as parasites. (A fuller account of the role of leucocytes in immunity is given in chapter 18).

An increase in the number of lymphocytes is referred to as a lymphocytosis; this means more antibodies may be produced to counter any infection. The most common cause of this is a viral infection, but it will also occur in tuberculosis.

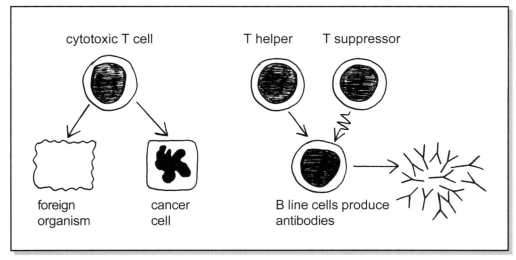

Diagram 4.4
Overview of the functions of the B and T lymphocytes. Cytotoxic T cells directly attack foreign organisms and cancer cells. T helper cells stimulate antibody production by B lymphocytes while T supressor cells inhibit production.

Monocytes

Monocytes are large phagocytic cells; they may grow up to 20 micrometres in diameter. The nucleus is relatively large and is usually oval or 'kidney' shaped. They are able to migrate through capillary walls, by the process of amoeboid movement, to live in organs or tissues. Amoeboid movement involves a flow of the cytoplasm within the cell membrane, moving the cell forward. Once in the tissues monocytes are referred to as macrophages. If any bacteria are encountered in the tissues they will rapidly be destroyed. Macro means big, and phage means to eat, so by name and by function they are literally 'big eaters'. The number of monocytes is particularly likely to rise in chronic bacterial infections.

Monocyte-macrophage cell system

Macrophages, derived from monocytes, are found in most tissues of the body. Sometimes they are fixed to tissue cells and sometimes they are free to patrol a tissue. Once in a tissue the macrophages may live for years before being required to perform an immune function. Tissue macrophages act as a first line of defence for the body tissues. They will phagocytose infecting viruses, bacteria or necrotic tissue which might have been killed as a result of trauma, infection or disease. If infection is detected in a tissue the macrophages will release a chemical messenger called a cytokine. This cytokine will circulate to the bone marrow where it will increase the release of neutrophils to fight the infection. Monocytes also produce pyrogens which act on the hypothalamus to increase body temperature during infection. These functions mean the tissue macrophages act as an early warning system for infection. The monocyte-macrophage cell system is the term used to describe all of the monocytes, fixed and mobile macrophages in the body. The old name for the monocyte-macrophage cell system was the reticuloendothelial system.

Thrombocytes

Thrombocytes or platelets are fragments of a type of white cell called a megakaryocyte. These are very large cells which fragment in the red bone marrow into over 2000 fragments. Each fragment is enclosed in a cell membrane and is an individual thrombocyte (platelet). Platelets are essential for the process of blood clotting. Initially platelets will stick together to form a platelet plug. Then their granules will release chemicals which promote blood clotting. If there is a deficiency of platelets then blood clotting will be inhibited resulting in haemorrhage and bruising. Lack of thrombocytes is termed thrombocytopenia.

Phagocytosis is cell eating

Granulocytes, monocytes and macrophages take part in the process of phagocytosis. This is the process whereby cells ingest and digest material the immune system

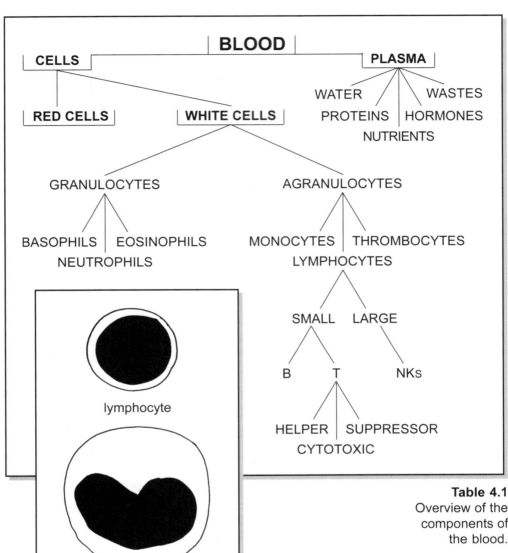

BLOOD

CELLS

RED CELLS   WHITE CELLS

PLASMA

WATER   WASTES
PROTEINS   HORMONES
NUTRIENTS

GRANULOCYTES   AGRANULOCYTES

BASOPHILS │ EOSINOPHILS   MONOCYTES │ THROMBOCYTES
NEUTROPHILS   LYMPHOCYTES

SMALL   LARGE

B   T   NKs

HELPER │ SUPPRESSOR
CYTOTOXIC

lymphocyte

monocyte

thrombocytes

Table 4.1
Overview of the
components of
the blood.

Diagram 4.5
The agranulocytic leucocytes are the
lymphocytes, monocytes and thrombocytes.

has identified for destruction. Phagocytes are able to detect the presence of foreign material by a chemical recognition system (in other words they can 'smell' it). They are also able to recognise and phagocytose dead and damaged tissue cells. Phagocytosis literally means 'cell eating'; the following account describes how a phagocyte eats a group of bacteria.

When the bacteria are detected the phagocyte moves towards them. Phagocytes are capable of an independent form of locomotion called chemotaxis which uses amoeboid movement. Once the phagocyte arrives next to the bacteria, it carries on moving towards them. The result of this is that the bacteria become engulfed by the cell membrane and cytoplasm of the phagocyte. Eventually the bacteria are completely enclosed in the cytoplasm of the phagocyte, within a vacuole composed of external cell membrane. After this, lysosomes move towards the newly formed vacuole. Lysosomes are specialist organelles which contain

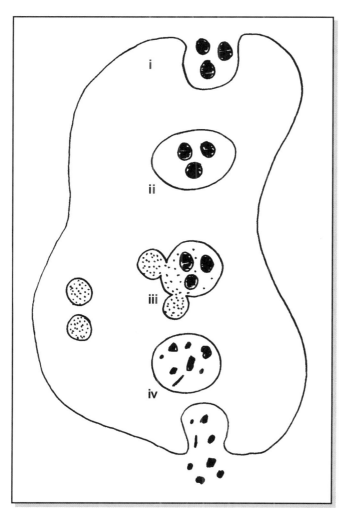

Diagram 4.6
Diagram of the sequential stages of phagocytosis.
(i) After moving towards the bacteria they are ingested; the phagocyte 'eats' them.
(ii) Bacteria are now isolated in a vacuole.
(iii) Lysosomes move towards the bacteria containing vacuole and the membranes merge. This pours digestive enzymes from the lysosomes onto the bacteria which are then digested.
(iv) Products of digestion which are not absorbed are excreted from the cell.

digestive enzymes such as lysozyme. When the membrane surrounding the lysosomes and the vacuole come into contact their membranes fuse, allowing the digestive enzymes to pour onto the trapped bacteria, which will then be digested into constituent carbohydrates, amino and fatty acids. These products of digestion are then absorbed by the phagocyte and surrounding cells as nutrients. A few break-down products from the bacteria which are not absorbed are ejected from the phagocytic cell.

ABO Rhesus system of blood grouping

People may be one of four possible major blood groups. They may be A, B, AB or O. In addition to these four groups there is a further group called the Rhesus factor. This is an additional group which a person may, or may not have, in addition to being A, B, AB or O. An individual may therefore be A Rhesus positive or Rhesus negative, B positive or negative, AB positive or negative or O positive or negative. The blood group a person has depends on the nature of their red cells, which is in turn genetically programmed. Blood groups are determined by protein based structures located on the external membranes of the red cells.

These grouping molecules are specific proteins which possess a particular molecular shape and are referred to as antigens. Someone is blood group A if they have A antigens on their red cells. In blood group B the person has B antigens on the surface of their red cells. The presence of group A and B antigens on the surface of the red cells means the individual would be group AB. People with group O have no antigens on the surface of their red cells. In fact O is a corruption of zero so really the blood groups should be A, B, AB and zero but we have changed this to O. So a person with blood group O actually has no ABO grouping antigens on the surface of their red cells. The Rhesus factor is also an antigen which is simply present or absent on the surface of the red blood cells.

Use of the term 'antigen' in reference to blood groups often causes confusion because an antigen is something the body recognises as foreign. Clearly the body should not recognise its own proteins as foreign. However, our understanding of blood groups was first developed with reference to blood transfusions, so the term antigen is used with reference to the recipient of donated blood. A recipient's immune system would recognise the group-defining proteins on donated red cells as antigenic, if they were from an incompatible group.

In addition to the antigens which determine blood group there are also associated antibodies present or absent in the plasma of particular blood groups. These antibodies are to all of the AB antigens the individual does not possess so, if a person is blood group A they will have antibodies to antigen B in their plasma. If a person is blood group B they will have antibodies to antigen A in their plasma. In blood group AB there will be no antibodies in the plasma, and if a person is blood group O they will have A and B antibodies in their plasma.

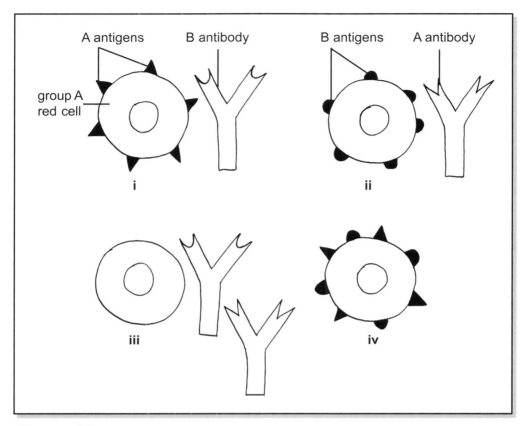

Diagram 4.7
The ABO blood grouping system.
(i)   Blood group A has A antigens on the red cells and B antibodies in the plasma.
(ii) Blood group B has B antigens on the red cells and antibody A in the plasma.
(iii) Blood group O has no (zero) antigens on the red cells and both antibodies A and B in the plasma.
(iv) Blood group AB has A and B antigens on the red cells but no antibodies in the plasma.

An antibody is a protein, found in the blood, which will bind to its specific reciprocal antigen. This means an A antibody will bind to an A antigen if the two come into contact. Therefore if a person with group A blood gives some blood to a person with group B blood, the A antibodies in the recipient's plasma will bind to the A antigens on the donor's red cells. This will cause many of the donated red cells to clump together in a process called agglutination.

This is a potentially life threatening complication of blood transfusion. It is therefore necessary that in a recipient's plasma there are no antibodies to the antigens on the donated red blood cells. If a person with group B blood donates blood to a person with group A blood then the B antibodies in the recipient's plasma will bind to the B antigens on the given red cells. This will cause agglutination (i.e. clumping) of the donated cells with the recipient's antibodies. Clumps of red cells will, over time, be broken down in the process of haemolysis which is why transfusion mis-matches are sometimes referred to as transfusion haemolytic reactions.

In theory each blood group can give to people with the same group as themselves, because they will share the same antibodies. Because people with group AB blood have no antibodies in their plasma they can, in ABO terms, receive blood from anyone. As they have no antibodies in their plasma, there will be no antibodies to bind to donated antigens, therefore there will be no agglutination. A person with group O blood can give blood to any other person because their blood contains no antigens. This means that whatever antibodies may be present in the recipient's plasma there will be no agglutination of donated cells. These principles explain why AB is sometimes referred to as the universal recipient and O as the universal donor.

Rhesus factor

The second common blood grouping uses the Rhesus factor (Rh factor), so called because it was first discovered in Rhesus monkeys. Rhesus factor is in addition to the ABO groups. This factor is simply present or absent on the red

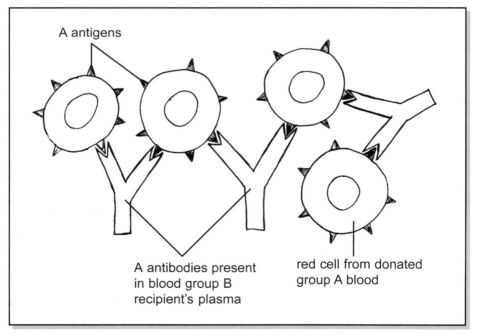

A antigens

A antibodies present in blood group B recipient's plasma

red cell from donated group A blood

Diagram 4.8
In this case group A blood has been given to a group B recipient by mistake. The result is that the A antibodies in the recipient's plasma bind to the A antigens on the surface of the donor's red cells. This results in agglutination.

cells. Unlike the ABO system there are no naturally occurring antibodies in the plasma, but antibodies may develop in a Rhesus negative individual if they are exposed to Rhesus positive blood.

Recipients who are Rhesus negative should therefore only receive Rhesus negative blood. If they were to be given Rhesus positive blood there would be

		DONORS			
		A	B	AB	O
RECIPIENTS	A	✓	X	X	✓
	B	X	✓	X	✓
	AB	✓	✓	✓	✓
	O	X	X	X	✓

Table 4.2
Summary of which donated blood may be given to which recipients in the ABO system.

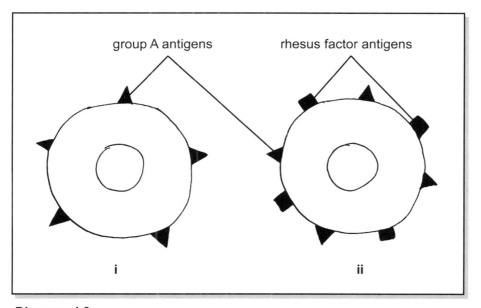

Diagram 4.9
The Rhesus factor is present or absent.
(i)   Group A red cell which is Rhesus negative.
(ii)   Group A red cell which is Rhesus positive.

no reaction on the first occasion, but the introduction of Rhesus antigens would cause the recipient to produce Rhesus factor antibodies. This means if the patient were to be given Rhesus positive blood on a second occasion, the new Rhesus factor antibodies would bind to the donated Rhesus factor antigen, leading to agglutination. Therefore Rhesus negative recipients may only receive Rhesus negative blood. However, in theory, Rhesus positive patients may receive Rhesus negative blood, as the red cells contain no antigens.

Once the Rhesus factor is taken into account it means that O negative is the universal donor and AB positive the universal recipient. The Rhesus factor is sometimes referred to as the D factor. This is because the most active component of the Rhesus factor antigen is termed the D factor.

Rhesus factor incompatibility in pregnancy and neonates

This problem arises as a result of the genetic transmission of Rhesus factor from parents to children. When a mother is Rh negative and the father is Rh positive there is a chance the baby will be Rhesus positive. There will be a 50% or a 100% chance of a baby being Rhesus positive depending on the genetic makeup of the father.

In Rh incompatibility the mother will develop Rh antibodies if there is blood to blood contact with her Rh positive baby. Mixing of maternal and baby blood may occur during birth. The rhesus factor in the baby's blood will act as an antigen in the circulation of the mother, causing her to produce Rh factor antibodies. This does not usually affect the baby during the first pregnancy, however during subsequent pregnancies she will already possess antibodies to the Rh factor. This can result in the mother's antibodies crossing the placenta and attacking the baby's blood, leading to a condition called haemolytic disease of the newborn. Affected babies have a reduced oxygen carrying capacity of the blood and are jaundiced due to the presence of red cell breakdown products such as bilirubin.

This complication should now be prevented by the administration of an Anti D injection, given to the mother after the birth of every baby. These injected D antibodies quickly destroy (mop up) any Rh-positive baby cells in the mother's blood. The result of this intervention is Rh-positive cells are not present in the maternal circulation for long enough to stimulate the mother's immune system to produce antibodies to the Rhesus factor.

Haemostasis

This describes the process whereby bleeding stops when a blood vessel is ruptured, the aim being to prevent ongoing blood loss. Bleeding may occur from any of the blood vessels, i.e. haemorrhage may be arterial, venous or capillary. Haemostasis may be considered under three headings; vascular spasm, platelet plugging and thirdly, the coagulation cascade.

Vascular spasm

In vascular spasm the smooth muscle of a blood vessel wall constricts after being damaged or cut. As a blood vessel constricts, the diameter of the lumen is reduced which reduces the amount of blood loss from the cut or damaged vessel. This mechanism is aided by cold and inhibited by heat. The cold was one reason why some severely injured soldiers survived in the Falklands war; the cold aided vascular shut down which prevented life threatening blood loss.

Platelet plugging

The second stage is referred to as platelet plugging. When the lining of a blood vessel is damaged substances are released which activate platelets, making them become very sticky. This means that the platelets adhere to the injury to form a temporary plug. This is sufficient to block small damaged vessels and prevent capillary bleeding.

Coagulation cascade

The third phase is referred to as the coagulation cascade. This is the actual process of blood clotting; there are twelve factors responsible for this denoted by the relevant Roman numeral. Overall the process converts liquid blood into a semisolid mass which forms a plug over the injury. Once formed, this can stay in position for several days.

Any cascade consists of a series of pre-synthesised components in an inactive form. In the case of the clotting cascade these components are present in the blood. A stimulus triggers off the first reaction in a cascade which triggers the second and so on. The activation of the final component of a cascade normally brings about a significant physiological change, in this case blood clotting. The advantage of having numerous steps to a cascade is that the process can be inhibited at any stage by negative feedback activity. This is important because if a blood clot forms within a blood vessel this can lead to serious complications. If a blood clot forms inside a blood vessel it is termed a thrombus. For example, when a blood clot forms inside a deep vein this is termed a deep venous thrombosis. If part of this thrombus breaks away it will be carried in the venous flow as an embolus. Such an embolus will pass through the right side of the heart and lodge in a branch of the pulmonary arterial tree of the lungs causing a condition termed pulmonary embolism. As this will block off the blood supply to an area of the lungs it is a potentially life threatening condition.

The process of clotting starts when factor XII (also called Hageman factor after the person it was discovered in) comes into contact with collagen in the damaged wall of a blood vessel. Factor XII is a plasma protein which is normally present in plasma, but in an inactive form. It is the contact with collagen which activates factor XII causing it to function as an enzyme.

Once activated, factor XII, in turn, activates further factors which eventually cause the inactive plasma protein called prothrombin to be broken down into thrombin, a much smaller protein. Factors derived from platelets and calcium ions are required for some of the steps in the process. Prothrombin is continually

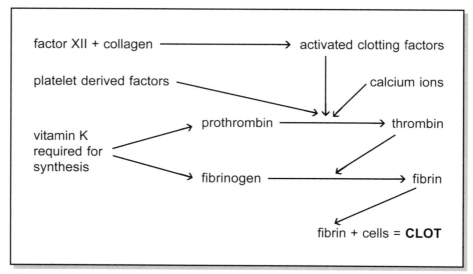

Table 4.3
The principle stages in blood clotting.

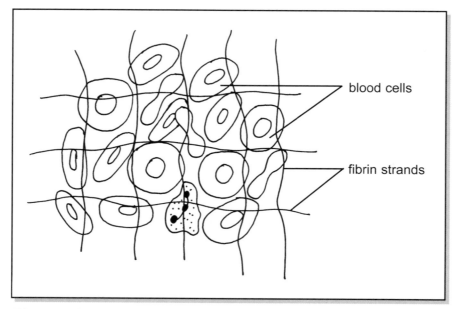

Diagram 4.10
A blood clot forms when blood cells adhere to sticky strands of fibrin.

used for blood clotting throughout the body so must be continually synthesised in the liver. Vitamin K is necessary for the formation of prothrombin and fibrinogen. This is why patients with liver failure or vitamin K deficiency may suffer from haemorrhagic features. Warfarin also acts by inhibition of vitamin K. This leads to lack of clotting factors in the plasma and so will cause anticoagulation.

Once formed thrombin acts on the large, soluble plasma protein called fibrinogen and converts it into the insoluble protein, fibrin. Fibrin forms long sticky threads which form the reticulum of the blood clot. The fibrin strands initially cover and reinforce the platelet plug. They will also stick to the cut or damaged edges of the blood vessel forming a network over the injury. Blood cells and other components of the plasma are caught in the fibrin network which holds everything together forming a blood clot.

Despite cold causing vasoconstriction, the efficiency of the coagulation cascade depends on the blood temperature being at physiological levels. This means if a patient is systemically hypothermic the blood will not clot normally, resulting in prolonged bleeding times. To prevent hypothermia injured patients should be kept warm and intravenous fluid replacements should be warmed before administration.

Breakdown of blood clot

A blood clot is a temporary measure to prevent blood loss. As the tissues regenerate to heal the initial injury, the blood clot needs to be removed. When a blood clot is formed, a plasma protein called plasminogen is trapped in the clot along with other plasma proteins. Damaged tissues and vascular endothelium release a substance called tissue plasminogen activator. Over the course of a few days this will progressively convert the trapped plasminogen into plasmin. Plasmin acts as a protein digesting (proteolytic) enzyme which breaks down the fibrin threads and so dissolves the blood clot. Plasmin is also sometimes called fibrinolysin (lysis means to breakdown).

CHAPTER 5

Respiratory System

Introduction

Respiration describes breathing and the utilisation of oxygen within the cells of the body. Traditionally the term external respiration has been used to describe the processes of ventilation and the transfer of oxygen from the lungs into the blood. Ventilation is the process of physically moving air in and out of the lungs. Internal respiration describes how oxygen is used within the cells of the body to oxidize food in order to generate energy.

Structures of the respiratory system

Nose and mouth

Air passes in and out of the nose via two openings called the external nares or nostrils. As air passes through the nose it is warmed when it comes into contact with the lining of the internal nasal passages as they are well perfused with warm blood. The vascular nature of the nasal cavities explains why a lot of blood can be lost through a nose bleed. Warming the air prevents the lower airways being chilled. As the lining of the nasal passages are moist, air passing through the nose is also humidified. This protects the lower airways from possible drying effects of air. The mucous lining, in combination with nasal hair, has the effect of filtering air passing through the nose, removing foreign bodies such as small insects.

Strangely the sense of smell provides much of the sensation of taste; this is why food seems to lose much of its taste when we have a cold. Smell also alerts us to the dangers of poisonous gases and bad food. Olfaction describes the sense of smell and there are olfactory sensory receptors found in the lining of the nasal cavity. These receptors are continuous with sensory nerve fibres which pass into the temporal lobes of the brain where smells are experienced.

A septum describes a structure which divides an area into two, so the nasal septum divides the nasal cavity into left and right sides. The back part of the septum is made of bony tissue and the front part of more flexible cartilage. Posteriorly the nasal cavity communicates with the nasopharynx through two openings called the internal nares. The mouth can increase the size of the airway opening to increase the volumes of air which can be inhaled. However, young babies breathe exclusively through the nose which means if their noses are blocked for any reason they will asphyxiate.

Sinuses

These are small air filled cavities in some of the frontal bones of the skull. They are lined with mucus which drains into the nasal cavity via small passages. The function of the sinuses seems to be to lighten the weight of the skull and to give resonance to the voice. Infection may spread from the nose into the sinuses giving rise to the common painful condition of sinusitis.

Pharynx

This is the passage which connects the back of the nose and mouth with the trachea and oesophagus. It is composed of three sections; the nasopharynx, oropharynx and laryngopharynx. The nasopharynx is behind the nasal cavity, below this is the oropharynx behind the mouth. The palatine tonsils are located in the oropharynx and can be seen through the open mouth. The lower section of the pharynx is called the laryngopharynx which leads down to the oesophagus and trachea.

Larynx

The larynx extends from the laryngopharynx to the start of the trachea. Because the structure is mostly composed of cartilage it can easily be felt in the middle of the neck, where it is commonly referred to as the 'Adam's Apple'. As the

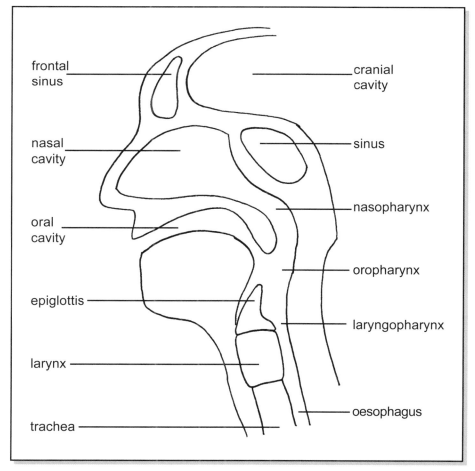

Diagram 5.1
Structures of the upper respiratory tract.

larynx contains the vocal cords it is often referred to as the voice box. The vocal cords are elastic ligaments which can be tightened or relaxed. As air passes over the cords they vibrate producing sound. The vibrations can be controlled by regulating how tight or relaxed the cords are. Tight cords will produce high pitched sounds, more relaxed cords will produce lower pitched sounds. If we vibrate the cords at a rate of 261 hertz (cycles) per second this will produce a musical middle C.

Epiglottis

During swallowing, food must pass over the entrance of the larynx to enter the oesophagus. The entrance to the larynx is termed the glottis, which consists of the vocal cords themselves and any space there may be between the cords. Just above the glottis (i.e. just above the vocal cords) is a sheet of elastic cartilage called the epiglottis. In order to allow movement, the epiglottis is attached to the cartilage of the larynx at the front forming a type of hinge. During swallowing the free, posterior portion, of the epiglottis flaps down to form a seal over the glottis. This seal prevents a food bolus entering into the airway by providing a pathway over the top of the epiglottis into the oesophagus. If this fails to work, food may enter the trachea, (going down the 'wrong way') causing choking. The most common cause of choking is talking and eating at the same time.

Respiratory lining

All of the respiratory passages from the nose down to the smallest bronchioles are lined with a layer of mucus to keep the surfaces moist. An internal surface lined with mucus is called a mucous membrane or mucosa. The presence of mucus aids in the moistening of inhaled air. In addition any inhaled particles, such as dust, smoke particles or aggregates of bacteria, stick to the mucus to prevent them being inhaled deeper into the lungs. This mucus is produced by numerous goblet cells present in the respiratory lining and by small mucus producing glands under the mucosa.

The epithelium which lines all respiratory passages is described as ciliated, which means the passages are lined with millions of cilia. Cilia are microscopic hair-like projections from cell surfaces. There may be as many as 200 cilia projecting from the surface of some cells. Cilia move back and forward to waft the mucus in one direction, away from the alveoli towards the pharynx. This has the effect of clearing mucus, together with any inhaled particulates, out of the lungs. Cilia can cause the mucus to move at a rate of 1 cm per minute forming a continuous clearance system. Once the mucus is in the trachea it may be coughed up, by a blast of air, through the vocal cords into the back of the mouth. From here it may be spat out or swallowed. The combination of the mucus and the wafting action of the cilia is called the mucocillary clearance system.

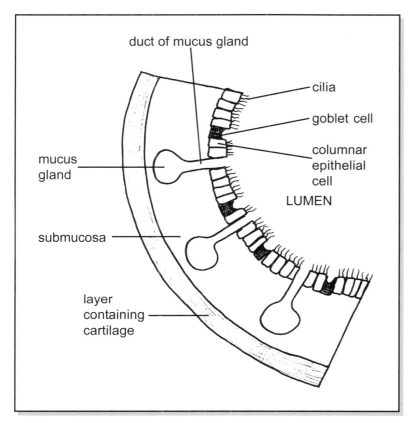

duct of mucus gland

cilia

goblet cell

columnar
epithelial
cell

LUMEN

mucus
gland

submucosa

layer
containing
cartilage

Diagram 5.2
Section of the wall of a bronchus. The lumen is lined with
mucus and ciliated columnar epithelium. This lining layer
comprises the mucous membrane or mucosa. Mucus producing
goblet cells are part of the mucosa. Under this is a submucosa
containing smooth muscle and larger mucus producing glands.
Both the goblet cells and submucosal mucus glands secrete
mucus into the bronchial lumen. Around the outside of the
bronchial tube is a layer containing rings of cartilage to ensure
the lumen of the bronchial passages is kept open.

Trachea

The trachea, or windpipe, is about 12 cm long and extends from the bottom of
the larynx to the bifurcation into the left and right main bronchus. Bifurcation
means to divide into two branches. It is vital that the trachea is patent at all times
as it is the only way air can enter and exit the lungs. To ensure it is kept open, the
walls contain rings of cartilage which are rigid to prevent collapse. The first ring
of cartilage is a complet ring and is termed the cricoid cartilage. All of the lower
rings are incomplete to allow the smooth passage of food down the oesophagus
which is immediately behind the trachea.

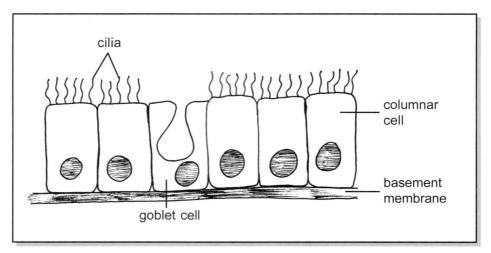

Diagram 5.3
Lining of a bronchial passage at higher magnification. The mucosa is composed of ciliated cells. Cilia waft mucus away from the alveoli towards the pharynx. All of the respiratory passages are lined with ciliated epithelium to provide the mucocillary clearance system.

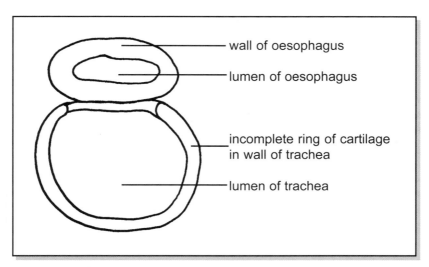

Diagram 5.4
Cross section of the trachea and oesophagus.

Left and right bronchus

The trachea divides into the left and right primary bronchi, one primary bronchus entering each lung (the primary bronchi are also called the main bronchi). The right primary bronchus is continuous with the trachea in more or less a straight line, taking an essentially vertical course into the right lung. However, the slightly narrower left primary bronchus branches away from the trachea at a greater angle into the left lung. This means that if a foreign body is accidentally inhaled it usually enters the right main bronchus. The place where the main bronchus passes into the lung is referred to as the hilum.

Bronchial tubes

Within each lung the primary bronchus divides into secondary bronchi, also referred to as lobar bronchi, because one supplies air to each lobe of the lung. The right lung is composed of three lobes while the left has two, so there are two lobar bronchi on the left and three on the right. In turn, secondary (lobar) bronchi divide into smaller tertiary bronchi. These are also referred to as segmental bronchi because one enters each bronchopulmonary segment of a lobe. Each lung has a total of ten segments with ten corresponding segmental bronchi. Within each bronchopulmonary segment the segmental bronchi rapidly and repeatedly divide into numerous progressively smaller bronchial passages.

Bronchioles

As the bronchial tree continues to divide into smaller airways, the rings of cartilage are lost. After 12 to 16 divisions the diameters of the airways are reduced to 1 mm or less and the tubes are referred to as bronchioles. These airways are still lined with mucus secreting columnar epithelium with cilia, to waft mucus upwards towards the trachea. In turn the bronchioles branch into still smaller terminal bronchioles but even in these smaller structures the walls are still too thick to allow any gaseous exchange to occur between the air and blood.

Terminal bronchioles further divide into respiratory bronchioles which terminate in the alveolar air sacs. The walls of the respiratory bronchioles have a few alveoli in their walls to increase internal surface area. Gaseous exchange between the air and blood only takes place in the microscopic respiratory bronchioles and alveoli.

As the airways form a branching structure they are referred to as the bronchial tree. The bronchial tree therefore consists of the trachea, primary, secondary and tertiary bronchi, numerous progressively smaller bronchi, very small bronchioles, terminal and respiratory bronchioles. If this analogy were to be extended, the respiratory bronchioles and alveoli would be the leaf stems and leaves. Overall the bronchial tree forms a fractal pattern with each smaller pattern duplicating the larger one it has branched from. This means that each terminal area of the tree receives equal volumes of fresh inhaled air and is able to exhale air equally freely.

Bronchial diameters

The smaller airways are able to dilate and constrict under the control of the autonomic nervous system. All of the airways contain smooth muscle fibres in their walls; when these contract bronchoconstriction will result and when they

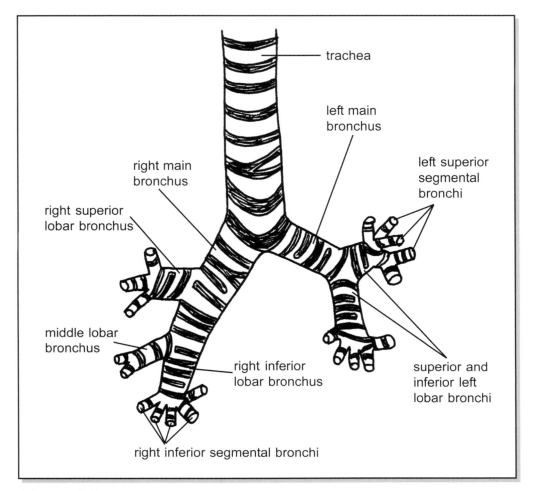

Diagram 5.5
The large structures of the bronchial tree; one trachea, two primary (main) bronchi, five secondary (lobar) bronchi and twenty tertiary (segmental) bronchi. Two left lobar bronchi branch into five segmental bronchi each. The right superior lobar bronchus branches into three segmental bronchi, the right middle into two and the right inferior into five.

relax there will be bronchodilation. During a 'fight or flight' reaction more oxygen is required for muscular activity. This is why sympathetic stimulation will relax the smooth muscle leading to airway dilation. This will also allow more carbon dioxide, produced by increased skeletal muscle activity, to be exhaled. If the airways were dilated all of the time, infection would be able to penetrate into the lungs more readily. This is why, when an individual is at rest, the parasympathetic nervous system constricts the airways to reduce their lumen. If irritants are inhaled there will also be a reflex bronchoconstriction to limit the amount that is able to enter the lungs.

Part of the problem in asthma is that there is excessive constriction of the smooth muscle in the walls of the bronchioles. This is why bronchodilating drugs will ease the condition. Some bronchodilating drugs will stimulate the bronchodilating effects of the sympathetic nervous system, other bronchodilating drugs work by inhibiting the bronchoconstricting effects of the parasympathetic nervous system.

Alveoli

Respiratory bronchioles terminate in groups of alveoli termed alveolar sacs. Alveoli have very thin walls with 90% of the surface area being composed of squamous cells. The remaining 10% of the alveolar wall is composed of septal cells which produce surfactant; this substance reduces the surface tension of the water which moistens internal surfaces of the air sacs. It is vital that the internal respiratory surfaces are moist as oxygen will not diffuse into a dry surface. However, the reduction in surface tension is also essential to prevent the walls of the alveoli sticking together after expiration. Premature babies often lack surfactant and this leads to the disorder called respiratory distress syndrome (RDS).

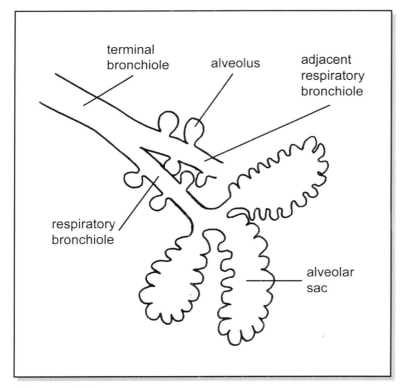

Diagram 5.6
A group of alveoli branching from a respiratory bronchiole.

Because the alveoli are the site of gaseous exchange the walls of the alveolar sacs are folded into structures which resemble hollow bunches of grapes. Infolding greatly increases the respiratory surface area to about 143 square metres in total, (71.5 m² per lung). There are about 300 million alveoli in the two lungs. Elastic fibres support the walls of the alveoli giving them natural elasticity.

The lungs

Lungs are very light organs as the alveoli are mostly filled with air. This is why lung fields appear dark on x-ray films. Because they do not contain a large mass of tissue most of the x-rays pass straight through. The superior part of each lung is described as the apex and these project above the level of the first rib. The lower parts of the lungs are described as the bases. All of the structures passing in and out of a lung do so at the hilum. Passing in and out of each lung, through the hilum is a pulmonary artery which carries deoxygenated blood into the lung. Two pulmonary veins leave each lung via the hilum; these transport oxygenated blood back towards the left atrium. A main bronchus, nerves and lymphatic vessels also pass through the hilum.

The left lung is composed of two lobes, each of which is, in turn, composed of five segments. These segments are correctly referred to as bronchopulmonary segments. The right lung is in three lobes. The superior lobe contains three segments, the middle lobe two and the inferior lobe five. This division of the lungs into lobes has an important role in compartmentalising some infections. For example, in lobar pneumonia the infection is usually confined to a single lobe. Pneumonia means infection of the lung tissue at the level of the alveoli.

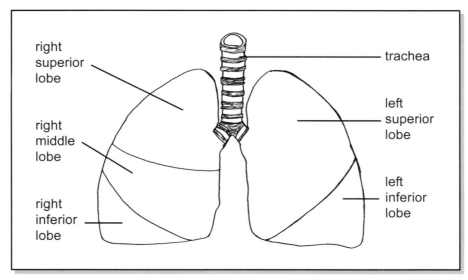

Diagram 5.7
Overall structure and lobes of the lungs.

Blood and lymphatic vessels

Deoxygenated blood is transported to the lungs via the pulmonary arteries. Oxygenated blood returns to the heart via the pulmonary veins. Each segment of the lung is individually supplied with blood via a pulmonary segmental artery and drained by a segmental vein. Each segment also has its own lymphatic drainage system. Like the bronchial tree, the arterial and venous pulmonary vessels also form a fractal pattern. A fractal arrangement ensures all areas of the lungs receive an equal supply of blood and are equally drained. This means that there are three superimposed fractal trees in the lungs; bronchial, arterial and venous.

Mechanical physiology of ventilation

Skeletal structures associated with ventilation

The lungs are surrounded with bones which provide protection against damage from outside trauma. Protection from the back is provided by the thoracic vertebral column. The breast bone or sternum is the flat bone in front of the chest. There are twelve pairs of ribs which form a cage like structure around the lungs, the first ten pairs of which are connected to the sternum via costal cartilage (costal means to do with ribs). Of course men and women both have the same number of ribs. In addition to protection the bony structures are also essential to facilitate the mechanical process of breathing.

Muscles associated with ventilation

The diaphragm is a sheet of skeletal muscle which divides the thoracic and abdominal cavities. When the muscle of the diaphragm is at rest the structure is domed upwards. Contraction causes it to flatten downwards. The ribs are joined together by sheets of intercostal muscles which follow the line of the ribs around the chest. These are the muscles you eat if you have barbecue spare ribs. There are two sets of intercostal muscles, the external and internal. The diaphragm and the intercostal muscles are referred to as the primary respiratory muscles. In addition there are some accessory muscles which are attached to the sternum and upper ribs and start to aid the expansion of the thorax during more vigorous respiratory activity.

Inspiration

To facilitate inspiration the diaphragm contracts, causing it to move down and flatten. At the same time the external intercostal muscles pull the rib cage up and out. Both of these movements result in an increase in the volume of the thoracic cavity. Because the volume of the thorax is increased the pressure of air left inside the thorax, in the lungs, is reduced. Gases will always move from areas of high pressure to areas of lower pressure. As there is a pressure reduction in the thorax, air moves in from the outside to equalise the pressures between

Diagram 5.8
A section of chest wall showing the ribs and intercostal muscles.

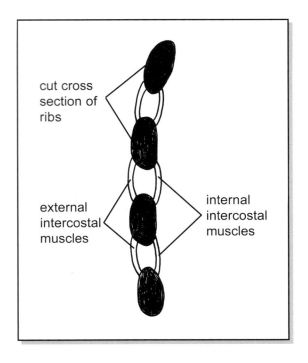

cut cross section of ribs

external intercostal muscles

internal intercostal muscles

the atmosphere and the reduced pressure inside the lungs. So in inspiration when air moves into the lungs the process is one of negative pressure ventilation. This is in contrast to artificial ventilation when air is actively blown into the lungs in the process of positive pressure ventilation. The increase in the volume of air in the lungs stretches the elastic tissues and smooth muscle associated with the walls of the bronchioles and alveoli. This is analogous to blowing up a balloon.

Expiration

During expiration, the smooth muscle and elastic tissue in the walls of the bronchioles and alveoli recoil. This reduces the volume of these structures and so increases the pressure of the air they contain. This is analogous to releasing the pressure on the neck of a balloon; as the elastic walls of the balloon recoil the pressure is increased so air is blown out. As a result of these elastic properties the lungs will passively recoil facilitating expiration. This increases the air pressure in the lungs as a whole, and air is blown out.

To assist this process the diaphragm relaxes and so moves up. The external intercostal muscles also relax which allows the ribs to fall down and in. The movement of the diaphragm up, and the ribs down and in, reduces the volume of the thoracic cavity. Because the volume is reduced the pressure will be increased. This means the pressure inside the lungs is now greater than in the external atmosphere so air will be blown out of the lungs. From this it can be seen that, while inspiration is an active muscular process, expiration is a passive process caused by elastic recoil and muscle relaxation. During vigorous respiration the process of expiration needs to be faster, so the process is aided by contraction of the internal intercostal muscles. These pull the ribs down and in rapidly and actively. These internal intercostal muscles are also essential during periods of increased airway resistance. For example, during an asthmatic attack when the bronchial lumens are narrowed meaning air needs be forced out against the increased resistance.

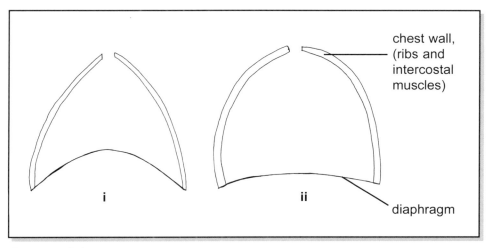

chest wall, (ribs and intercostal muscles)

diaphragm

Diagram 5.9
(i)   At the end of expiration the ribs are down and in and the diaphragm is domed upwards.
(ii) To facilitate inspiration the ribs move up and out while the diaphragm flattens.

Monitoring the rate, depth and rhythm of breathing is a fundamental aspect of clinical observations. One respiratory cycle consists of one inspiration followed by one expiration. These may be counted by observation of chest movements and should be recorded over a period of one minute. The respiratory rhythm should be regular and a rate of about 12 breaths per minute is normal during periods of rest. In emergency situations assessment of the airway is always the first priority. If we put our ear near the patients mouth and look down at their chest we are able to 'look, listen and feel' the breathing.

Pleural membranes

There are two pleural membranes surrounding the lungs. Firstly, the visceral is the inner membrane with one visceral membrane surrounding the surface of each lung. Secondly, the parietal is the outer membrane lining the inside of the thoracic cavity; this pleural membrane also lines the superior surface of the diaphragm. Between these two membranes there is a film of fluid and a negative pressure of about -4mm of mercury. This negative pressure has the effect of sucking the two membranes together which means the area between the two pleural membranes is only a potential space. A potential space is when two membranes are immediately adjacent to each other but not directly connected by tissue, the result of which is that a space could be created should something be introduced between the two layers.

When the ribs move up and out, while the diaphragm moves down, the parietal pleural membrane will move with these structures as it is adherent to them and invaginates them. Because there is a negative pressure between the parietal and visceral pleural membrane, the visceral pleural membrane will be drawn up and out with the chest wall, and down with the diaphragm. As the visceral pleural membrane is adherent to the surface of the lungs, the lungs expand with their visceral pleural membrane. This is why the lungs expand with the chest wall and diaphragm.

The visceral pleural membrane expands because of the suction of the visceral pleural membrane onto the parietal pleural membrane. Therefore if any air gets into the potential pleural space (that is between the visceral and parietal pleural membranes) for example, through a stab wound, the negative pressure will be lost. Movement of the parietal pleural membrane would then no longer result in movement of the visceral pleural membrane and the lung would collapse. This condition is known as a pneumothorax and requires immediate emergency medical treatment. Fortunately there is usually time to transfer such patients to hospital as the two lungs are each surrounded by a separate visceral and parietal pleural membrane. This means one penetrating injury only results in the collapse of one lung and it is possible to survive on the other single lung for a time.

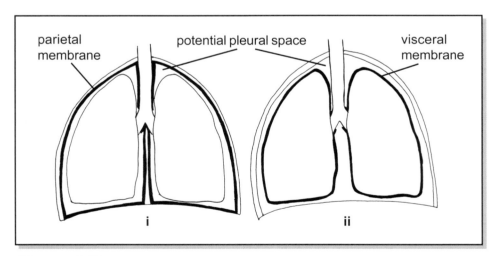

Diagram 5.10
(i)   Parietal pleural membrane.
(ii) Visceral pleural membranes.

Ventilatory volumes

During normal, quiet breathing, about 500 mls of air moves in and out of the respiratory system per breath. The volume of inspired or expired air is referred to as the tidal volume. During exercise the tidal volumes will increase. The minute volume of respiration can be calculated by multiplying the tidal volume by the minute respiratory rate. If the rate is 12 and the tidal volume 500 mls the minute volume would be 6 litres. During inhalation not all of the air reaches the respiratory surfaces. About 150 mls of air is left in the nose, pharynx, larynx and bronchial passages. This volume is referred to as the 'dead air volume' and the space occupied by this volume of air is called the 'dead space'. The presence of dead space means only about 350 mls of fresh atmospheric air reaches the lungs as a result of each inspiration at rest.

It is possible to increase the tidal volume intake of air by about 3 litres per breath; this additional reserve volume is termed the inspiratory reserve volume.

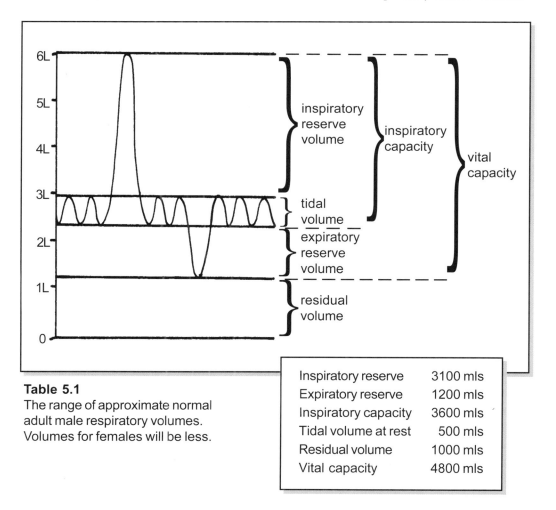

Table 5.1
The range of approximate normal adult male respiratory volumes.
Volumes for females will be less.

Inspiratory reserve	3100 mls
Expiratory reserve	1200 mls
Inspiratory capacity	3600 mls
Tidal volume at rest	500 mls
Residual volume	1000 mls
Vital capacity	4800 mls

Likewise it is possible to breathe out more air than normal; this is called the expiratory reserve volume. However, even with full strained expiration there will always be at least one litre of air left in the lungs, the residual volume. The combination of the expiratory reserve volume and the inspiratory reserve is termed the vital capacity. The total lung capacity is normally about 6 litres.

Cough reflex

If any foreign material or nasty gases are inhaled these will stimulate the very sensitive linings of the trachea and bronchial passages. From these sensitive linings, sensory nerve fibres pass up the vagus nerve to the medulla oblongata of the brain stem. When the medulla receives nerve signals that represent irritation of the lining of the trachea or bronchi the medulla oblongata initiates and coordinates coughing.

Firstly there is a deep inspiration, filling the lungs with air. Next the epiglottis and vocal cords close tightly to trap this large volume of air in the lungs. Immediately after this the diaphragm contracts, supported and strengthened by contraction of the abdominal muscles. The internal intercostal muscles will also forcibly contract. Contraction of these muscles greatly increases the pressure of the air which is trapped in the lungs by the closure of the epiglottis and vocal cords. Next the epiglottis and vocal cords both suddenly open. This means the pressurized air which was trapped in the lungs explodes outwards at high velocity. As the air passes outwards it carries inhaled foreign material, along with some mucus, out of the bronchi and trachea, into the pharynx or mouth where it can be swallowed or spat out.

It is always vital to make sure our patients are able to cough effectively. If a person cannot cough there will be a build up of mucus in the trachea and bronchial passages which will result in stasis with the probability of infection.

Gaseous exchange

The right ventricle contracts, ejecting blood through the pulmonary arterial valve into the pulmonary artery. The pulmonary artery subdivides into smaller arteries and ultimately, via arterioles, into the capillaries which surround the alveoli. Because the blood in the right ventricle has returned from the body it is deoxygenated which means the blood in the pulmonary arterial system is low in oxygen and relatively high in carbon dioxide. The walls of the pulmonary capillaries and the walls of the alveoli are both very thin, made of squamous epithelial cells. This means the diffusional distance between air and blood is small. The lining of the alveoli is moist, allowing oxygen to diffuse into the surface. Oxygen is therefore able to diffuse through the cell walls of the alveoli and capillaries into the blood, and carbon dioxide from the blood into the alveoli. This means that the blood leaving the lungs, to return to the left side of the heart via the pulmonary veins, is now high in oxygen and low in carbon dioxide.

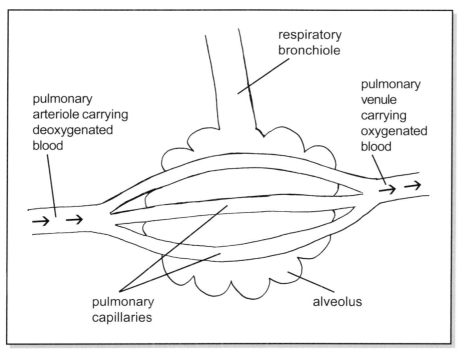

Diagram 5.11
Pulmonary capillaries surround the alveoli; arrows indicate direction of blood flow.

Blood flow through the lungs

Perfusion of blood through the lungs is achieved as a result of the pumping effect of the right ventricle. This generates a systolic pulmonary arterial blood pressure of about 25 mmHg and a diastolic pressure of 8 mmHg. In order to maximize the volumes of oxygen the blood is able to absorb as it passes through the lungs, blood needs to pass through the segments of the lungs where the alveoli are most oxygenated. If the levels of gaseous oxygen in an area of lung are reduced for any reason there is no point distributing a lot of blood there, as there is not much oxygen to be obtained. To reduce blood supply to poorly oxygenated areas of the lung the smaller pulmonary arteries and arterioles constrict. This means more blood is left over to perfuse well oxygenated areas of the lungs. By this mechanism blood is distributed to areas of the lung where it can pick up most oxygen.

It is interesting to note that this vasoconstricting response to reduced levels of oxygen by the pulmonary arterial vessels is the opposite of that which occurs in the systemic vessels supplying the body. In systemic small arteries and arterioles there is vasodilation in response to tissue hypoxia. Hypoxia means reduced levels of oxygen in the tissues. This response in the systemic arterial vessels is logical as an increased volume of perfusing blood will transport more oxygen to the hypoxic tissue.

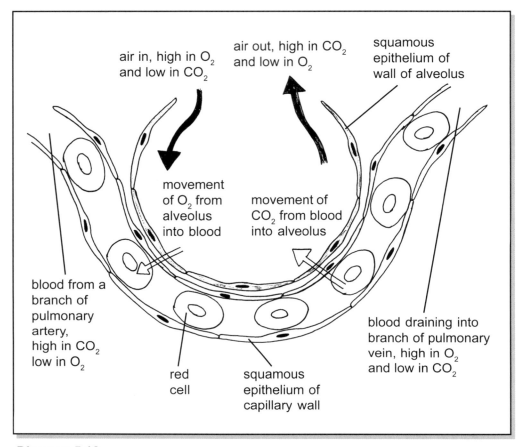

Diagram 5.12
The walls of the capillaries and alveoli are both composed of squamous cells. This means the diffusional distance between the air and blood is small to allow gaseous exchange. Each alveolus is about 0.2 mm in diameter and the two lungs contain 300 million alveoli.

Transport of gases in blood

Approximately 98.5% of the oxygen (O_2) absorbed into the blood is transported by haemoglobin molecules in the red cells. The remaining 1.5% is transported in solution in plasma. These figures explain why people who have lost a lot of blood require blood transfusions. Replacement of fluids alone will result in an inadequate ability to transport oxygen from lungs to tissues. Oxygen saturation monitoring is common in clinical practice and this reveals that blood is normally 98-99 % saturated. This indicates how efficiently oxygen is absorbed by the blood passing through the lungs.

Carbon dioxide (CO_2) is carried from tissues to the lungs in three ways. Firstly about 7% of the total CO_2 is simply carried in solution after dissolving into the plasma. Secondly a further 23% combines with haemoglobin and is

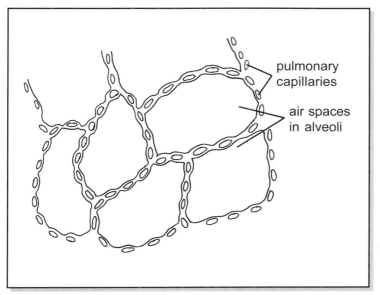

pulmonary
capillaries

air spaces
in alveoli

Diagram 5.13
Cross section of a group of alveoli with their associated
pulmonary capillaries. Between the thin walls of the alveoli is
an almost solid network of pulmonary capillaries. This
provides a large surface area to facilitate rapid diffusion of
large volumes of oxygen from the air in the alveoli to the red
cells in the capillary blood.

transported in red cells. Thirdly 70% forms bicarbonate ions (HCO_3^-) in combination with water in the plasma. In the lungs these ions dissociate back into CO_2 which then diffuses into the alveoli. A small amount is also transferred in the form of carbonic acid (H_2CO_3) explaining why blood pH reduces (becomes more acidic) if there is carbon dioxide retention.

Composition of air

Atmospheric air is a mixture of approximately 21% oxygen, 78% nitrogen, 0.04% carbon dioxide and several other trace inert gases are also present such as argon, helium and neon. The proportion of water in the air is variable and determines the ambient humidity. Because some oxygen is absorbed into the blood, expired air contains about 16% oxygen. The presence of this oxygen in expired air is why exhaled air in mouth to mouth ventilation may be used to keep a patient oxygenated for a short time. As carbon dioxide is excreted from the lungs, the proportion rises to around 4% of the exhaled air volume. There is an equilibrium between nitrogen in the air and in solution in plasma, so the proportion of this inert gas in inhaled and exhaled air is the same.

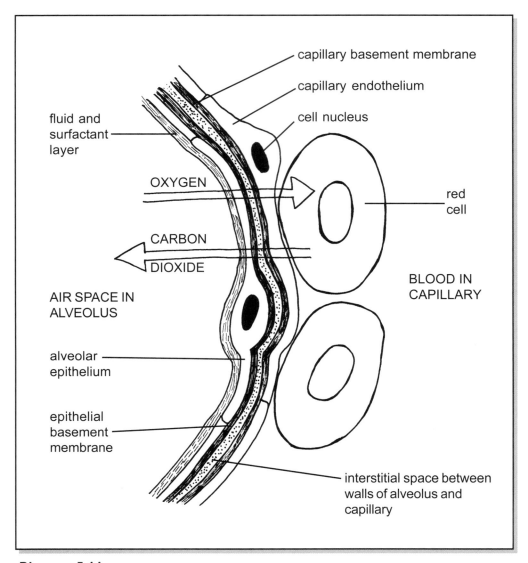

Diagram 5.14
Higher magnification of the relationship between the air in the alveoli and the blood.
The surface through which gaseous exchange takes place is called the respiratory
membrane. The average distance between the blood and air is 0.6 micrometres.
Oxygen first diffuses into the fluid and surfactant layer then through the alveolar
epithelium, interstitial space, capillary endothelium and finally into the red blood cells.

Regulation of respiration

Respiration is controlled by the respiratory centre located in the medulla
oblongata, which is the lowest component of the brain stem. Respiratory cells
located in the respiratory centre of the medulla oblongata coordinate a natural

rhythm which generates nerve impulses to stimulate inspiration. The activity of the respiratory centre therefore generates the regular rhythmic pattern of normal breathing. Because the diaphragm and intercostal muscles are skeletal, they will only contract when stimulated to do so by nerve impulses from motor neurones. From the medulla oblongata nerve fibres carry the respiratory impulses down the spinal cord towards the diaphragm and intercostal muscles.

The two phrenic nerves leave the spinal cord via the cervical nerve roots 3, 4 and 5. You may find the following rhyme helpful, 'C 3 4 5 keep the diaphragm alive'. After passing through the chest, one phrenic nerve stimulates each side of the diaphragm. This explains why patients with high cervical spinal cord damage are unable to breath. Cervical vertebral damage must always be assumed in traumatised patients until x-rays can be taken. Intercostal nerves leave the spinal cord via thoracic nerve roots to stimulate the intercostal muscles. When the inspiratory impulses generated in the medulla stop, the lungs and respiratory muscles passively recoil causing expiration.

In addition to the normal rhythmic breathing pattern coordinated by the respiratory centre, breathing will be further stimulated by increases in the levels of carbon dioxide in the blood. Increases in the plasma volumes of carbon dioxide are detected in the respiratory centre which then stimulates increased respiratory effort in order to excrete the excess.

Other factors which stimulate the respiratory centre include messages from chemoreceptors located in the aorta and carotid bodies. These specialised receptors detect falls in the level of oxygen. However, the degree to which oxygen lack stimulates respiration in normal physiology is small compared to the effect of carbon dioxide increase. Patients with chronic bronchitis have difficulty excreting carbon dioxide so their blood levels of this waste gas are chronically high; this overwhelms the carbon dioxide detectors in the respiratory centre of the medulla oblongata. The result of this is that CO_2 excess no longer stimulates the respiratory drive, as a result such individuals become dependent on this secondary, oxygen lack drive, from chemoreceptors.

These patients may sometimes need to be given high concentrations of oxygen if their saturations are very low. It used to be thought that if these patients were given high concentrations of oxygen this may switch off their oxygen lack respiratory drive causing them to stop breathing. In practice it is more likely such poorly people will die from lack of oxygen if it is withheld. Oxygen may therefore be given provided such patients are closely observed.

Additional factors which may influence ventilation of the lungs include messages from the higher centres of the brain, for example in anxiety. Decreased pH of the blood may also stimulate respiration; this is seen in the 'air hunger' characteristic of ketoacidosis in poorly managed diabetes mellitus.

Essential science

In order to understand internal respiration and many other aspects of physiology it is necessary to have a knowledge of elements, compounds and chemical reactions.

Elements

An element is a pure substance which cannot be chemically split into simpler substances. There are 92 naturally occurring elements although people have made a few more using nuclear physics. All substances are made up of various proportions of these basic building blocks, chemically combined together. Symbols are used as shorthand to identify elements; the following selection are some of those we frequently come across in physiology and clinical practice.

Hydrogen	H	Carbon	C	Nitrogen	N
Oxygen	O	Fluorine	F	Sodium	Na
Magnesium	Mg	Phosphorus	P	Sulphur	S
Chlorine	Cl	Potassium	K	Calcium	Ca
Iron	Fe	Copper	Cu	Zinc	Zn
Selenium	Se	Iodine	I	Mercury	Hg
Lead	Pb				

Compounds

When two or more elements chemically combine together a compound is formed. Individual atoms of the original element are combined into a molecule of compound. Water is a compound of hydrogen and oxygen, carbon dioxide is a compound of carbon and oxygen, sugars are compounds of carbon, hydrogen and oxygen. Although oxygen is an element, in gaseous form two atoms of oxygen combine to form a single oxygen molecule; this is referred to as a diatomic molecule. In a chemical formula the symbol for the element and number of atoms in the molecule are given (e.g. CO_2, O_2, H_2O).

Chemical reactions

These occur when two or more elements or compounds chemically interact together, resulting in the formation of new compounds, or liberation of elements. Chemical equations are used to record the original reactants and products. Because matter cannot be created or destroyed, the number of atoms of each element must always be the same before and after the reaction has occurred. Chemical bonds hold elements together in new compounds. The creation of new chemical bonds requires an input of energy. For example, energy from sunlight is required in photosynthesis to synthesise sugars from water and carbon dioxide. When these bonds are broken down in internal respiration this energy is released and may be used to do useful work.

Internal respiration

Internal respiration is a term which should be restricted to describing the events that go on inside mitochondria located in the cells. Oxygen is essential to all animals. Each living cell must have a constant supply of oxygen if it is to survive. The reason oxygen is required is that all cells must produce energy to fuel the processes of life. Life needs energy. In the mitochondria glucose and other fuels (correctly termed metabolic substrates), are combined with oxygen to produce energy. When fuel molecules such as glucose are oxidised, the chemical bonds that hold the atoms together are broken, this has the effect of releasing the energy which was stored in those bonds. This energy was ultimately derived from sunlight when the fuel molecule was produced in the process of photosynthesis. Internal respiration may be summarised as follows;

glucose + oxygen → water + carbon dioxide + energy

that is $C_6H_{12}O_6 + 6O_2 \rightarrow 6H_2O + 6CO_2$ + energy

In order to oxidise one molecule of glucose, six molecules of oxygen are required. In addition to the energy derived, six molecules of water and carbon dioxide are also produced. This explains that the carbon, in exhaled carbon dioxide, is derived from ingested carbohydrates. The six H_2O molecules are referred to as metabolic water. The energy derived from this reaction is initially used to generate ATP from ADP.

ATP and ADP

Energy production in internal respiration is common to all animals and most bacteria. The process is termed oxidative phosphorylation. Oxygen is used to facilitate phosphorylation. This means the addition of a single phosphate unit to an existing two phosphate unit. Energy is used to convert ADP (adenosine diphosphate) into ATP (adenosine triphosphate). The bond between the single phosphate unit and the ADP is energy rich, therefore energy is required to unite the phosphate unit with the ADP. However, when the phosphate unit dissociates from the ATP, energy, which may be used in living processes, is liberated. This liberation of energy where it is required, converts the ATP back to ADP. In other words the ATP stores energy in a chemical form and transfers it, from the mitochondria where it is produced, to wherever it is required. ATP is sometimes referred to as the 'energy currency' of the cell. Energy generation may be summariesd as follows;

$$ADP + P + energy \rightarrow ATP$$

When this energy is subsequently used, in energy demanding cellular processes the process may be summarised as;

$$ATP \rightarrow ADP + P + energy$$

Hypoxia

This refers to a shortage of oxygen at the level of the tissues. This may arise because of a lack of oxygen in the atmosphere or drowning. In addition hypoxia may develop if the mechanisms of ventilation are deficient. This may occur in some forms of paralysis when the respiratory muscles do not function normally. Almost any form of lung disease may lead to hypoxia. If the blood is unable to transport oxygen hypoxia will also result. In some rare conditions hypoxia may also present if the mitochondria are unable to chemically process oxygen to produce energy.

CHAPTER 6

Nervous System

Introduction

The nervous system is an internal communication system allowing for rapid transport of messages within the body. This includes perception, processing of information and control of responses. Anatomically the nervous system may be divided into the central nervous system (CNS) and the peripheral nervous system (PNS). The CNS consists of the brain and spinal cord and the PNS consists of all of the other nervous tissue in the body such as the nerves going to and from the spinal cord and the nerves in the limbs.

Nerve cells

The nervous system is composed of billions (thousands of millions) of individual specialised nerve cells referred to as neurones. These cells interconnect with other nerve cells to form networks which perform specific functions. Like any other cell, neurones are surrounded by a membrane and contain cytoplasmic organelles and a nucleus. There are different types of neurones which perform various functions, for example motor, sensory and relay neurones.

Motor neurones

Motor means to do with movement. When we decide we want to move part of the body a motor neurone in the brain will generate a new nerve impulse. The same neurone will then carry this impulse away from the brain towards a synapse with an other motor neurone which will then carry the impulse into the PNS.

A nerve impulse is electrical in nature and is generated in the cell body. This is an enlarged area of the cell which contains the nucleus and most of the cell organelles. From here the impulse travels away, along a fibre of the motor neurone called an axon. Any nerve fibre which carries information, in the form of an electrical nerve impulse, away from a cell body is defined as an axon.

There are also dendrites connected to the motor neurone cell body. A dendrite is defined as any nerve fibre which carries information towards a cell body. Typically a motor neurone consists of short dendrites conveying information towards the cell body and a longer axon carrying information away. Nerve fibres are essentially long thin projections of the cytoplasm. Despite being very thin, nerve fibres can be very long. For example, some motor neurone axons originate in the spinal cord and run the full length of the legs into the feet.

Because motor neurones initiate movement they often connect to skeletal muscles. When an axon approaches the muscle it supplies it divides into a number of smaller fibres which end in specialised structures called the synaptic end bulbs. These bulbs are responsible for conveying the impulse from the axon into the muscle. A muscle will only contract when it is stimulated to do so by the nerve impulse. As motor neurones carry impulses out from the CNS they are sometimes referred to as efferent neurones (remember 'e' for Efferent and for Exit).

The importance of motor neurones is clearly seen in motor neurone disease in which motor neurones progressively die resulting in increasing paralysis. Because it is only the motor neurones which die in this disease sensation is not affected at all.

When we want to move a muscle, a new nerve impulse is generated in the motor neurone cell body which is located in the motor cortex of the brain. The motor cortex is the area of the brain which initiates all movement of the skeletal

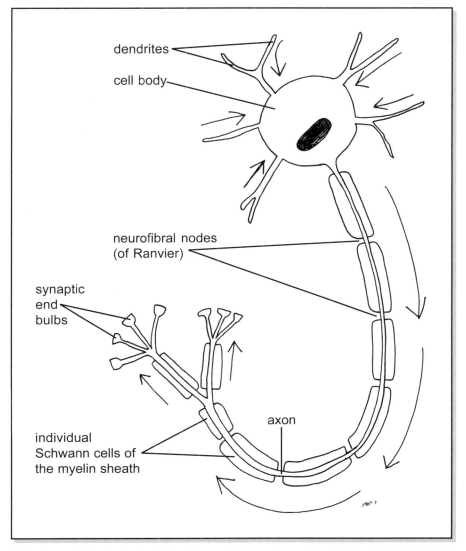

Diagram 6.1
A motor neurone. Arrows indicate the direction of the one way transmission of a nerve impulse. Note the dendrites carry the impulse towards the cell body and the axon carries the impulse away.

muscles. Nerve fibres from the motor cortex pass through the brain in a pathway called the internal capsule. Most of the descending motor fibres cross over to the opposite side of the body at the level of the lower brain stem, before passing down the spinal cord. At the correct level in the spinal cord the first motor neurone connects with a second motor neurone via a small gap referred to as a synapse. This second motor neurone carries impulses from the spinal cord to the appropriate muscle. All of the motor neurones leave the spinal cord from the front; the pathway they take is referred to as the anterior nerve root.

Sensory neurones

Stimuli from all five senses are transmitted via sensory neurones. Sensory neurones carry sensations from the environment to the sensory cortex in the brain. This is the area of the brain which allows us to detect the presence and location of sensation from the body. In sensory neurones the nervous impulse is not generated in the cell body but in a peripheral sensory receptor. This is a specialised structure designed to detect a particular sensation, for example touch in the fingertips. When a sensation is detected the receptors generate a new nerve impulse which represents the external stimulus. Impulses from the neck and below, and from the back of the head, travel to the brain via spinal nerves and the spinal cord. Impulses from the front of the head, including the face, mouth, teeth and eyes do not travel via the spinal cord, but are relayed directly to the brain stem via the cranial nerves.

From the sensory receptor the impulse is transmitted along the dendrite of a sensory neurone to the cell body. This first fibre, between the receptor and the cell body, is referred to as a dendrite because it carries information towards the cell body. From a cell body in a spinal nerve, an impulse is carried into the spinal cord via the axon of a sensory neurone. After entering the spinal cord the impulse travels upwards, towards the brain in an ascending sensory pathway. The first sensory neurone will synapse with a second in the spinal cord or brain stem. All sensory neurones cross over (decussate) to the opposite side at the level of the spinal cord or brain stem. In the case of cranial nerve this crossing over (or decussation) occurs at the level of the brain stem. This means sensation from the left side of the body is experienced in the right side of the brain. Likewise, sensations from the right side of the body are experienced in the left hemisphere of the brain.

All sensory impulses then pass up through the brain stem to the thalamus where the second sensory neurone synapses with a third. The thalamus is an area of the brain with many interconnections, communicating between the brain and spinal cord. The thalamus acts as a relay station, coordinating communications between various components of the brain. A third sensory neurone from the thalamus finally carries the impulse into the sensory cortex of the brain where it is experienced as sensation.

The arrival of a sensory stimulus in the sensory cortex generates the experience we call tactility or feeling. This means that, ultimately, all sensation is generated by the brain. This means if I hit my thumb with a hammer, it feels to me like the pain is in my thumb. In fact the pain is experienced in the area of my sensory cortex which corresponds to my thumb. Like motor neurones the fibres of the sensory neurone have a myelin sheath. Because sensory neurones carry information into the CNS they are sometimes referred to as afferent neurones.

Sensory neurones enter the spinal cord from the back, via the posterior nerve root. All of the cell bodies of the sensory neurones, carrying information into the spinal cord at a particular level, are located in a group or cluster. This group of cell bodies is referred to as the posterior root ganglion. A ganglion is a

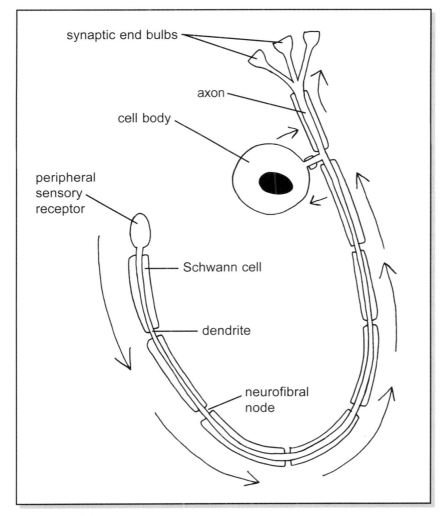

Diagram 6.2
A sensory neurone.

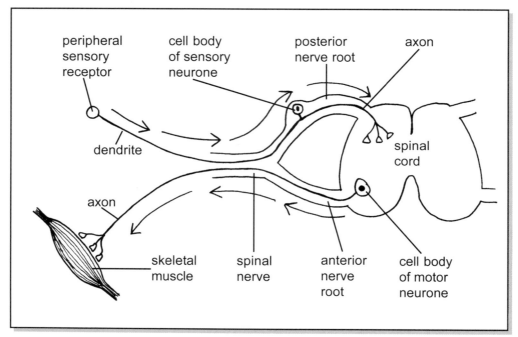

Diagram 6.3
Transverse section of the spinal cord showing motor and sensory nerve roots.
Arrows illustrate the direction the nerve impulses follow. The motor neurone would
receive impulses from a descending neurone coming down from the brain and the
sensory neurone would connect to an ascending neurone which carries the impulse
up towards the brain. Note only the nerve roots on the right side of the body are
illustrated.

cluster of cell bodies in the PNS. (If a group of cell bodies is found in a cluster
in the CNS this is referred to as a nucleus.) On entering the spinal cord some
sensory neurone axons synapse, and cross over to the opposite side and then
travel up the spinal cord. Other sensory neurones, as discussed, do not cross
over until the level of the brain stem. However, the end result is always that
sensation from the right side of the body is experienced in the left side of the
brain and sensation from the left side of the body is experienced in the right
side of the brain. The physiological reason for this cross over is currently unclear.

The motor and sensory nerve fibres leave and enter the spinal cord separately.
However, a short distance away from the cord they join to form a single spinal
nerve.

Relay neurones

In addition to motor and sensory neurones there are other nerve cells which
connect these together. Sometimes referred to as relay neurones, they relay an
impulse from one neurone to another. More correctly they are termed

interneurones or association neurones. These interneurones also consist of a cell body with associated nerve fibres.

Myelin

Nerve cells and fibres are of course microscopic. A group of nerve fibres will run together in a bundle forming a macroscopic structure referred to as a nerve. Macroscopic means large as opposed to microscopic which means small. As a nerve consists of many nerve fibres carrying electrical nerve impulses, there is a risk that the impulses will jump from one fibre to another forming a short circuit. In order to prevent this, most individual nerve fibres are insulated. This insulation is provided by a specialised form of cell. In the PNS these specialised insulating cells are referred to as Schwann cells which wrap themselves around the nerve fibres. Schwann cells are composed of an insulating fatty material called myelin which forms a sheath around a nerve fibre. The myelin sheath is therefore like the plastic insulation which surrounds an electrical copper wire. However, unlike an electrical insulator there are small gaps between the Schwann cells called the neurofibral nodes (formally called the nodes of Ranvier).

In addition to insulating the nerve fibres, myelin increases the speed at which a nerve impulse passes along the fibre. In other words the myelin sheath increases the rate of neuronal transmission. Myelin also protects the nerve fibres from damage and helps with their nourishment. The vital function of the myelin sheath is illustrated in the condition of multiple sclerosis where there is a loss of myelin in the CNS.

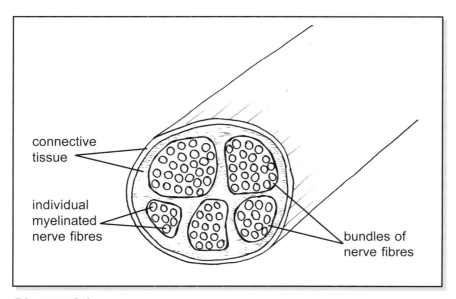

connective tissue

individual myelinated nerve fibres

bundles of nerve fibres

Diagram 6.4
Cross section of a nerve composed of possibly thousands of nerve fibres in combination with fibrous tissue.

Essential science

In order to understand the nature of a nerve impulse it is necessary to understand how atoms can be electrically charged.

Atoms are electrically neutral

An atom is made up of protons and neutrons which are closely grouped together in the atomic nucleus. Surrounding this core are orbiting electrons. These three sub-atomic particles possess mass and have a charge which may be positive, negative or neutral. The charge is electrical in nature. Protons carry a positive charge of plus one and electrons have a negative charge of minus one. Neutrons are electrically neutral. Atoms are always electrically neutral. This means they must have the same number of positive protons as negative electrons. In this way, all of the negative and positive charges will cancel out to make the atom electrically neutral overall.

Ions have an electrical charge

If an atom loses an electron it will lose one of its negative charges. This will mean there is one more positive charge than negative charge. This will give the atom an overall charge of plus one. When an atom has an electrical charge it is no longer referred to as an atom but an ion. If an atom loses two electrons it will lose two negative charges and so will become an ion with an overall charge of plus two. Conversely if an atom gains an electron it will become an ion with a charge of negative one and if it gains two electrons it will become an ion with a charge of negative two.

Diagram 6.5
Atoms and ions.
(i)   A sodium atom containing 11 protons and 11 electrons is electrically neutral.
(ii) A sodium ion forms when the atom loses an electron and so has an overall charge of plus 1.

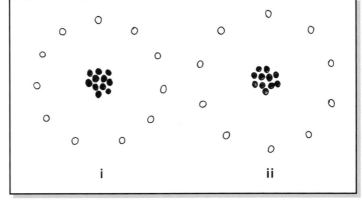

Neuronal transmission

We have already mentioned that a nerve impulse is electrical. This electrical charge is generated by the relative distribution of ions on both sides of the cell membrane. If there are more negative ions inside the cell with relatively more positive ions outside, the overall charge will also be negative on the inside and positive on the outside. This state is sometimes referred to as the resting potential. This is the electrical condition a nerve fibre will be in when there is no nerve impulse passing a particular point. Because in this situation there is a negative pole inside and a positive pole on the outside, the cell is described as being polarized. These are the same as the poles of a battery, one of which is negative and the other positive.

However, when a nerve impulse is passing a point on a nerve fibre, the polarity across the cell membrane reverses. There is a change in the permeability of the membrane surrounding the nerve fibre. This allows ions to pass through the cell membrane leading to a change in the relative distribution of positive and negative ions on the two sides of the membrane. The result is the inside becomes positive and the outside negative. This reversal of polarity is referred to as depolarization. After the nerve impulse has passed, the polarity reverts back to being negative inside and positive outside. The process by which resting polarity is restored is termed repolarization. From this it can be seen that a nerve impulse is a wave of depolarisation which passes along a nerve fibre. It is this electrical wave which constitutes the nerve impulse. Changes in polarity necessary for the propagation of the impulse are brought about by changes in the relative distribution and concentration of ions. These concentrations may change because ions are able to pass through the cell membrane in specialised small gaps called ion channels.

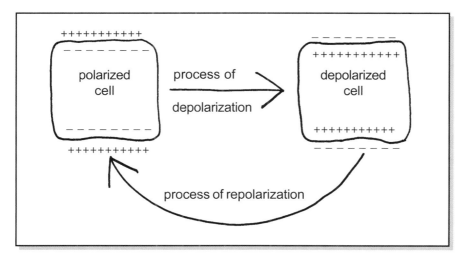

Diagram 6.6
An area of nerve fibre is polarized at rest. When the nerve impulse is passing it becomes depolarized; after the impulse has passed repolarization occurs.

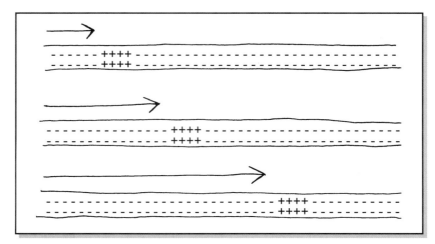

Diagram 6.7
This shows the same length of nerve fibre as a nerve impulse passes along. The three illustrations are a fraction of a second apart.

Speed of a nerve impulse

The speed at which a nervous impulse travels varies, depending on the type of neurone involved. Wider diameter fibres transmit impulses faster than narrow fibres. However, in humans the main factor influencing the rate of transmission is the presence of the myelin sheath. Myelinated fibres transmit the impulse quickly because the impulse does not need to travel along the full length of the fibre but is able to 'bounce' from one neurofibral node to the next. This is referred to as saltatory transmission. In unmyelinated fibres the speed of transmission may be as slow as 0.5 meters per second, however in some myelinated fibres the rate may be over 100 meters per second.

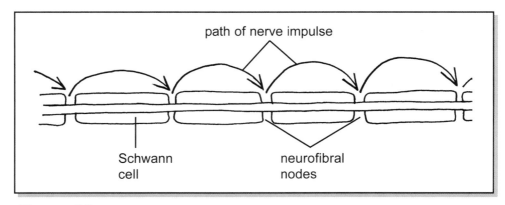

Diagram 6.8
Saltatory or 'bouncing' transmission. This is analogous to a flat stone skimming over the surface of a lake; it hits the water then bounces further on.

The synapse

There are very small gaps between individual nerve cells and between motor neurones and muscles. These gaps are called synaptic gaps. The gap is a physical space and the electrical nerve impulse is unable to jump across. The synapses are necessary to limit the propagation of an impulse around the nervous system. If all of the neurones were directly physically interconnected then any one nerve impulse would be propagated around the whole nervous system resulting in gross over-activity (this would probably result in continuous convulsions).

However, despite this need for electrical limitations, it is essential that nerve impulses can pass from one neurone to another when required. To allow this to happen the nerve fibre at one side of the synaptic gap releases a chemical called a chemical transmitter (neurotransmitter). This transmitter will then diffuse across the gap and generate a further electrical nervous impulse in the second neurone. Only the nerve fibre on one side of the synapse is able to secrete chemical transmitter. This means an impulse can travel from this first neurone to the second but not back in the other direction. The result is that synapses act as valves, only allowing one way transmission of impulses.

The neurone before the gap is termed the pre-synaptic neurone and the one after the gap as the post-synaptic neurone. Just before the gap, the pre-synaptic neurone widens out into a structure called the synaptic end bulb. This contains mitochondria to provide energy for the function of the synapse. The bulb also contains vesicles of chemical transmitter substances which have been previously synthesised by the neurone. When a nerve impulse arrives in the synaptic end bulb it causes some secretory vesicles to fuse with the pre-synaptic membrane releasing some chemical transmitter into the gap. After diffusing across the gap these transmitter molecules bind onto specific receptor sites on the post-synaptic membrane. Binding of transmitter into the receptor site activates the site. When enough of these receptor sites are activated by the chemical transmitter a further electrical impulse is generated in the post synaptic neurone.

If an impulse should arrive at the synapse via the post-synaptic neurone it will not be able to cross the gap and so will terminate. So, a nerve impulse is electrical when traveling along nerve fibres and chemical when traveling across a synaptic gap. A synapse may occur between two nerve fibres or between a nerve fibre and a cell body.

The connection between the synaptic end bulb of a motor neurone and a muscle is also via a synapse. Because this junction connects a nerve to a muscle it is referred to as a neuromuscular junction. As in a nerve to nerve connection, chemical transmitter is released, diffuses across the gap and binds onto specific receptor sites. When sufficient of the receptor sites are activated by the binding of transmitter, the muscle will be stimulated to contract. The surface of the muscle where the receptor sites are located is termed the motor end plate.

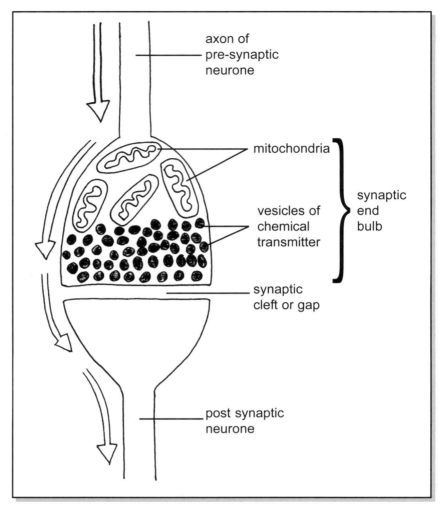

Diagram 6.9
The synapse. Arrows illustrate the direction of the nerve impulse.

Chemical transmitters carry an impulse across the synaptic gap

There is a wide range of chemical transmitter molecules used in the nervous system. Two common transmitters are acetylcholine and noradrenalin (also called norepinephrine). Acetylcholine is also the neuromuscular transmitter molecule used at the neuromuscular junctions. Once any chemical transmitter has activated the post synaptic membrane it must be removed from the synaptic gap. If this is not done there will be continued stimulation of the receptor sites. Some of the transmitter simply diffuses away into the tissue fluid. However, some is actively reabsorbed by the pre-synaptic neurone for recycling. In addition, in the case of acetylcholine, the molecule is broken down and inactivated by a tissue enzyme called acetylcholinesterase.

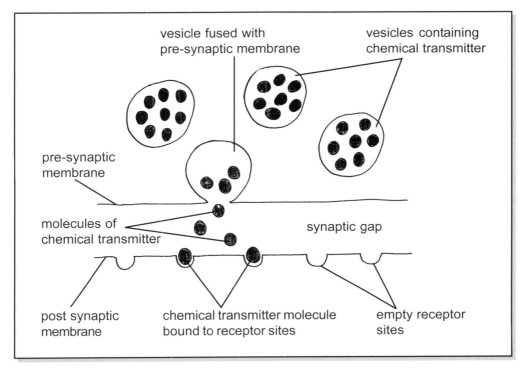

Diagram 6.10
This diagram illustrates the synapse at greater magnification. Chemical transmitter is released from vesicles in the pre-synaptic neurone, these then diffuse accross the synaptic gap. Transmitter molecules of a particular shape are able to fit into, and so activate, specific receptor sites on the post synaptic membrane.

There are a large number of different transmitter molecules found in the CNS with a wide variety of functions. For example, there is a transmitter called GABA which inhibits the activity of many neurones. If the levels of GABA are increased, the individual feels relaxed and at ease. Anti-anxiety drugs often work by increasing GABA activity. Another transmitter is dopamine; this is vital for normal control of movement and deficiency causes Parkinson's disease. In other parts of the brain dopamine causes the person to experience pleasure. Levels of dopamine are increased by many drugs people take for their enjoyable effects such as alcohol or cocaine. Antidepressants work by increasing the amounts of serotonin in the synaptic gaps; they do this by inhibiting pre-synaptic reuptake. This indicates a feeling of depression may be caused by low levels of serotonin. Endorphin is a transmitter molecule which reduces pain. Morphine based drugs work because they activate endorphin receptor sites, simulating an endorphin effect.

When people artificially stimulate the levels of chemical transmitters by taking drugs the body often responds by producing less of its own. This is why many drugs have withdrawal or abstinence syndromes.

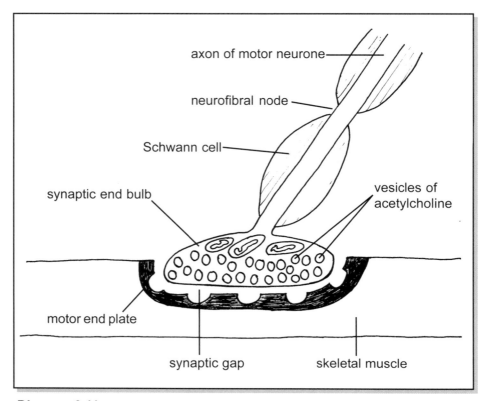

Diagram 6.11
A neuromuscular junction. Acetylcholine carries the impulse from the nerve to the muscle.

The reflex arc

Reflexes occur to protect the body from tissue damage; they are rapid involuntary actions. For example, the arm will suddenly be withdrawn if it touches a very hot object. A reflex arc describes an arrangement of three neurones which detect the stimulus and relay the information across the spinal cord to a motor neurone which will move an appropriate muscle.

The initial sensation is detected by peripheral sensory receptors and transmitted along the dendrite of a sensory neurone to the cell body. From the cell body it is then transmitted along the axon of the sensory neurone. This fibre then goes into the spinal cord where it synapses with a relay neurone. The relay neurone will carry the impulse across the spinal cord from the back, where the sensory neurones enter, to the front where the motor neurones leave. This relay neurone then synapses with the cell body of a motor neurone which carries the impulse away from the spinal cord to the appropriate muscle which is innervated to contract, withdrawing the hand away from the hot object.

In addition an ascending neurone carries the information up the spinal cord to inform the brain of what has happened. This means that the reflex can occur before the brain becomes aware that there is a problem. This saves a lot of time; if the message had to go up to the brain and a further message sent down to the muscle there would be a time delay during which injury could occur. There are many other examples of reflexes including the eyelash and gag reflexes.

Sensory neurones always approach the spinal cord from the back and the motor neurones always leave the spinal cord from the front. The nerve containing the sensory neurones which pass into the spinal cord is termed the posterior root and the one containing motor neurones the anterior root. Posterior always means towards the back and anterior towards the front.

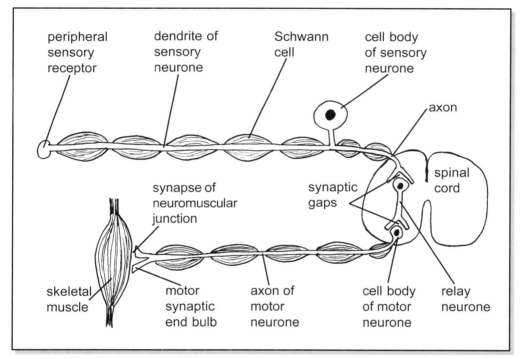

Diagram 6.12
A reflex arc.

The brain

The human brain is composed of about a hundred thousand million (10^{11}) neurones, together with supporting glial cells. Each neurone makes synaptic interconnections with between one thousand and ten thousand other neurones. The number of neurones and their interconnected networks means the human brain is the most complicated known structure in the universe. A brain is composed of grey and white matter; grey matter is mostly nerve cells and white matter is mostly nerve fibres. It is useful to think of the brain as consisting of four basic areas. These are the cerebrum, cerebellum, diencephalon, and brain stem.

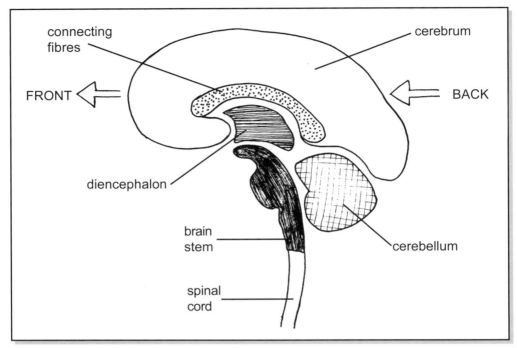

Diagram 6.13
Four main areas in the brain; cerebrum, diencephalon, cerebellum and brain stem. The connecting fibres of the corpus callosum allow communication between the right and left hemispheres of the cerebrum.

Neuroglia

Neuroglia (also simply referred to as glia) describes the tissues of the nervous system which are not neurones. In the PNS the myelin sheath surrounding nerve fibres is composed of a form of neuroglial cells called Schwann cells. There are four types of neuroglial cells found in the CNS; these are astrocytes, oligodendrocytes, ependymal cells and microglia.

Astrocytes provide physical and nutritional support to neurones, they also have processes which wrap around blood capillaries. These processes are referred to as astrocyte end feet and they help to keep potentially toxic substances in the blood out of the brain. Oligodendrocytes form and maintain the myelin sheaths in the CNS. Ependymal cells form layers which line internal surfaces of the ventricles in the brain and the central canal of the spinal cord, spaces which are filled with cerebrospinal fluid. Microglial cells function as phagocytes in the CNS; they will phagocytose infecting particles or damaged tissue.

As neuroglial cells can carry on dividing throughout adult life they are able to maintain the integrity of the brain and spinal cord. However, as they are capable of ongoing mitosis they also have the potential to generate tumours. These CNS tumours are termed gliomas.

Cerebrum

The cerebrum is the largest part of the brain and is made up of the left and right cerebral hemispheres. These two sides of the brain are connected by a large number of internal connecting white fibres. The outer layer of the cerebrum is called the cerebral cortex. This layer is folded into gyri and sulci to give a large surface area. A gyrus is one of the raised folds of the cerebral cortex while a sulcus is one of the grooves between the gyri. Each of the hemispheres are composed of four lobes, the frontal, parietal, temporal and occipital lobes.

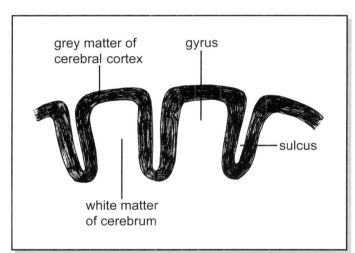

grey matter of cerebral cortex

gyrus

sulcus

white matter of cerebrum

Diagram 6.14
The cerebral cortex of the brain is a layer of grey matter, mostly composed of nerve cell bodies. This outer cortex of the brain is only 2-4 mm thick but contains billions of cell bodies. Under this layer is the white matter, mostly composed of nerve fibres and their associated glial cells.

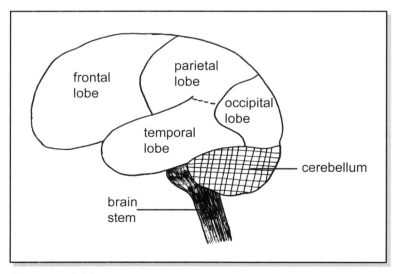

frontal lobe

parietal lobe

occipital lobe

temporal lobe

cerebellum

brain stem

Diagram 6.15
Four main areas or lobes in the cerebrum, frontal, parietal, temporal and occipital (the brain stem and cerebellum are also identified.)

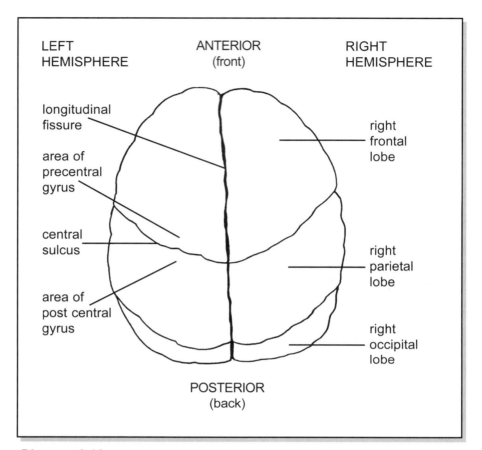

LEFT
HEMISPHERE

ANTERIOR
(front)

RIGHT
HEMISPHERE

longitudinal
fissure

right
frontal
lobe

area of
precentral
gyrus

central
sulcus

right
parietal
lobe

area of
post central
gyrus

right
occipital
lobe

POSTERIOR
(back)

Diagram 6.16
From above the cerebrum is seen to be composed of the right and left
cerebral hemispheres. The central sulcus divides the frontal and the
parietal lobes. Immediately anterior to the central sulcus is the precentral
gyrus which is where the motor cortex is located. Immediately posterior to
the central sulcus is the postcentral gyrus which houses the sensory cortex.

The motor area of the brain is located in the frontal lobes. This area contains
the cell bodies of the motor neurones. Speech is generated in an area of the frontal
lobe closely associated with the motor cortex. Also in the frontal lobes are the
frontal eye areas; these control and coordinate movement of the eyes so we can look
at a particular point in space. You have just used this area to scan the words of this
paragraph. Frontal cortical areas of the brain are also concerned with various functions
such as reasoning and abstract thinking. In addition, much of the personality and
character seem to be generated in this area of the brain. If the frontal lobes are
damaged the person becomes socially disinhibited, often severely.

The parietal lobe contains the sensory cortex. This is the area of the brain that
collects information about the body generated in the peripheral sensory receptors

and transmitted via sensory neurones. Different parts of the sensory cortex generate perception of sensation from different parts of the body. This area also generates our positional sense (proprioception) so we know where various parts of the body are in space. This is why we can still clap hands with our eyes shut. The speech sensory area is also largely located in the parietal lobe and is essential to enable the understanding of language.

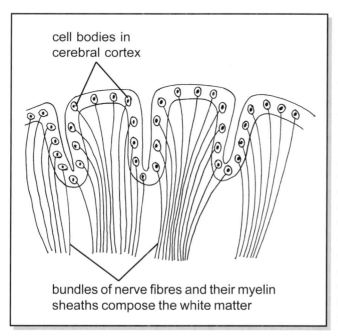

cell bodies in
cerebral cortex

bundles of nerve fibres and their myelin
sheaths compose the white matter

Diagram 6.17
Cell bodies are located in the cortex and their connected nerve fibres project down into the white matter of the cerebrum. For example, in the motor cortex of the precentral gyrus the cell bodies of the motor cortex generate new nerve impulses which are transmitted via their axons, down through the white matter of the cerebrum, towards the spinal cord. In the sensory cortex of the post central gyrus the neuronal cell bodies receive impulses which have ascended through the white matter via their dendrites.

The auditory area which is concerned with hearing is in the temporal lobe, just underneath the sensory cortex. This lobe also contains the olfactory area which generates the sense of smell from information received from the nose. The temporal lobe also seems to allow us to have religious experiences, and aids in the formation of emotions.

The occipital lobe is located at the back of the cerebrum and is the area where vision is generated. Nerve impulses arrive from the eye and the occipital lobe allows us to perceive these as vision.

While it is true that these brain areas have many specific localised functions, it seems that much of the activity of the cerebral cortex is more diffuse. Processes such as thinking, memory and reasoning can still carry on even if some localised areas of the cortex are damaged. The experience of consciousness is also probably a diffuse product of the function of the cerebrum. This is why we measure Glasgow Coma Scales in head injuries. If the cortex is being compressed by rising pressure within the skull there will be a generalised reduction of cortical function, resulting in a corresponding reduction in the level of consciousness and so in GCS.

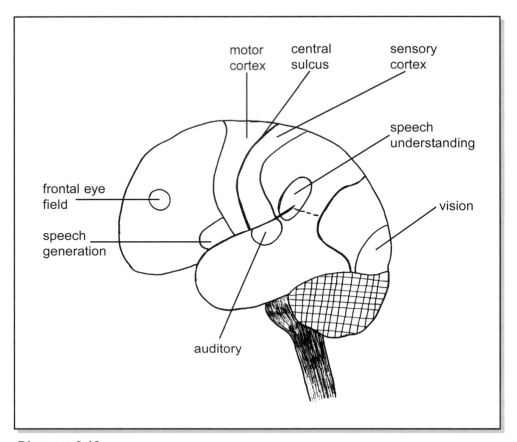

Diagram 6.18
Examples of specific functions carried out in particular areas of the cerebral cortex.
While most areas are present in both hemispheres, in the majority of people the
areas which generates speech, and understanding of speach, are only found in the
left hemisphere.

The cerebral cortex is particularly well developed in people compared to
animals. It gives us the ability to function in groups, to relate to other people
and to co-operate. If the activity of the cerebral cortex is reduced then the social
inhibitions, which allow us to function in groups, are inhibited. Alcohol causes
loss of inhibitions by depressing the function of the cortex. This means that
while drunk, people may engage in behaviours that have social and personal
consequences, which they would not take part in if their cerebral cortex was
functioning normally. Violent and sexual behaviour are the obvious examples.

Cerebellum

The cerebellum controls automatic learnt functions such as writing, walking,
making beds and riding a bike. Once these complex skills have been well learned
the cerebellum can co-ordinate them, leaving the rest of the higher parts of the

brain free to think about something else. This is why we can walk or drive a car while chatting about something more interesting. The cerebellum is also involved in functions such as balance, maintenance of posture, fine motor coordination and dexterity. The cerebellum also receives impulses from the semicircular canals in the inner ear which it uses to coordinate reflexes which maintain an upright posture.

Diencephalon

This contains two structures; the thalamus and below this the hypothalamus. The thalamus is responsible for such apparently diverse functions as language, sleep and wakefulness, recent memory and emotion. It also acts as a relay centre, receiving information from the body via the spinal cord and relaying this on to appropriate areas of the brain. The hypothalamus is the main brain centre for regulation of the internal environment of the body; this means it controls several aspects of homeostasis. Among the parameters it regulates are body temperature, hunger, thirst, emotional balance, sexual behaviour and endocrine hormone homeostasis. It is also the hypothalamus which regulates the activity of the pituitary gland and hence the endocrine system.

Brain stem

The brain stem acts as a connection between the spinal cord and the rest of the brain. Throughout the brain stem is a complex network of neurones called the reticular activating system which generates consciousness. Although consciousness is generated in the brain stem it is probably mostly experienced in the cerebrum.

Anatomically the brain stem is described in three areas. The upper region is the midbrain. This contains fibres to allow communication between the brain above and the body below. Below the midbrain is an area called the pons. Nerve fibres running through the pons are continuous with those of the midbrain above and medulla below. It also contains nuclei involved in motor and sensory innervation of the face in addition to areas which affect respiration.

The lower section of the brain stem is the medulla oblongata but is often simply called the medulla. Again nerve fibres running through this area are continuous with the spinal cord below and the pons above. It is at the level of the medulla that many of the motor and sensory fibres cross over from left to right and vice versa. This is why if a person has a stroke which affects the right side of the brain the left side of the body is affected. Many vital nuclei are contained in the medulla oblongata. These include the respiratory centre which controls breathing. Also in this region is the vasomotor centre which controls the tone of blood vessels and regulates blood pressure on a second by second basis. There is a cardiac centre which influences the activity of the heart. It is because of this association between the brain stem with these vital physiological functions and consciousness that death is often now defined as death of the brain stem.

Diagram 6.19
The three
areas of the
brain stem.

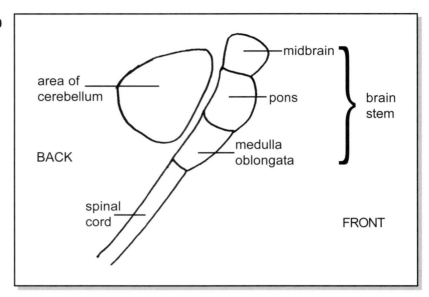

area of
cerebellum

midbrain

pons

medulla
oblongata

brain
stem

BACK

spinal
cord

FRONT

Cranial nerves

These are the nerves which communicate directly with the brain without going via the spinal cord. There are 12 pairs of cranial nerves which are usually numbered with Roman numerals. The cell bodies for these nerves are located in the brain. Cranial nerve I is the olfactory nerve carrying the sense of smell from the nose into the brain. Cranial nerve II is also sensory, it is the optic nerve carrying vision from the eyes to the occipital brain areas. Cranial nerves III to XII arise from the brain stem, III and IV from the midbrain, V to VIII from the pons and IX to XII from nuclei in the medulla oblongata. Some cranial nerves carry motor fibres, others sensory and a few carry motor and sensory fibres. Sensory functions include sight, smell, hearing and sensation from the face, lips and teeth. Because these structures are physically above the level of the spinal cord it makes sense that they communicate with the brain directly. Cranial nerve motor functions include movement of the eyeball, control of the pupil, and movement of the tongue and facial muscles.

Cranial nerve control of the pupil explains why we check the response and diameter of the pupil in cases of head injury. The pupil is controlled by the third cranial nerve which runs under the base of the brain. If this nerve is compressed by pressure from above it will not function properly causing the pupil it controls to become sluggish and ultimately fixed in response to light.

Spinal cord

The spinal cord is the main communication between the brain and body. In an adult it is about 45 cm in length. The meninges and cerebrospinal fluid (CSF) continue around and below the cord. The outside of the cord is composed mostly of white matter and an area in the centre is composed mostly of grey matter. As in the brain the grey matter is mostly nerve cell bodies and white matter is the nerve fibres. White matter in the spinal cord consists of tracts containing bundles of ascending and descending neurones. Ascending tracts carry information up towards the brain while descending tracts carry information down from the brain to the body.

In cross section the spinal cord has a roughly H shaped central area of grey matter, arranged into ventral and dorsal horns. Motor neuronal cell bodies are located in the ventral horns; their axons leave in the ventral nerve roots to innervate muscles. In the dorsal horns the grey matter is largely composed of the cell bodies of interneurones (relay neurones) which process signals from the axons of sensory neurones entering via the dorsal nerve root. Overall the spinal cord communicates with the body through 31 pairs of spinal nerves which arise from both sides of the cord. These spinal nerves then carry on to supply the

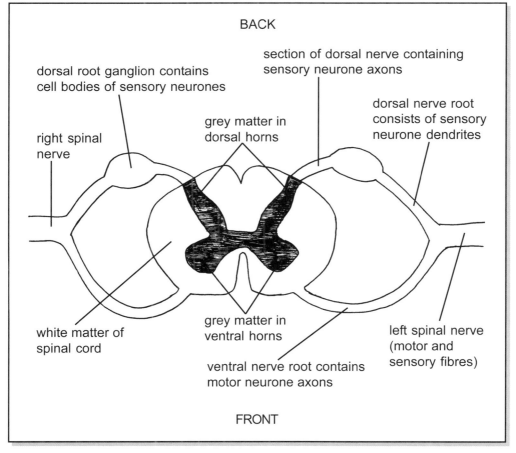

Diagram 6.20
Cross section of the spinal cord.

same side of the body. The dorsal (posterior) nerve roots contain sensory neurones carrying sensory afferent information into the spinal cord. Ventral (anterior) nerve roots contain motor neurones carrying motor, efferent impulses out from the spinal cord. If there is a transverse injury to the cord the person will not be able to feel or move anything below the level of the lesion.

The spinal cord is anatomically described in sections; these are named according to the vertebrae in the region the cord is passing through. The top section is continuous with the medulla of the brain stem and passes through the neck; this is the cervical region. The second thoracic region passes through the thorax. Thirdly, the lumbar region passes into the small of the back. In most people the spinal cord terminates between the level of the first and second lumbar vertebrae. This is why if a specimen of CSF is needed the lumber puncture is normally performed below the third lumbar vertebra to prevent accidental damage to the cord. Below the level of the second lumbar vertebra, large spinal nerves form the lower lumbar, sacral and coccyx sections. As the spinal cord has terminated by this level these large nerves are no longer part of the spinal cord. They are collectively referred to as the cauda equina which is Latin for 'horse's tail'.

Protection of the central nervous system

Nervous tissue is delicate and must be protected from trauma. To achieve this there are several layers of protection around the brain and spinal cord. The skull is surrounded by skin and subcutaneous tissue, which provides some cushioning effect against knocks. Hair may also provide a cushioning effect from outside forces. Under the subcutaneous tissue there is the periosteum and bone of the skull. The bone is strong and ridged and the skull forms a closed vault around the brain. The spinal cord runs through the vertebral canal so is protected by the bony vertebrae which surround it.

Meninges

Under the bone there is a layer called the dura mater composed of tough fibrous tissue which supports and protects the brain and spinal cord. Underneath the dura mater is a web-like structure referred to as the arachnoid mater. Underneath the arachnoid mater is the cerebrospinal fluid (CSF). The compartment containing the CSF, under the arachnoid mater, is referred to as the subarachnoid space. Numerous blood vessels supplying the brain run in this subarachnoid space. In adults there is about 150 mls of this fluid surrounding the brain and spinal cord. This layer of CSF surrounds the brain and the spinal cord meaning the CNS is essentially floating in CSF. This is important because fluid is an excellent shock absorber. If this shock absorbing layer were not present even minor jolting, like stepping off a curb, would cause delicate neuronal tissues to strike the overlying bony structures. Underneath the cerebrospinal fluid, and lining the surface of the brain itself is the pia mater. (Memory point - the CSF is at 'lunch time', between the morning and the afternoon, i.e. between the a.m. and the p.m.).

Collectively the dura, arachnoid and pia mater are called the meninges. Inflammation of the meninges causes meningitis. (Also remember that the meninges PAD the brain - Pia, Arachnoid, Dura). So the brain is protected from damage by hair, skin, subcutaneous tissue, bone, dura mater, arachnoid mater, cerebrospinal fluid and pia mater.

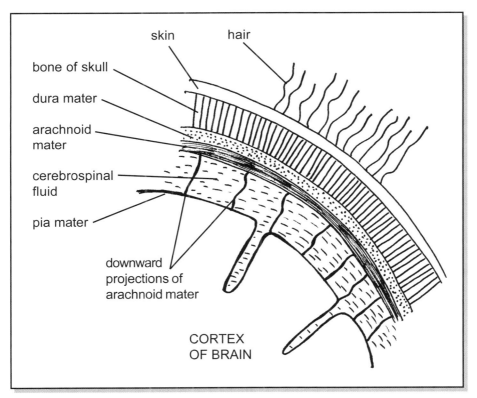

Diagram 6.21
Protection of the central nervous system from damage.

Blood brain barrier

The blood brain barrier is a physiological barrier between the blood supply to the brain and the brain interstitial fluid, which bathes the neuronal cells. This barrier is located in and around the capillary walls which carry blood through the brain tissue. The first layer of the blood brain barrier is provided by the endothelial cells which make up the capillary walls. These endothelial cells are tightly packed and are sealed together at their edges by tight junctions. The second layer of the barrier is composed of the flattened 'end feet' processes of astrocytes which wrap around the capillaries. This protective barrier keeps many toxins out of the brain, even if they are present in the blood.

Autonomic nervous system

In physiological terms the nervous system can be divided into the voluntary nervous system under the control of will and the autonomic nervous system which functions automatically. The voluntary nervous system allows us to implement voluntary movements, for example, when we decide to move a hand or foot. The autonomic nervous system looks after the automatic functions controlled by the nervous system. The autonomic nervous system is itself subdivided into two sub categories known as the sympathetic autonomic nervous system and the parasympathetic autonomic nervous system.

Sympathetic

The sympathetic nervous system prepares the body for 'fight or flight', to escape from dangerous situations, or to fight, if necessary. Sympathetic activity increases in an emergency, excitement or exercise (known as the 3 Es). In order to prepare the body for fight or flight there is an increase in heart rate and the amount of blood pumped out per cardiac contraction (known as stroke volume). The combination of these factors increases cardiac output. Increased stroke volume and strength of cardiac contractions explains why we can feel our hearts beating when we are anxious or after exercise. There is also dilation of the coronary arteries to increase the blood supply to the myocardium to allow maintenance of the increased cardiac work load.

Increased sympathetic activity increases respiratory rate and dilates the bronchial passages. These effects increase the amount of oxygen the lungs can absorb and the volume of carbon dioxide they can excrete. Again this prepares us for the vigorous exercise required to run or to fight. Consistent with preparing the body for increased activity sympathetic innervation also causes dilation of the blood vessels supplying skeletal muscles. This will allow them to exercise at increased rates by increasing their supply of glucose and oxygen and increasing the removal of waste products such as carbon dioxide.

However, because the blood volume is limited, increased blood supply to some areas means there must be an equivalent reduction to others. This is achieved by vasoconstriction of the blood vessels carrying blood to the skin and the gut. Vasoconstriction of arterial vessels supplying the skin explains why someone may appear white when they are frightened. Reduced blood supply to the gut probably explains the feeling of 'butterflies' in the stomach when we are anxious.

So reduced blood flow to the skin and gut leaves more blood to circulate around the heart, lungs and skeletal muscles. Peripheral vasoconstriction, especially in combination with increased heart rate will also increase systemic arterial blood pressure. This will further improve the circulation of blood to the myocardium, skeletal muscles and brain. Peripheral vasoconstriction will also mean that if superficial injuries are sustained there will only be small volumes of blood loss. Sympathetic stimulation dilates the pupil of the eyes to allow more light in, so that the environment may be sensed and danger recognised. All of these effects make the body ready to take emergency action which will increase the chances of individual survival.

Nerves carrying sympathetic innervation leave the CNS and enter the PNS from spinal nerves T1 (thoracic) all the way down to L3 (lumbar), a total of 15 spinal nerves. This is why the sympathetic division of the autonomic nervous system is sometimes referred to as the thoracolumbar outflow. The final synapse between most sympathetic nerve fibres and the organ or structure innervated uses norepinephrine (also called noradrenalin) as the chemical transmitter. These neurones are therefore referred to as adrenergic neurones.

Parasympathetic

The parasympathetic nervous system usually has the opposite effect of the sympathetic. It reduces heart rate and stroke volume and also slows down the respiratory rate as well as constricting the bronchioles. This is appropriate when less air is required to go in and out of the lungs; if the airways remained wide open all of the time infection would be more likely. Vasodilatation increases the blood supply to the skin and the gut. Parasympathetic stimulation increases gut motility and stimulates the release of digestive enzymes to promote digestion. Vasoconstriction decreases the blood supply to skeletal muscles and the pupils constrict. The generally reduced level of activity facilitated by parasympathetic activity allows the body to conserve energy supplies. So the parasympathetic nervous system is concerned with the more routine, low key, function of the body. It is the relative balance of innervation of the sympathetic and parasympathetic nervous systems which maintains the body in a healthy physiological balance.

Nerves carrying parasympathetic innervation leave the CNS and enter the PNS through cranial nerves III, VII, IX and X. Parasympathetic innervation also leaves via spinal nerves S2 to S4 (sacral spinal nerves). This is why the parasympathetic division of the autonomic nervous system is sometimes referred to as the craniosacral outflow. The final synapse between parasympathetic nerve fibres and the organ or structure innervated uses acetylcholine as the chemical transmitter. These neurones are therefore referred to as cholinergic neurones.

Repair of the nervous system

Neurones in some of the central areas of the brain are capable of some limited mitotic division throughout adult life. However the neurones of the cerebral cortex have essentially no powers of mitosis, they cannot divide to regenerate damaged nervous tissue. This means that damage to the brain or spinal cord after birth will usually result in a deficit of function. For example, if there are complications during birth and the baby is deprived of oxygen for a period of time, areas of the brain will die as a result. As cerebral cortical neurones cannot regenerate this damage can leave a child with cerebral palsy (spasticity) or learning difficulties for the rest of their life. Another application of the inability of neurones to divide is dementia. In dementia there is a progressive, irreversible decline in intellectual function as a direct consequence of global death of cerebral neurones. Once lost these neurones cannot regenerate by mitosis explaining why dementia is irreversible by definition.

If the spinal cord is severed the nerve cells cannot divide to regenerate the lost tissues. This means the person will be left without sensation and will be paralysed below the level of the lesion. This is why it is vital to assume unconscious traumatised patients have cervical spinal damage until proved otherwise. When tumours arise in the nervous system they are caused by excessive mitosis of the neuroglial cells, not of the neurones. The neuroglial cells are supporting and structural cell types found in the nervous system.

Sleep

Sleep is marked by a reduced level of brain activity which reduces the level of consciousness. Sleep and wakefulness are both controlled by activity of the reticular formation which is a network of neurones distributed throughout the brain stem. This network will increase stimulation of the cerebrum during wakefulness and reduce stimulation during sleep. There is also diminished activity of skeletal muscles and a lowered metabolic rate. There are basically two types of sleep, rapid eye movement sleep (REM) and non rapid eye movement sleep (NREM). NREM sleep is also called slow wave sleep as there is a slowing of the brain waves as detected using an electroencephalogram (EEG). Brain wave activity may slow down to one or two waves per second (1-2 Hz). During this slow wave sleep the pupils of the eyes also constrict.

The first REM period during a nights sleep usually lasts for about 20 minutes with later periods becoming progressively longer. During a typical nights sleep there may be 4 or 5 periods of REM sleep alternating with NREM, slow wave sleep. During REM periods the brain wave activity increases to about 60-70Hz. REM sleep is when dreaming occurs and if a person is woken up they can remember their dreams. During REM sleep there are alterations in pulse, blood pressure and respiratory rate and men often have erections. The amount of sleep required by an individual changes throughout life from as much as 20 hours a day in infancy to as little as 6 hours a day in old age. Insomnia describes a difficulty in getting to sleep or waking during the night or early morning.

Stages of sleep

NREM sleep is often described in four stages. Stage one is a transitional stage between waking and sleeping that normally only lasts for a few minutes when someone is falling asleep. Stage two is the first stage of true sleep. It is a light sleep and fragmentary dreams may be experienced despite it being NREM. Stage three represents a moderately deep sleep, body temperature begins to fall and blood pressure decreases. Stage four is deep sleep. The person responds only slowly if they are vigorously woken up. The deeper phases of sleep are more likely to occur during the first few hours of sleep.

Possible reasons for sleep

Sleep allows the CNS to reduce its level of activity and so recuperate from the previous days activity. Dreaming may be necessary for the normal functioning of the CNS; some have suggested it is necessary for encoding learnt information or for forgetting. People who have been deprived of sleep also start to hallucinate and are unable to concentrate effectively. The rest time associated with sleep allows for maintenance and repair of damaged body tissues. This is why it is important for people to get plenty of sleep when recovering from illness or injury. After vigorous exercise people also have more slow wave sleep. In children most growth occurs while they are asleep, so sleep is necessary for normal growth.

Circadian Rhythm

This is a pattern based on a 24 hour day cycle so it describes rhythms which occur on a daily basis for example waking and sleeping. Many physiological parameters have a circadian rhythm, e.g. body temperature drops at night. Urine production is reduced overnight and increased during the day. Metabolic rate is less during the night and several hormones have a circadian variation in serum levels.

A developing field

I hope you have now understood some of the physiological processes going on in the nervous system. If everything does not seem to make sense just now do not worry; much of the function of the brain is still a mystery to science and neuroscience is still very much a developing field. For example, it is not clear how consciousness is generated, or indeed what consciousness is. It is hard to imagine how some nerve cells, neuronal impulses and neurotransmitters generate consciousness. We mentioned that sight is perceived in the occipital lobe. In a place where there is in fact no light at all we see all of the colours, textures and beauty of the world. When we do something we enjoy we feel pleasure but even this phenomenon is generated by the activity of dopamine in the brain and why this should be pleasurable is not clear. Perhaps if all of these things cause us to reflect on the amazing nature, and remaining mysteries of human physiology it is a good thing.

CHAPTER 7

Endocrine System

Types of gland

A gland is a structure which produces and secretes a chemical product. There are two forms of gland in the body; these are referred to as exocrine and endocrine. An exocrine gland secretes a product via a duct into a localised area whereas an endocrine gland always secretes the product directly into the blood.

Exocrine glands

An exocrine gland produces a product which is then directly exported from the gland. Exocrine gland products are usually secreted onto an internal or external body surface. Exocrine products are directly secreted locally and are not exported into the blood. This means the products perform some local function and are not systemically distributed in the blood.

Exocrine glands may be unicellular, meaning they are composed of one cell. Other exocrine glands are multicellular; these are more complex structures composed of many cells. Goblet cells are an example of a unicellular gland. These are so called because their internal structure resembles the shape of an old style drinking goblet. Goblet cells produce and secrete mucus directly onto the surface of mucous membranes. Once on an epithelial surface mucus provides protection and lubrication. Production of mucus by goblet cells in mucous membranes can be stimulated by the presence of infection or other irritants. For example, more mucus will be produced to protect the linings of the airways from inhaled smoke. The need to expectorate this excess mucus from the airways explains why smokers often have a cough.

There are many different forms of multicellular exocrine glands but they all have secretory cells which secrete a product, and a duct which transports the product to a release site. For example, a sweat gland produces sweat and a duct carries this product to the surface of the skin. Other examples of exocrine glands are mammary glands which produce milk, sebaceous glands – sebum, salivary glands – saliva, pancreas – digestive enzymes and the prostate gland – seminal fluid.

Endocrine glands

Endo means inside. Endocrine glands release their products directly into the blood and so into the internal systemic environment. These glands have no ducts and for this reason, in the past, were called ductless glands. Endocrine products are released directly into the blood circulating through a gland. This means that the endocrine products are rapidly systemically distributed.

Endocrine products are referred to as hormones. A hormone is a chemical messenger which circulates in the blood at low concentrations. After being produced in an endocrine gland a hormone circulates in the blood until it reaches a specific target tissue. The hormone will then bind onto a specific receptor on the target tissue. It is the combination of a hormone and the receptor site which then initiates a physiological response in the target cell.

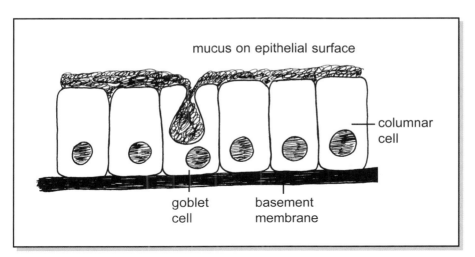

mucus on epithelial surface

columnar
cell

goblet
cell

basement
membrane

Diagram 7.1
A goblet cell in the internal lining of the small intestine. Produced mucus
first passes into the 'goblet' and then out to line the epithelial surface
where it will protect and lubricate the lining of the gastrointestinal tract. The
layer of mucus provides the epithelial cells with protection from potentially
damaging substances such as digestive enzymes. Mucus also lubricates
the passage of the partly digested food along the lumen of the tract.

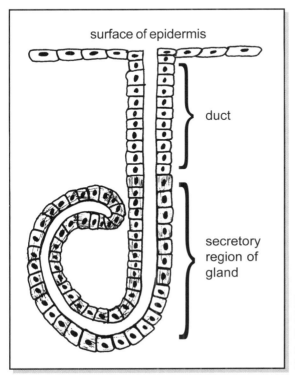

surface of epidermis

duct

secretory
region of
gland

Diagram 7.2
Example of a coiled exocrine gland.
Sweat is produced in the lower
secretory portion then passes up,
through the duct, to the skin surface.

Diagram 7.3
Endocrine product is
secreted directly into the
blood; arrows represent
flow of endocrine
product.

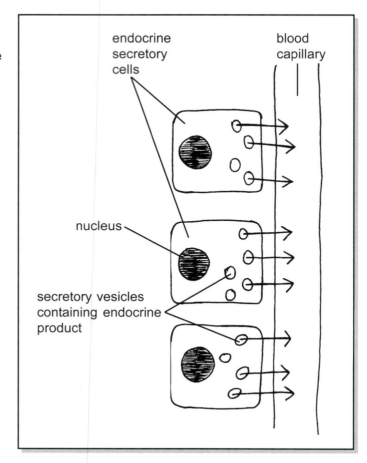

Signals and receptors

Because a hormone carries a chemical message it is sometimes referred to as a
signal. A signal molecule has a particular shape and defined chemical properties.
This means the signal will only bind to a specific receptor site. Receptor sites are
made of protein and located on, or in, target cells. The hormone is analogous to a
key, and the receptor to a lock. A specific key is required to open a particular lock.
The cells which comprise the tissues of the body have many receptor sites on
internal and external cell surfaces. However, only the signal with the correctly
shaped 'key' can activate a specific receptor site. A target cell may have between
2000 and 100,000 receptors for a particular hormone. Signal molecules may
also be referred to as ligands.

Endocrine glands

Hormones are produced by endocrine tissue which is usually concentrated in
specialised glands designed for this purpose (there are also a few hormones produced
by endocrine tissue in organs which have another prime function).

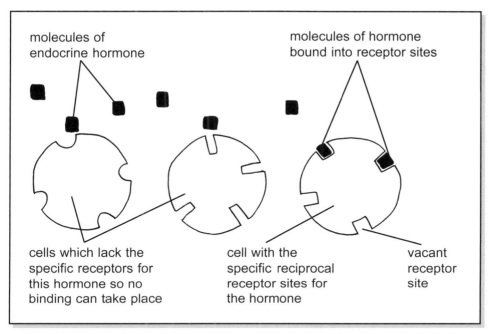

molecules of
endocrine hormone

molecules of hormone
bound into receptor sites

cells which lack the
specific receptors for
this hormone so no
binding can take place

cell with the
specific reciprocal
receptor sites for
the hormone

vacant
receptor
site

Diagram 7.4
The square shaped signal molecule does not fit into a round or oblong receptor
site. It can only fit into, and bind with, the reciprocal shaped receptor. Once the
endocrine signal has bound to the receptor a physiological change will be
initiated.

Pituitary gland

The pituitary gland is about 1-1.5 cm in diameter and sits in the pituitary fossa
which is a small bony depression in the base of the skull. The gland is attached to
the base of the brain by a stalk underneath the hypothalamus. It is composed of
two adjacent but separate lobes. The larger anterior (frontal) lobe is composed of
glandular tissue. Anterior glandular tissue produces hormones and releases them
directly into the blood.

The posterior lobe is made of neurological tissue; hormones released from this
lobe are actually produced in cell bodies located in the hypothalamus. Once
synthesised these hormones are packaged into granules which then travel down
secretory axons before release from the posterior lobe. Because posterior lobe
hormones are produced in nerve cells the process is termed neurosecretion.

The scientifically correct name for the pituitary gland is the hypophysis. The
anterior lobe is called the adenohypophysis because it is composed of glandular
tissue (adeno means to do with glandular tissue). Because the posterior lobe is
made of nervous tissue it is termed the neurohypophysis.

There are only two hormones secreted by the posterior lobe; oxytocin and
antidiuretic hormone.

Diagram 7.5
The distribution
of endocrine
glands within
the body.

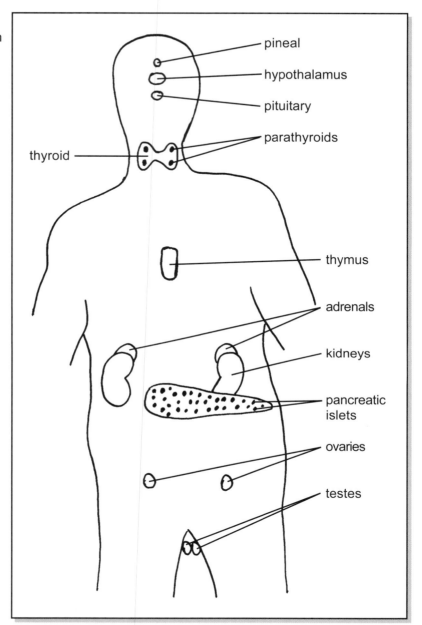

- pineal
- hypothalamus
- pituitary
- parathyroids
- thyroid
- thymus
- adrenals
- kidneys
- pancreatic islets
- ovaries
- testes

Posterior pituitary hormones

Oxytocin

Oxytocin has two functions. Release of this hormone may be stimulated by distension of the uterus in the later stages of pregnancy. Oxytocin then stimulates the contraction of the uterine muscles during delivery. This explains why oxytocin may be used clinically to induce labour. The second role of oxytocin is during

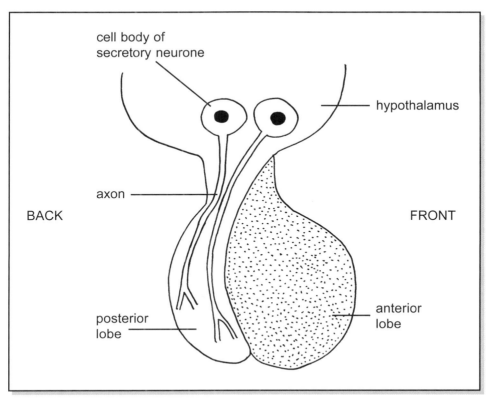

Diagram 7.6
Two lobes of the pituitary gland. Note the neurosecretory neurones arise in the hypothalamus and terminate in the posterior lobe from where the hormones are released into the blood.

lactation. When a baby suckles at the nipple this stimulates a reflex which leads to oxytocin release. In this case the oxytocin contracts the milk ducts to stimulate the release of milk from the nipples in the process of milk let-down. In both cases oxytocin is working by stimulating smooth muscle contractions.

Antidiuretic hormone (ADH)

Diuresis refers to the production of a large volume of urine. Diuretic drugs such as furosemide are given to increase urine volumes. An antidiuretic has the opposite effect; it acts against diuresis to reduce urine volumes. This means that the more ADH in the blood the less urine will be produced. In the absence of ADH the urine volumes will increase.

   When the volume of water in the blood drops this has the effect of increasing the concentration of the blood. As a result the osmotic potential is increased, so increasing osmolarity which is detected in the hypothalamus and causes ADH to be released. This hormone then travels to the kidneys in the blood. ADH acts on distal portions of the nephrons in the kidneys to increase the volume of glomerular filtrate which is reabsorbed back into the blood. If more water from the glomerular filtrate is reabsorbed back into the blood this means there is less left in the lumens of the nephrons to enter the urine. The result of this is that urine volumes drop so conserving water in the blood.

Conversely, if someone drinks large volumes of water, the blood will become too dilute, reducing blood osmolarity. This is detected in the hypothalamus and causes the pituitary gland to release less ADH. When there is less ADH in the blood, less water is reabsorbed from the glomerular filtrate in the nephrons. This means more water is retained in the nephron so more water will pass on into the urine.

Alcohol inhibits the release of ADH; this means there is less antidiuretic effect, so urine volumes are large. This is why alcohol drinking causes dehydration (one of the causes of a hangover). Diabetes insipidus (nothing to do with diabetes mellitus) is a disease where there is a lack of ADH production. These patients will develop a polyuria, passing up to 20 litres of urine per day. This severe water loss will lead to extreme thirst causing the patient to drink large volumes of water. Fortunately this disorder can be treated using synthetic ADH given through skin patches.

By regulating plasma levels of ADH the body is able to regulate the amount of water in the blood. This keeps the blood at the correct osmolarity. If the blood is too dilute the osmolarity will fall. In dehydration the osmolarity will tend to rise. This maintenance of equilibrium by ADH is an example of the principle of homeostasis. Homeo means 'same'. There are many parameters in the body which need to be maintained in the same state or at the same level, and homeostatic mechanisms exist to ensure this. (Other examples of homeostasis are discussed later in this chapter and in subsequent chapters.) ADH is also a potent vasoconstricting agent, reducing the lumens of arterioles; this is why it is also referred to as vasopressin. This vasoconstriction is particularly important after haemorrhage or during times of dehydration when it will help to maintain blood pressure.

Anterior pituitary

Anterior pituitary function is controlled by the hypothalamus

Traditionally the pituitary gland has been described as the master gland or the leader of the endocrine orchestra. This is because the anterior lobe produces trophic hormones which coordinate the activity of other endocrine glands. While this is true, the anterior pituitary gland is itself regulated by the hypothalamus. This part of the brain produces a range of hormones which act on the anterior pituitary so in this sense the hypothalamus has an endocrine function.

The hypothalamus regulates anterior pituitary function by producing a range of neurohormones which regulate the release of the trophic hormones. These

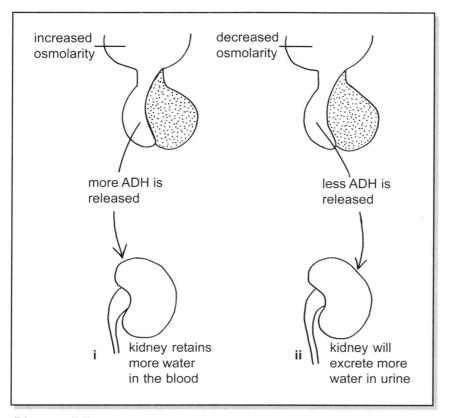

Diagram 7.7
(i)   When blood osmolarity rises (i.e. there is less water in the blood) this is detected by the hypothalamus which causes more ADH to be released leading to lower urine volumes.
(ii) A reduction in blood osmolarity (this will happen when the blood is too dilute) will be detected by the hypothalamus which reduces the amount of ADH released leading to greater urine volumes.

neurohormones are also called releasing hormones as their function is usually to stimulate the release of the trophic hormones.

Hypothalamic neurohormones include growth hormone-releasing hormone (GHRH) which stimulates anterior pituitary cells called somatotrophs to release growth hormone (GH) into the blood. There is also a hypothalamic neurohormone called growth hormone release-inhibiting hormone (somatostatin) which inhibits release of GH. Thyrotrophin-releasing hormone (TRH) stimulates the release of thyroid stimulating hormone (TSH) which is produced by a group of specialised anterior pituitary cells called thyrotrophs.

Corticotrophin-releasing hormone (CRH) causes the pituitary to release adrenocorticotrophic hormone (ACTH) from specialised pituitary cells called corticotrophs. Gonadotrophin-releasing hormone (GnRH) stimulates the release of follicle stimulating hormone (FSH) and luteinising hormone (LH) which are produced by pituitary cells called gonadotrophs. Hypothalamic vasoactive intestinal peptide (VIP) stimulates the release of prolactin from pituitary cells called lactotrophs. From this it can be seen that the anterior pituitary tissue is composed of five different types of cell, somatotrophs, thyrotrophs, corticotrophs, gonadotrophs and lactotrophs producing the different trophic hormones.

Neurohormones from the hypothalamus are not released into the systemic circulation in the way that other endocrine hormones are. Once produced in the hypothalamus they are absorbed by capillaries which drain into portal veins which then run down the pituitary stalk. Once the portal veins reach the anterior pituitary they divide into capillaries which supply the neurohormones directly to the pituitary cells. This means the neurohormones can be produced in very small volumes as they are not systemically diluted before exerting their effect. As these hypothalamic hormones regulate pituitary function the hypothalamus is ultimately the 'master gland'.

Anterior pituitary hormones

Thyroid stimulating hormone (TSH)

Homeostasis refers to the maintenance of a constant internal environment; this is maintained in different ways in different parts of the body. One group of parameters which need to be finely regulated are the levels of endocrine hormones in the blood. If these levels are not kept relatively constant the tissues of the body will be over or under stimulated. One type of homeostatic mechanism is known as a negative feedback system. An example of this is the control of the amount of thyroid hormone (TH or thyroxine) in the blood. Low levels of thyroid hormone in the blood are detected by specialised cells in the hypothalamus. The hypothalamus responds to these low levels of TH by releasing a substance called thyrotrophin-releasing hormone (TRH). This TRH then stimulates the anterior lobe of the pituitary gland to release the trophic hormone which is thyroid stimulating hormone (TSH). TSH then stimulates the thyroid gland itself to produce more TH. As the levels of TH in the blood rise, the TH inhibits the release of further TRH from the hypothalamus.

The underlying mechanism involved in this process is increased levels of thyroid hormone in the blood inhibits the release of its own initial releasing factor, that is the TRH. This is an example of a negative feedback system. A negative feedback system is when the end result of a process, e.g. TH, inhibits (has a negative effect on) the release of the initial releasing factor for its own production - in this case TRH.

Adrenocorticotrophic hormone (ACTH)

This anterior pituitary hormone stimulates the release of hormones from the adrenal cortex, both hydrocortisone (cortisol) and corticosterone. These are steroid

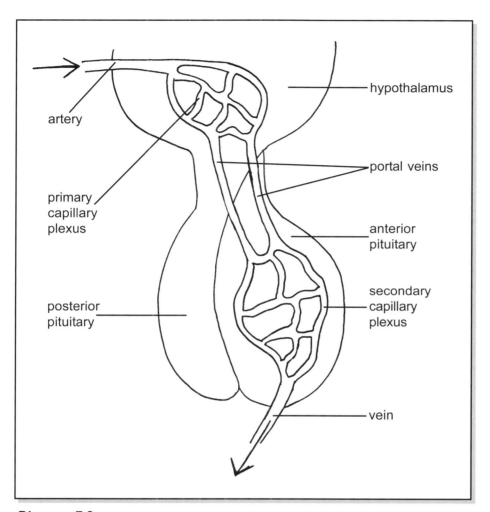

Diagram 7.8
Portal veins carry neurohormones from the hypothalamus directly to the
anterior pituitary gland where they regulate the release of trophic hormones.
These trophic hormones in turn regulate the activity of the endocrine glands
in the rest of the body. Blood enters the hypothalamus via an artery then
circulates through the hypothalamus in a group of capillaries called the
primary capillary plexus. Blood from these capillaries drains through larger
portal veins into a secondary capillary plexus in the anterior pituitary gland
before finally draining into the systemic venous circulation.

type hormones and are collectively called glucocorticoids. ACTH also stimulates
the release of androgens (male type hormones) from the adrenal cortex. Levels of
these adrenal cortical hormones are detected by specialised cells in the
hypothalamus in a similar way to the levels of thyroid hormone discussed above.
The hypothalamus responds by secreting the hormone which stimulates the release

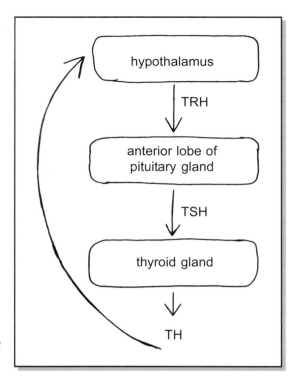

Diagram 7.9
The homeostatic control of TH levels in the blood via a negative feedback system. Rising levels of TH inhibit further release of TRH, falling levels of TH allows increased release of TRH.

of ACTH, which is called corticotrophin-releasing hormone (CRH). CRH then stimulates the release of ACTH from the anterior pituitary and the ACTH in turn stimulates the release of the adrenal cortical hormones. Increases in the blood levels of adrenal cortical hormones inhibit the release of CRH from the hypothalamus. When this happens less ACTH is secreted so less adrenal cortical hormones are released by the adrenal cortex. This is another example of the end product of a process inhibiting the release of its own initial releasing factor, in other words it is a negative feedback system. The end result of this mechanism is that plasma levels of adrenal cortical hormones are maintained at homeostatic levels.

Follicle stimulating hormone (FSH)

FSH is an interesting hormone as it has different functions in men and women. In men FSH stimulates the production of sperm in the testes using the process termed spermatogenesis. The word genesis refers to 'beginning' as in the first book of the bible, so spermatogenesis is literally the beginning of sperm. In women FSH has two functions. Firstly it stimulates the development of the ova each month in the ovaries. The structure, within the ovary, containing an ovum is called the follicle which is where FSH gets its name. An ovum is the female gamete (i.e the egg cell) which can be fertilised by a sperm. Secondly, FSH stimulates the ovaries to release the female hormone, oestrogen.

Luteinising hormone (LH)

This hormone again has a different function in the two sexes. In women it stimulates the ovary to release an ovum, normally around day 14 of the menstrual cycle. LH also regulates the release of progesterone from the corpus luteum during the second half of the menstrual cycle. In men, LH stimulates the endocrine tissue in the testes to produce the male hormone, testosterone. The release of FSH and LH are both regulated by the levels of a specific releasing hormone produced in the hypothalamus called gonadotrophin releasing hormone (GnRH). Both FSH and LH are produced by the gonadotrophs of the anterior pituitary. This may be because they both act on the gonads.

Prolactin

Prolactin is also released as a result of stimulation by a hormone from the hypothalamus. In the case of prolactin, the releasing hormone is called vasoactive intestinal peptide (VIP). VIP is released in response to nervous impulses stimulated by the sucking action of an infant on the nipple. Prolactin acts on the breasts to initiate and sustain the synthesis of milk, a process which is called lactation. Lact means to do with milk, for example lactose is the sugar found in milk. The action of prolactin should not be confused with that of oxytocin. Prolactin stimulates the actual synthesis of milk whereas oxytocin stimulates the ejection of the produced milk from the breasts. In men prolactin reduces blood levels of testosterone and at high levels may inhibit sperm production.

Growth hormone (GH)

GH is also sometimes referred to as somatotrophin. Several factors are involved in the process of growth including genetic potential and adequate nutrition. Several hormones, in addition to GH, also influence growth these include sex hormones, thyroid hormones and insulin. It is the action of GH which causes children to grow. There are two periods of rapid growth in a child's development; the first is in the first two years of life with a second 'spurt' at the time of puberty. Growth stops around the age of 18-20 years when the growing ends of the long bones fuse over in the process of epiphyseal closure. GH acts on body cells to increase the rate of mitosis and the production of new proteins, muscle and bone are particularly stimulated. In bone it stimulates the proliferation of cartilage cells and osteoblasts in the growth plates; it will also stimulate the production of collagen and the mineralization of bone. If there is too much GH during development a giant will result, too little GH during childhood will lead to dwarfism. Most of the growth initiated by GH takes place at night; this is why it is very important that children get plenty of sleep.

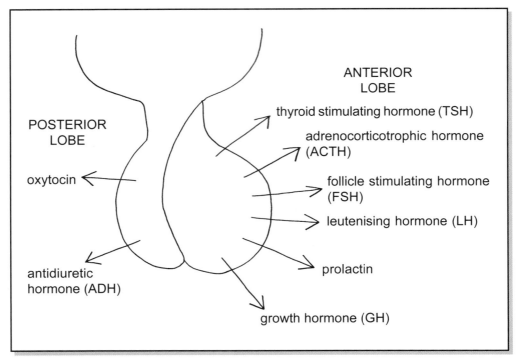

POSTERIOR
LOBE

oxytocin

antidiuretic
hormone (ADH)

ANTERIOR
LOBE

thyroid stimulating hormone (TSH)

adrenocorticotrophic hormone
(ACTH)

follicle stimulating hormone
(FSH)

leutenising hormone (LH)

prolactin

growth hormone (GH)

Diagram 7.10
Hormones secreted from the two lobes of the pituitary gland, ADH and oxytocin from
the posterior lobe and the trophic hormones from the anterior lobe.

Thyroid gland

This endocrine gland is located in the neck, in front of the trachea, just below the
larynx. The gland consists of two lobes on either side of the thyroid cartilage and
trachea. These two lobes are joined by a narrow section of thyroid tissue termed
the thyroid isthmus. Within the gland there are a large number of follicles, which
are surrounded by secretory epithelial cells. Within these thyroid follicles thyroid
hormone is stored in combination with a protein in the form of thyroglobulin.
Two forms of secretory cells are contained in the thyroid gland. The most common
form are called follicular cells and these produce thyroid hormone. There are two
forms of thyroid hormone; T3 contains three iodine atoms and T4 contains four
iodine atoms in the molecule. Both of these thyroid hormones perform the same
function but the T3 is physiologically more active.

From this, it is clear that iodine is essential for the formation of thyroid
hormone. Iodine comes primarily from the sea, so people who do not have
access to fish or sea salt may become deficient. In the UK this used to be common
in Derbyshire because of its distance from the sea. When iodine is deficient the
thyroid gland swells to try to extract more iodine from the blood. A swelling in
the thyroid gland is called a goitre, the traditional English name for this is

Derbyshire neck. However, it is important to realise the thyroid gland may swell in other disorders and produce toxic amounts of thyroid hormone; this pathological swelling is still referred to as a goitre.

The second form of secretory cells in the thyroid are the C cells which are also sometimes called parafollicular cells. Para means beside, so these cells are beside the follicular cells. C cells secrete calcitonin.

Thyroid hormones

Secretion of the two forms of thyroid hormone is stimulated by TSH. Thyroid hormone acts on a wide range of body cells where it increases the metabolic rate. This will mean that thyroid stimulated cells will use more glucose, fatty acids and oxygen to produce more energy. If a patient is over-producing thyroid hormone they will usually lose weight and feel hot. This is referred to as hyperthyroidism (hyper means high). Such patients lose weight because they use up the energy reserves of the body. Whenever energy is used, heat is always produced, explaining why the patients tend to feel hot. Conversely if a patient has hypothyroidism, (hypo means low), resulting in low levels of TH in the blood, they will tend to put on weight and feel cold, due to metabolic under-activity.

Thyroid hormone is also needed for the normal development of the brain. This is why if a person has low levels of thyroid hormone during fetal life or during the growing years, the brain does not develop normally leading to mental retardation. In childhood, thyroid hormone is also needed for normal growth, so a child with low TH levels does not grow properly. This combination of stunted growth and mental retardation caused by childhood hypothyroidism is referred to as cretinism. This used to occur in the UK in areas where there was a deficiency of iodine in the diet and is still seen in some areas of the world. Child or adult hypothyroidism can now be readily treated with oral iodine or thyroxine.

Calcitonin

Secretion of calcitonin by the C cells of the thyroid is stimulated by increased levels of calcium in the blood. The calcitonin lowers plasma levels of calcium in two ways. Firstly it causes more calcium to be deposited in the bones. Secondly calcitonin increases the excretion of calcium by the kidneys.

Parathyroid glands

There are four parathyroid glands located within the tissue, but to the back, of the thyroid gland itself. These produce parathyroid hormone (PTH).

Parathyroid hormone

This is produced by the parathyroid tissue in response to decreasing levels of calcium in the blood. Once released, parathyroid hormone increases plasma calcium levels in three ways. Firstly it increases the amount of calcium which is released from stores in the bone. Secondly parathyroid hormone increases the amount of calcium which is reabsorbed by the nephrons in the kidney, resulting in less calcium being lost in the urine. Thirdly it acts on the small intestine to increase the amount of calcium which is absorbed from food. If there is a deficiency of parathyroid hormone this will lead to reduced blood levels of calcium. This hypocalcaemia causes muscle spasms, a condition called tetany. This is a rare complication of thyroid surgery and will occur if too much parathyroid tissue is accidentally removed. Tetany may be treated with calcium supplements. It is the combined action of calcitonin lowering and parathyroid hormone raising blood calcium levels which maintains the mineral at homeostatic levels.

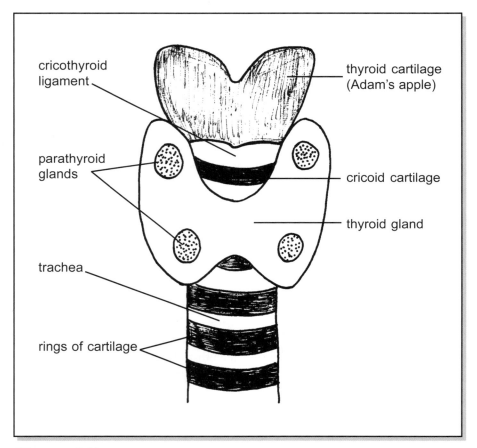

Diagram 7.11
Thyroid and parathyroids. The thyroid gland is about the same size and position as a bow tie. (If emergency access to the airway is needed, for example in choking or suffocation, an opening may be made through the cricothyroid ligament in a procedure called a cricothyrotomy).

Pancreas

Endocrine tissue in the pancreas is located in over a million small pancreatic islets (of Langerhan). The pancreas is located in the curve of the duodenum in the upper area of the abdominal cavity behind the stomach. Most of the pancreatic tissue produces exocrine digestive enzymes which drain into the duodenum via the pancreatic duct. This means the pancreas has exocrine and endocrine functions. The islets form small 'islands' of tissue throughout the substance of the gland. Within each islet or cluster of endocrine tissue there are two main forms of cells called alpha and beta. Pancreatic islets also contain D (or delta) cells which secrete somatostatin, a product which is the same as the growth hormone release-inhibiting hormone produced by the hypothalamus.

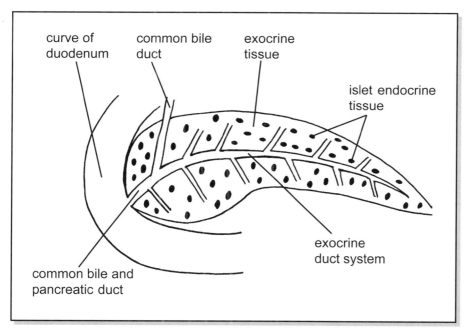

Diagram 7.12
Pancreas showing islet tissue. In reality these are a million or more isolated clusters of cells in a 'sea' of exocrine tissue. Only about 2% of the mass of the pancreas is islet tissue, the rest is exocrine.

Pancreatic islets

Another example of the endocrine system maintaining homeostasis is the physiology of blood glucose regulation. If the amount of sugar in the blood drops too low this condition is referred to as hypoglycaemia and the person will feel shaky, sweaty and hungry. Conversely, if the concentrations of glucose in the blood rise too high this is referred to as hyperglycaemia. In the short term, hyperglycaemia may lead to glucose in the urine with increased urine volumes. In the longer term hyperglycaemia is very harmful to the body and is responsible for most of the long term complications of diabetes mellitus. So both hypoglycaemia and hyperglycaemia are abnormal conditions and need to be avoided. Physiological mechanisms of homeostasis maintain the blood concentration of glucose at a relatively constant normal of around 4.5-7 mmol/L (millimoles of glucose per litre of blood).

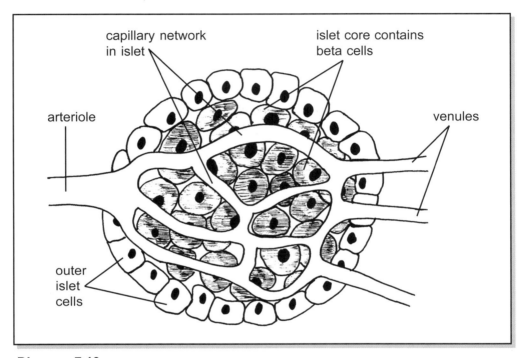

Diagram 7.13
A single pancreatic islet is supplied with blood from an arteriole. As this blood passes through the islet it picks up endocrine hormones produced and secreted by the islet cells. This blood then returns to the systemic venous circulation via some venules. The core of each islet contains beta cells which are sensitive to increases in blood glucose levels and respond by secreting insulin. The cortex of an islet contains alpha cells which are sensitive to falls in blood glucose and respond by secreting glucagon. The cortex of each islet also contains PP (also referred to as F) cells which produce pancreatic polypeptide and delta cells which produce somatostatin.

Insulin from beta cells will lower blood glucose levels

After eating a meal containing carbohydrates, such as sugary or starchy foods, blood glucose levels will start to rise. These rising levels of blood sugar are detected by the beta cells in the pancreatic islets. The same beta cells respond by secreting insulin. Insulin is released directly into the blood where it facilitates the conversion of soluble glucose into insoluble glycogen which can then be stored in the liver and muscles. When glucose is converted to glycogen it is no longer in the blood, but being stored in the muscles and liver in insoluble form. Therefore blood sugar levels will drop down, back towards a normal homeostatic level.

In addition to this mechanism, insulin also facilitates the transfer of glucose across cell membranes, from the tissue fluids and blood, into the cells of the body. In the absence of insulin, most cell membranes are impervious to the passage of glucose. This is because glucose is a water soluble molecule while cell membranes are lipid based. When an insulin molecule arrives at a cell membrane it combines with a specific insulin receptor protein in the cell membranes. The combination of the insulin and the insulin receptor trigger changes within the cell which results in the opening of glucose channels or 'gates' through which glucose may pass. This means more glucose, under the influence of insulin, passes from the tissue fluids of the body into the cells. Once in the cells, glucose may be metabolised in the mitochondria to produce energy. Clearly, if the glucose is in the cells it is no longer in the blood, so again blood levels are lowered. The combination of the glucose to glycogen mechanism and the transport of glucose into cells means that insulin causes the level of blood glucose to drop back down towards a normal homeostatic level. Insulin is actually a small protein made up of 51 amino acid units. This is why insulin used therapeutically must be injected if it is required; if it were swallowed the protein digesting enzymes in the stomach would simply digest it making it ineffective.

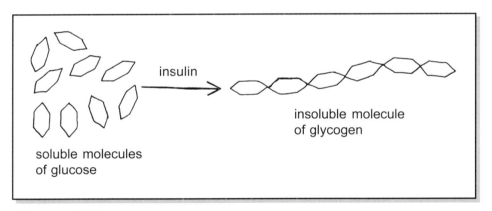

Diagram 7.14
Many molecules of soluble glucose are joined together under the influence of insulin to form a large glycogen molecule. Once formed the large insoluble glycogen molecules may be stored in the liver or muscles.

Glucagon will raise blood glucose levels

Conversely if an individual has not eaten for a few hours or takes active exercise, the levels of glucose in the blood will start to fall. Reductions in blood glucose levels are detected by the alpha cells of the pancreatic islets. The same alpha cells respond by secreting a hormone called glucagon. Glucagon acts on stored

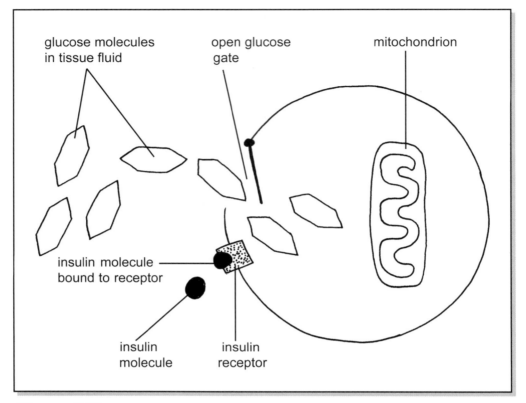

Diagram 7.15
Insulin gates the passage of glucose from tissue fluid into the cells. Insulin molecules combine with insulin receptors on the cell membrane causing the glucose 'gate' to open allowing glucose to be gated into the cell. Once in the cell the glucose can be used in the mitochondria as a substrate, combining with oxygen to produce energy.

glycogen to reconvert it back into glucose. This means insoluble glycogen stored in the liver and muscles is converted back into soluble glucose which will dissolve in the blood. The liberation of this soluble glucose raises blood sugar levels. In addition, low blood sugar levels will make the individual feel hungry; therefore they will eat if food is available. When the carbohydrate component of this food is absorbed it will also increase blood sugar levels.

Insulin lack will cause hyperglycaemia

In diabetes mellitus type 1 the beta cells are all systematically destroyed by the immune system. This is an example of an autoimmune disease where the immune system destroys one of the bodies own tissues. (In military terms this would be described as a 'friendly fire' incident). Over a few years this autoimmune process results in the total eradication of the beta cells in all pancreatic islets meaning the body can no longer produce insulin. The result of this is that blood glucose

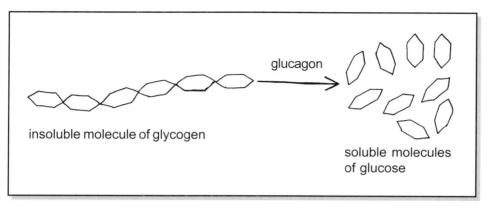

Diagram 7.16
The action of glucagon converting stored glycogen back into glucose.

levels rise. Despite high blood glucose levels, the lack of insulin means that the glucose present in the blood and tissue fluids cannot be gated into the cells. So, there are abnormally high blood glucose levels but abnormally low levels in the cells where it is needed by the mitochondria. This means these patients are dependent on injected insulin in order to survive; the condition is described as insulin dependent diabetes mellitus (IDDM). Before insulin was isolated young people would die within several months of diagnosis.

Adrenal glands

There are two adrenal glands, one located above each kidney; this is why they were previously referred to as the suprarenal glands. The outer layer of the adrenal gland is referred to as the cortex and the centre as the medulla. There are three layers or zones in the adrenal cortex which secrete a range of steroid type hormones; firstly there is an outer layer which produces aldosterone. Underneath this, but still part of the cortex, is a larger layer which produces and secretes the glucocorticoid hormones, which are hydrocortisone (also called cortisol) and corticosterone. The inner layer of the cortex produces sex hormones, mostly the male hormones called androgens. The medulla at the centre of the gland produces adrenaline and noradrenaline (epinephrine and norepinephrine).

Adrenal cortical hormones

Hydrocortisone (cortisol) is the main glucocorticoid produced by the adrenal cortex. The functions of hydrocortisone are complex but basically it increases the probability of survival in difficult or dangerous situations. One function is to ensure the body has enough available sources of energy to deal with times of stress. This is why it increases the levels of nutrients in the blood, such as amino acids, fatty acids and glucose. These nutrients are all required to facilitate the metabolic reactions which produce energy, and will be mobilised from body reserves if necessary. Glucose and fatty acids are used by the body cells as fuels while the amino acids may be synthesised into proteins which act as enzymes to facilitate metabolic processes. In many survival situations the body may need to use large amounts of energy over prolonged periods of time. This may be to escape from predators or to seek out new sources of food.

Hydrocortisone also increases the probability of survival by inhibiting the inflammatory process. Inflammation is necessary for wound healing. However, inflammation also causes pain which may inhibit essential body movement and activity. Because hydrocortisone inhibits the inflammatory process it also inhibits pain. This means that movements essential to survival may carry on, such as fighting a predator or running away. These mechanisms explain why levels of hydrocortisone are increased during periods of stress and anxiety. Hydrocortisone and other related steroid compounds may be given as drugs; in high doses they are very anti-inflammatory which is sometimes a desirable therapeutic outcome.

Aldosterone

The adrenal cortex also produces aldosterone. This has the effect of increasing the reabsorption of sodium from the renal nephrons so retaining more sodium in the blood. As sodium is an osmotic molecule it will tend to attract more water into the blood. This will increase overall blood volume and so will increase blood pressure. Again, in a survival situation, high plasma salt levels and consequent water levels will reduce the blood pressure lowering effects of haemorrhage. This means aldosterone will help to maintain blood pressure if blood is lost. If blood pressure is adequate, the perfusion of blood around vital organs such as the heart, lungs and brain will be maintained. Again this effect can increase the probability of surviving a difficult situation where blood has been lost. The main factor increasing the secretion of aldosterone is the renin-angiotensin mechanism, mostly under the influence of angiotensin II.

Adrenal medullary hormones

Adrenaline and noradrenaline (also called epinephrine and norepinephrine) are both released from the adrenal medulla; collectively these two hormones are described as catecholamines. Adrenaline works in a similar way to the sympathetic nervous system, to help the body to prepare rapidly for a fight or flight situation. Adrenaline will therefore increase the rate and force of cardiac contractions and will dilate the bronchial passages to increase air entry to the alveoli. Blood supply to the skin and gut will be reduced by vasoconstriction to leave more blood for the skeletal muscles, heart and lungs. Adrenaline will also dilate the pupils of the eyes to increase light entry. Adrenaline even prepares the body for possible injury and blood loss by constricting peripheral blood vessels and by causing the blood to clot more quickly. Adrenaline and noradrenaline have similar effects and the adrenal

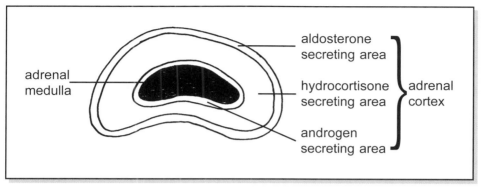

Diagram 7.17
The layers of the adrenal glands, a central medulla surrounded by three layers
of cortex.

medulla secretes 80% adrenaline and 20% noradrenaline. The effects of adrenalin
start a few seconds after the hormone is released, this means the body can be
placed on an emergency footing as soon as danger is detected. The release of
catecholamines is stimulated by action of the sympathetic nervous system. This
sympathetic activity is initiated by the hypothalamus in response to pain, anxiety,
excitement, haemorrhage, cold or hypoglycaemia.

Stress

Stress describes the physiological response of an individual to actual or perceived
threats. Other factors which can cause a physiological stress reaction include blood
loss, hypoxia, pain, cold, bacterial infection, hypoglycaemia and tissue injury. Any
factor causing stress is called a stressor. As discussed these stressors will lead to a
'fight or flight' response, often with feelings of anxiety. In all stress reactions there
is an increase in cortisol and catecholamine secretion. In stress this response of
the adrenal cortex and medulla are both initiated by the hypothalamus. If stress is
prolonged the high levels of cortisol will suppress the immune response. There
will be atrophy of lymphatic tissues with a corresponding reduction in circulating
lymphocytes. It seems likely that ongoing stress also inhibits production of
antibodies. These factors, combined with the suppression of the inflammatory
response, mean the body is more prone to viral and bacterial infections as a result
of ongoing stress.

Kidneys

The prime function of the kidneys is to remove impurities and excess water from
the blood and incorporate these into urine; however, the kidneys also have
endocrine functions. Two hormones are produced by the kidney, erythropoietin
and calcitriol. An enzyme called renin is also produced by the kidneys and is part
of the renin-angiotensin mechanism.

Erythropoietin (EPO)

The kidneys are able to detect the amount of oxygen in the blood which is perfusing them. If levels of oxygen drop, the kidneys respond by releasing erythropoietin. (The liver also produces small amounts of erythropoietin). Erythropoietin stimulates the process of erythropoiesis, which is the production of new erythrocytes (i.e. red blood cells). This cell forming process takes place in the red bone marrow and once formed the cells are released into the systemic circulation. If the number of red cells in the blood is increased this will increase the oxygen carrying capacity of the blood. This in turn will result in increased levels of oxygen in the blood perfusing the kidneys. When the levels of oxygen in the renal blood supply are increased this will again be detected and the kidney will respond by secreting less erythropoietin.

This regulation of the secretion of erythropoietin is therefore one of the mechanisms which controls the numbers of red cells and therefore influences the oxygen carrying capacity of the blood. In health EPO physiology is the main mechanism ensuring that the rate of new red blood cell production balances the rate at which old cells are destroyed. However, there can be alterations to this balance. For example if a person goes to live at altitude there will be a lower partial pressure of oxygen in the air and so the volumes of oxygen in the blood will drop. This will stimulate erythropoietin release and increase the proportion of red cells in the blood to increase oxygen carrying capacity. As red cells take time to manufacture the consequent adaptation to altitude takes time.

Regular aerobic activity will also stimulate erythropoietin release and so increase red cell production. In some cases of renal failure the kidneys are no longer able to produce erythropoietin resulting in anaemia. Such patients may therefore be treated by giving recombinant EPO injections. EPO has also been used by cheating endurance athletes to increase their aerobic capacity. The danger of injecting synthesised EPO, or living at high altitude, is that the increased numbers of red cells causes blood viscosity to increase. This in turn increases the probability of thrombus formation (a thrombus is a clot in a blood vessel and can result in death).

Calcitriol

The second hormone produced by the kidneys is calcitriol. This is in fact the active form of vitamin D. Inactive forms of vitamin D are generated by the skin when exposed to sunlight and absorbed from ingested food. However, the body is unable to use these forms until they have been activated in the kidneys. Calcitriol is classified as a hormone because it is produced in the body from a chemical precursor and is transported in the blood to target tissues. Loss of this ability to convert vitamin D into an active form explains why patients with chronic renal failure lose bone mass, as vitamin D is essential for normal bone metabolism.

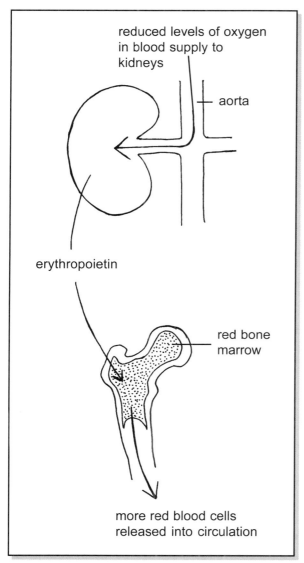

reduced levels of oxygen
in blood supply to
kidneys

aorta

erythropoietin

red bone
marrow

more red blood cells
released into circulation

Diagram 7.18
Reduced levels of oxygen in renal arterial blood are detected and stimulate release of erythropoietin. Erythropoietin circulates in the blood to red bone marrow where it increases red cell production. As increased numbers of red cells increase oxygen carrying capacity of the blood this will reduce erythropoietin release.

Gonads

Gonads is a collective term including both ovaries and testes. The ovaries are located in the female pelvis and the testes in the scrotal sack. Ovaries are responsible for the development and release of the ova. They also produce two hormones, oestrogen and progesterone. The testes produce sperm and the principal male sex hormone called testosterone.

Ovarian hormones

The main hormones secreted by the ovaries are oestrogen and progesterone. These are both steroid type hormones synthesized from cholesterol. Secretion of oestrogen is mostly stimulated by the pituitary hormone follicle stimulating hormone (FSH) although luteinising hormone (LH) also has some stimulating effect. Just before each menstrual cycle begins there is an increase in FSH secretion which stimulates the early ovarian follicle to grow and to start secreting oestrogen. Oestrogen is secreted by the developing ovarian follicle during the first 14 days of a menstrual cycle. The first five days of the cycle is described as the menstrual phase when the old endometrium breaks down and is expelled through the vagina. After this oestrogen stimulates the build up of the lining of the endometrium and increases its vascularity. This means the endometrium is ready to receive an embryo should fertilization occur that month. In addition to these effects oestrogen stimulates the secretion of mucus from the cervical glands and causes changes in the mucus which facilitates the passage of sperm through the cervix, from the vagina into the uterus. On day 14 of an idealised menstrual cycle ovulation occurs. This is mostly stimulated by a surge in LH, released from the anterior pituitary.

After ovulation the LH causes the ovarian follicle to change into the corpus luteum. This conversion is achieved by LH changing the nature of the cells in the ovarian follicle, converting them into lutein cells. These lutein cells in the corpus luteum secrete some oestrogen, but mostly they secrete progesterone. This means blood levels of progesterone are higher during the second half of the menstrual cycle. It is progesterone which maintains development of the endometrium, ready to receive and nourish an embryo should one be formed after ovulation. Progesterone stimulates growth of the mammary glands in the breasts ready for milk secretion. Progesterone also changes the nature of the cervical mucus, but unlike oestrogen it makes it more viscous and so resistant to the penetration of sperm. If pregnancy does not occur the corpus luteum degenerates completely in a process called involution.

If pregnancy does occur the newly developing embryo (when it reaches the blastocyst stage) secretes a hormone called chorionic gonadotropin (CG). This hormone has an effect on the corpus luteum which is similar to that of LH. This means that if pregnancy does occur, the corpus luteum does not undergo involution, but will be maintained for the first three months of the pregnancy by the CG. As a result the corpus luteum will continue to secrete increasing quantities of oestrogen and progesterone. These hormones will prevent menstruation and further promote the development of the endometrium. Sensitive tests can measure the presence of CG in the blood about 9 days after fertilization. The rates of CG secretion then rise rapidly and reach a maximum around weeks 10 to 12 of pregnancy. The presence of CG is commonly used as a pregnancy test.

Later in a pregnancy oestrogen and progesterone are produced by the placenta, the structure connecting the mother and the baby. This means that for the duration of pregnancy the placenta is functioning as an endocrine gland. However, the primary role of the placenta is to allow the diffusion of oxygen and nutrients from mother to baby and the passage of carbon dioxide and waste products of metabolism from baby to mother. Oestrogen and progesterone secreted by the placenta maintain the lining of the uterus and prepare the breasts to secrete milk. During pregnancy, high levels of oestrogen and progesterone prevent further pregnancies by inhibiting ovulation. Combined oral contraceptive pills work by artificially increasing blood levels of oestrogen and progesterone to inhibit ovulation and therefore prevent conception.

It is largely the increase in the blood levels of oestrogen which stimulates puberty in girls. Oestrogen causes development of the female reproductive organs as well as secondary sexual characteristics, such as breast development and female body hair distribution. Oestrogen also promotes growth by stimulation of protein synthesis, an effect which promotes growth in bones and muscles during puberty. Small amounts of androgens are also produced by the ovaries, (and as already mentioned by the adrenal cortex in women). These androgen hormones seem to increase female libido (i.e. the desire for sexual activity).

Testicular hormones

The testes are located in the scrotal sack and produce testosterone. They secrete the hormone testosterone which is the principle adrogenic male hormone. Like oestrogen and progesterone, testosterone is a steroid type hormone synthesised from cholesterol. Testosterone is produced by the interstitial cells of Leydig, which lie scattered between the sperm producing tubules. Secretion of testosterone is stimulated by LH. It is increasing levels of testosterone which stimulates puberty in boys. The hormone causes development of external genitalia and stimulates sperm production. By promoting protein synthesis, testosterone stimulates growth of the bones and muscles. It also leads to male secondary sexual characteristics such as deepening of the voice and the growth of facial hair. Testosterone also promotes male libido and aggression. If a boy is castrated before puberty most of these developmental changes do not occur, nor do castrated males demonstrate male pattern baldness.

Other endocrine glands

Thymus gland

This gland is located in the chest behind the sternum between the lungs. Several hormones are produced in the thymus such as thymosin and thymic factor. These hormones stimulate the maturation and activity of the T lymphocytes.

Pineal gland

This tiny (weight is only 0.1-0.2g) and somewhat mysterious gland is attached to the roof of the third ventricle in the brain. Ventricles in the brain are spaces filled with cerebrospinal fluid. The pineal gland secretes the hormone melatonin. This secretion depends on how much light enters the eyes over the course of a day. If there is more light then less melatonin is secreted. In darker conditions more melatonin in secreted. It is believed that melatonin may play a role in coordinating the circadian cycle, promoting alertness during the day and sleepiness at night. This may be one reason it is so difficult to change between day and night shifts.

In many animals, light levels and pineal gland secretions are used to influence the release of gonadotrophic hormones from the anterior pituitary gland. This has the effect of regulating their reproductive cycles so offspring are born at the time of year which is most likely to promote their survival e.g. in the UK lambs are born in spring. It is currently unclear if the pineal gland influences human sexual and reproductive behaviour.

CHAPTER 8

Digestive System

Introduction

The functions of the digestive system can be summarised as ingestion, digestion, absorption and elimination. Ingestion refers to taking food and water into the body, the processes of eating and drinking. Ingested food molecules are often large and insoluble; in order for them to be absorbed into the body they must first be broken down into smaller units. The process of converting large, ingested food molecules into a form which may be absorbed is termed digestion. After food has been digested it must then be absorbed into the blood or lymphatic systems of the body before it can be utilised. The process whereby digested food is transferred from the lumen of the gut into the circulatory systems is called absorption. Not all ingested material is absorbed, some continues along the length of the digestive tract and is eliminated as waste. Fibre is not broken down by any digestive processes and is eliminated in the same form it was eaten. Water is absorbed unaltered into the blood.

Structures of the digestive system

Essentially, the gastrointestinal (GI) tract or gut is a single tube which runs from the mouth to the anus. The old fashioned name for the GI tract is the alimentary canal. The digestive system consists of the organs which compose the GI tract and the accessory organs of digestion. These accessory organs are not part of the tract but produce and secrete fluids and enzymes essential for the digestive process. Different sections of the GI tract have different properties and diameters of lumen, which allow for the specific functions necessary.

Layers composing the wall of the digestive tract

The walls of all the sections of the GI tract from the oesophagus to the rectum have the same basic layered structure. The lumen is surrounded by mucosa, submucosa, a muscular layer and an outer serosa.

Mucosa

The inner layer, immediately surrounding the lumen, is called the mucosa. This is composed of a mucous membrane, lined with mucus. A mucous membrane is simply a layer of tissue which secretes mucus. Mucus protects the underlying cells and also acts as a lubricant to ease the passage of material along the lumen. The thickness of the mucosal epithelium varies along the length of the tract. In areas such as the mouth, oesophagus and anus, which are subject to a lot of mechanical forces and abrasion, the mucosa is composed of a stratified epithelium. In sections associated with absorption it is important for the lining to be thin enough to facilitate diffusion of nutrients. In these areas the mucosa is composed of a simple columnar epithelium.

Underneath the epithelium but still part of the mucosa is a layer of connective tissue containing small blood vessels. These vessels supply nutrients and oxygen to the epithelial cells. In some areas of the GI tract these vessels will also be involved in the process of absorption. Under the connective tissue is a thin layer of smooth muscle. This supports the overlying connective and epithelial

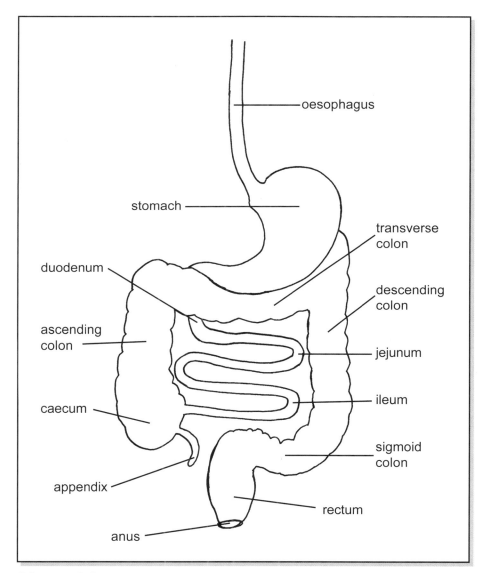

Diagram 8.1
Principle sections of the GI tract. The oesophagus passes through the thoracic cavity and diaphragm. The stomach lies over the front of the second part of the transverse colon. The duodenum loops behind the first part of the transverse colon. In reality the small intestine loops around on itself many times in the abdominal cavity before connecting with the colon. The sigmoid colon passes backwards, towards the rectum and anus.

tissues and in some areas of the gut pulls the lining up into a series of folds. These folds have the effect of increasing the internal surface area of the lumen which increases the rate of digestion and absorption.

Submucosa

The layer underneath the mucosa is called the submucosa. This is composed of loose connective tissue and also carries numerous blood vessels which perfuse the gut wall with blood. In certain areas of the GI tract the submucosa contains exocrine glands which produce some of the digestive enzymes. Areas of lymphatic tissue are found in the submucosa; these are referred to as lymphatic nodules and provide an immune function. This layer also contains a network of intrinsic nerve fibres collectively called the submucosal plexus. Plexus means a network of blood vessels or nerve fibres.

Muscular layer

Under the submucosa is the muscular layer or muscularis. There are two layers of smooth, involuntary muscle; the outer layer is composed of longitudinal muscle fibres and the inner layer of circular muscles. The wall of the stomach has an additional inner layer of muscle fibres which run obliquely. Activity of the muscular layer is coordinated by a network of intrinsic, autonomic nerve fibres called the myenteric plexus.

Contraction and relaxation of these muscle layers allows material to be propelled along the GI tract. This muscular contraction also helps with the physical breakdown of food and aids the mixing in of digestive enzymes. In addition to the involuntary muscles found in the wall of the GI tract, the mouth, pharynx, oesophagus and anus also contain voluntary muscles.

Serosa

The outer layer of the gut wall is called the serosa. This is composed of loose connective tissue with a serous membrane on the external surface of the bowel. Like all serous membranes it secretes a small volume of serous fluid (fluid derived from serum, i.e. plasma). This acts as an external lubricant, allowing sections of bowel to move freely over each other. Below the level of the diaphragm, the serosal layer is called the visceral peritoneum.

Peritoneum

This is the thin membrane which lines the surface of the organs in the abdominal cavity and also lines the inner abdominal wall. The peritoneum immediately surrounding the organs is referred to as visceral and the layer lining the abdominal wall as parietal. Between these two layers is a potential space called the peritoneal cavity which contains serous lubricating fluid. This allows areas of the intestine to move slightly relative to other lengths. The parietal peritoneal membrane

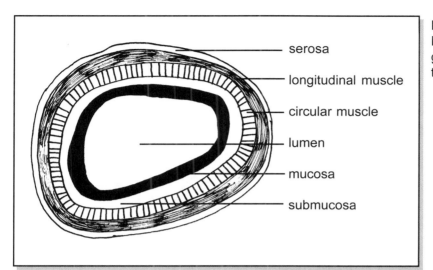

Diagram 8.2
Layers of the gastrointestinal tract.

- serosa
- longitudinal muscle
- circular muscle
- lumen
- mucosa
- submucosa

contains many pain receptors which makes it a very sensitive tissue. Folds of the peritoneal membranes form the mesenteries and are discussed below. Abdominal organs which are suspended in these mesenteric folds of the peritoneum are described as intraperitoneal, for example, the large and small intestine. Other abdominal organs are outside the peritoneal cavity, or are only covered by peritoneum over one of their surfaces. Such organs are described as retroperitoneal, for example the pancreas and kidneys.

Sometimes as a result of infection, or after surgery, areas of the visceral and parietal peritoneum become physically connected by scar tissue; this disorder is referred to as adhesions and often requires surgery to separate them. If gastrointestinal contents escape through a perforation in the wall of the gut this will cause inflammation of the peritoneum, a life threatening condition called peritonitis. In other abnormal conditions excessive volumes of fluid may accumulate in the peritoneal cavity, converting the potential space into an actual space. This is referred to as ascites. In peritoneal dialysis, dialysing fluid is introduced between the parietal and visceral layers and then drained off.

Mesentery

This is a double layer of peritoneum which connects the jejunum and ileum to the posterior abdominal wall. Blood vessels which supply the small intestine run between the layers of the mesentery, carrying blood from large blood vessels to the gut wall. Venous and lymphatic drainage vessels also run through the mesentery, draining blood and lymphatic fluid from the intestines. This arrangement keeps all of the vessels which supply and drain the intestines neatly in one place; if there were free individual vessels supplying areas of gut they could readily get tangled up.

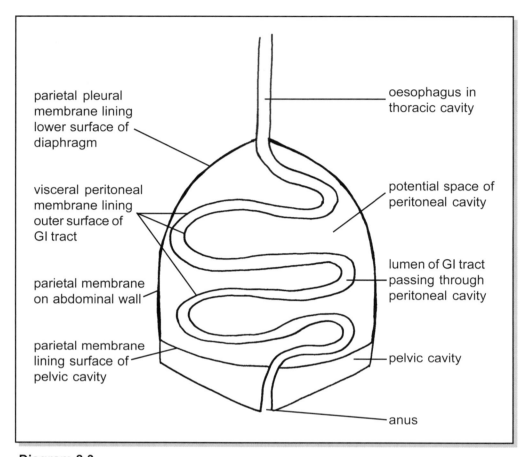

Diagram 8.3
Highly simplified diagram of the abdomen. The GI tract is essentially one long tube, from mouth to anus. The walls of the abdominal cavity are lined with parietal peritoneal membrane and the GI tract is lined with visceral peritoneal membrane. The last part of the colon passes out of the peritoneal cavity and into the pelvic cavity. Untold billions of bacteria live in the lumen of the gut; however, the peritoneal cavity is completely sterile. In life the potential space of the peritoneal cavity is completely filled with abdominal contents.

The mesentery is fan shaped, starting with a 15 cm length which connects the whole structure to the posterior abdominal wall. This is called the root of the mesentery. By the time the same double sheet of mesentery reaches the small intestine it is six metres long. Despite this length the height is only 20 cm at the centre and much less towards the edges. Major blood vessels supplying the gut run behind the peritoneum. Branches of the aorta project through the root of the mesentery then travel through the mesentery to the small intestine. In the same way venous branches drain from the gut, through the mesentery, then through the root of the mesentery into branches of what will become the hepatic portal vein. There is a similar double layer of tissue called the mesocolon which connects the duodenum and part of the colon to the posterior abdominal wall.

There are three main blood vessels which supply the GI tract. The coeliac artery leaves the aorta and divides to perfuse the stomach, duodenum, liver and spleen. Blood is supplied to the rest of the small intestine via the superior

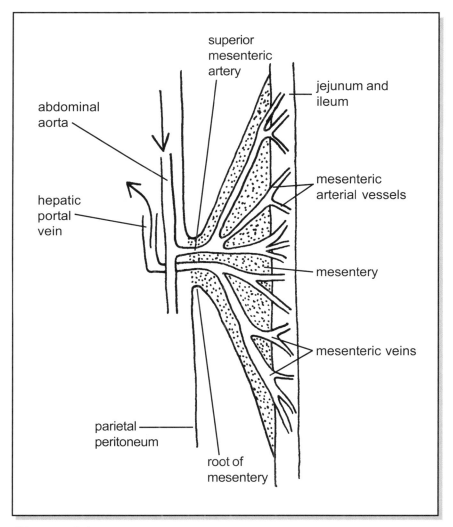

Diagram 8.4
Blood vessels to and from most of the small intestines run in between the layers of the mesentery. Starting from a 15 cm connection, the mesentery provides vascular and neuronal support for a 6 metre length of small intestine. For simplicity this diagram shows the arterial supply at the top and the venous drainage at the bottom. In reality, arterial, venous, lymphatic and nervous connections run together.

mesenteric artery which also supplied the ascending and most of the transverse colon. Remaining areas of the colon are supplied by the inferior mesenteric artery. Venous drainage occurs via splenic and gastric veins with an inferior and superior mesenteric vein, all of which drain directly into the hepatic portal vein to convey blood to the liver.

Omentum

The greater omentum is a large, apron-like peritoneal fold of tissue which lies in front of the organs of the GI tract. The omentum is often called the policeman of the abdomen. This is because it is able to seal off and consolidate areas of infection; this prevents spread throughout the peritoneal cavity. Infection in the peritoneal cavity is called peritonitis and is life threatening. In addition to this protective role the omentum stores adipose tissue and is one reason why people often get a fat abdomen when they become obese. There is another lesser omentum between the stomach, liver and duodenum.

Gastrointestinal regulation

The activity of the GI tract and accessory organs must be controlled and regulated. This is achieved by neural and hormonal control mechanisms. There are two aspects to neural control referred to as intrinsic and extrinsic. The intrinsic nerves are autonomic fibres located in the walls of the tract which coordinate local muscular and secretory activity. Extrinsic nervous control involves autonomic nerves which communicate directly with the central nervous system (CNS). Afferent, sensory neurons convey information from the gut into the CNS. Efferent, motor fibres carry information from the CNS to modify the activity of the digestive system. There are some sympathetic fibres involved in control of the gut but most of the extrinsic neuronal control is parasympathetic, often via the vagus nerve. Sympathetic nerve fibres exert an inhibitory effect on the activity of the GI tract whereas parasympathetic fibres stimulate activity.

Some of the cells which line the gut produce endocrine hormones. These specialised cells are called enteroendocrine cells. The hormones they produce are systemically absorbed but affect and regulate other organs of the digestive system.

Appetite

The desire to eat is stimulated by a specialised group of neurones in the hypothalamus which form the appetite centre. It is the hypothalamus which generates the sensation of hunger and the desire to search for food. In addition eating increases the release of dopamine from some areas of the brain which generates a sensation of pleasure. If a person has experienced pleasure in the past from eating a particular food they will have a desire to reproduce this sensation by further eating. When enough food has been eaten another area of the hypothalamus produces a feeling of satisfaction. This group of neurones is referred to as the satiety centre.

Peristalsis

This is the term used to describe the coordinated waves of muscular contraction that occur in the walls of the gut. Muscles in a short length of the GI tract will contract, while those immediately in front relax. This allows contents to be squeezed along a length of lumen. The area of muscle which was relaxed then contracts, while the length in front of this section will relax, propelling the material further forward. As a result of this co-ordinated muscular activity waves of contraction pass along the length of the gut wall, progressively transferring material from mouth to anus. Peristalsis should always occur in the mouth to anus direction. However, in vomiting material is propelled in the opposite direction by antiperistalsis, first in the small intestine then in the wall of the oesophagus.

Digestion

In digestion food molecules are broken down into simpler components which may later be absorbed. This is achieved by the operation of the two processes of mechanical and chemical digestion. By the end of the overall digestive process proteins are broken down into amino acids, carbohydrates to simple sugars, and fats into fatty acids and glycerol.

Mechanical digestion

Food is physically broken down by chewing (i.e. mastication) in the mouth. Once food is in the stomach there are regular peristaltic contractions about every 20 seconds, which are called mixing waves. These churn the gastric contents into a mixture called chyme. As chyme is peristaltically squeezed along the small intestine it is subject to further mixing. These physical processes break up and therefore increase the surface area the food. This gives a larger surface area over which enzymes may subsequently act.

Chemical digestion uses digestive enzymes

In Chapter 1 we considered intracellular enzymes which catalysed all biochemical reactions in the cell. The enzymes concerned with digestion however, only break down large molecules into smaller ones. Digestive enzymes are produced by exocrine glands and act in the lumen of the gut.

Many digestive enzymes are made as enzyme precursors to prevent the enzyme products digesting the glands in which they are produced. Enzyme precursors are normally converted into an active form of enzyme in the lumen of the GI tract. For example, trypsin is an enzyme which will digest proteins; this is formed as trypsinogen in the pancreas. Trypsinogen is inactive and will not break down protein molecules. However, when exported from the pancreas into the lumen of the small intestine it is then converted into its active form which is trypsin. If it were synthesised in the pancreas as the end product of trypsin, the pancreas

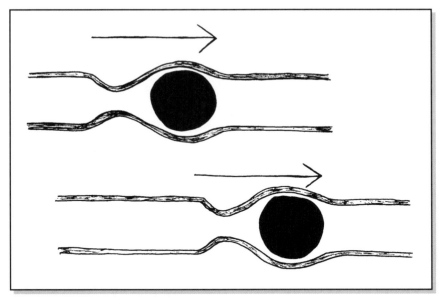

Diagram 8.5
A food bolus is propelled along a length of GI tract by a wave of peristalsis; arrows indicate the direction of bolus movement.

itself would be digested as it is largely composed of protein. Active enzymes are unable to damage body tissues in the gut lumen as the mucosa is protected by a layer of mucus.

Mouth

Teeth

Children have 20 deciduous or 'milk' teeth. Adults should have 32 teeth, shaped to perform particular functions. The incisors at the front are chisel shaped to bite into food, for example cutting into an apple. Behind these are the canines, which are pointed to stab into and tear food, such as tearing off a piece of meat. Next there are the premolars, which crush and grind food, so are important in eating vegetables and grains. Finally at the back of the mouth are the molars which also crush and grind. The upper and lower jaw bones each have two pairs of incisors, one pair of canines, two pairs of premolars and three pairs of molars.

Teeth are lined with hard enamel; under this is a bone like substance called dentine. The inner pulp cavity contains sensory nerve fibres, blood and lymphatic vessels. Teeth are described in three regions; the top part is the crown, under this is the neck and the root is the part which connects with the jaw bone. Teeth are firmly held in sockets within the jaw bones by cementum and fibres of the periodontal ligament. The bottom teeth are held in the mandible and the top ones in the maxilla.

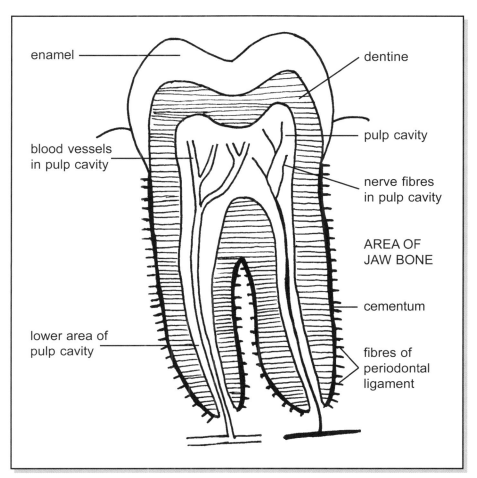

Diagram 8.6
Generalized structure of a tooth.

Saliva

Three pairs of salivary glands, the parotid, submandibular and sublingual, all produce saliva which is drained into the mouth via salivary ducts. Saliva is continually secreted in small volumes to keep the mouth moist; however, the sight, smell or taste of food may increase production by as much as 20 times. Secretion of saliva is stimulated by activity of the parasympathetic vagus nerve under the control of two salivary nuclei located in the brain stem. Water is the principle component in saliva but it also contains some sodium chloride and an enzyme which acts against bacteria called lysozyme. Mucus acts as a lubricant and softening agent. Salivary amylase is the digestive enzyme present; this starts the digestion of carbohydrates by breaking starch molecules into maltose. Starch is a polysaccharide which means it is composed of a long chain of sugar units chemically bonded together. A single sugar unit is referred to as a monosaccharide; a double sugar unit is a disaccharide. Amylase breaks some of the bonds holding the individual sugar units together, resulting in maltose which is a disaccharide.

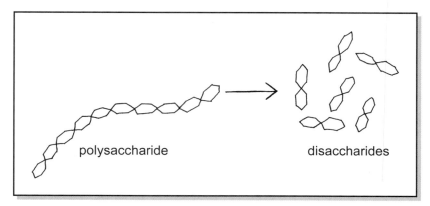

Diagram 8.7
Amylase breaks polysaccharide chains down into disaccharides.

Eating and swallowing

The teeth close on food which is thereby crushed and displaced. The tongue, lips and cheeks repeatedly push the food back between the teeth for further mechanical processing. During this grinding process, food is mixed with saliva and formed into a bolus. Swallowing (or deglutition) occurs in stages. Firstly the mouth is closed. Next, starting from the front, the tongue moves the food backwards along the palate, which forms the roof of the mouth, towards the oropharynx. Contact of the food bolus with the back of the mouth initiates the swallowing reflex. Respiration is stopped as part of the reflex to prevent aspiration of food into the trachea. Return of food, back into the mouth, is prevented by the tongue, and food is also prevented from going up into the nose. Movement of the epiglottis prevents food entering the trachea. Next, the muscular walls of the pharynx contract pushing the food in the only direction left open, into the oesophagus.

Oesophagus

This is a muscular tube which extends from the laryngopharynx, down through the chest. It passes through the diaphragm into the abdominal cavity where it joins the stomach. Oesophageal lumen is lined with stratified squamous epithelium; mucus is secreted from this lining to lubricate the passage of food. Once a food bolus enters the oesophagus, peristaltic waves of contraction in the muscular wall propel food down towards the stomach.

At the bottom end of the oesophagus is the lower oesophageal sphincter (also called the cardiac sphincter) which regulates the passage of food into the stomach. This sphincter is located in the terminal 4 cm of the oesophagus and it is normally closed. After swallowing the lower oesophageal sphincter relaxes for about eight seconds to allow the bolus through into the stomach, then it contracts again to prevent regurgitation. If acid contents from the stomach do reflux into the oesophagus heartburn is usually experienced. Evidence for the peristaltic action of the oesophagus is seen in the ability to swallow upside-down although gravity does assist normal swallowing.

Difficulty swallowing is called dysphagia and may be caused by diseases of the mouth or tongue, neuromuscular disorders, oesophageal disorders, foreign bodies or psychological problems. If food enters the airway when an individual is conscious this will lead to choking. The most common cause of this is trying to talk and eat at the same time. As unconscious patients are unable to swallow they must never be given anything by mouth because the food or fluid will simply run down into the lungs causing aspiration of the food or fluid.

Stomach

Basic structure

The stomach is a widened area of the GI tract which expands when it fills with food. It receives, stores, mechanically and chemically breaks down food. Finally, it controls the release of gastric contents into the first stage of the small intestine (gastric simply means to do with the stomach). This gastric emptying is regulated via a second ring of muscle called the pyloric sphincter.

The proximal (first part) of the stomach has a relatively thin wall and is highly distendable, allowing it to store an ingested meal. The distal (lower) part of the stomach has a thicker muscular layer and there is a greater level of peristaltic activity to churn the contents. Anatomically the upper area of the stomach is called the fundus, the middle area the body and the lower area the pylorus.

Mucosa lines the inside of the stomach

Gastric mucosa lies in large folds called rugae when the stomach is empty. These increase the surface area of the stomach and allow for expansion after meals. Gastric lumen is lined with simple columnar epithelial cells. Close inspection of the mucosa lining reveals numerous gastric pits which project down into the mucosa. These pits contain the gastric glands.

Gastric glands are lined with several types of specialised exocrine cells which secrete the various gastric juices (gastric juice is also referred to as peptic juice). Cells around the neck of the pits are mucous cells which secrete mucus. This is essential to protect the stomach lining from the irritating effect of other gastric juices. If the mucous lining is disrupted a gastric ulcer may result as gastric juices attack and digest underlying tissue. A gastric ulcer is a type of peptic ulcer, a peptic ulcer being any ulcer caused by peptic (i.e. gastric) juice.

Diagram 8.8
Areas and sphincters associated with the stomach.

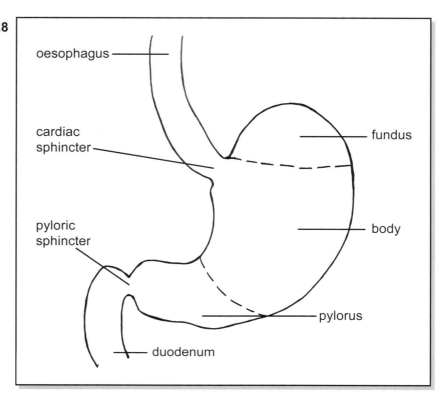

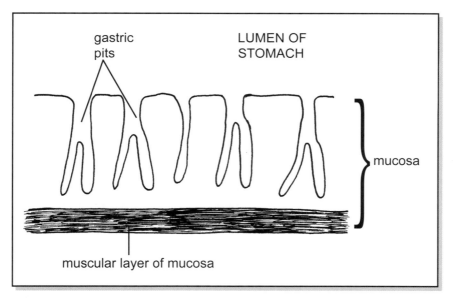

Diagram 8.9
Gastric mucosa with pits containing gastric glands. Gastric juice is secreted from the pits into the lumen of the stomach. In the proximal area of the stomach there are about 100 gastric pits per mm² of gastric mucosa.

The most common cell type in the pits are the chief cells (also called zymogenic cells). These produce the enzyme precursor called pepsinogen, which travels out of the gastric pit into the lumen of the stomach. Parietal cells (also called oxyntic cells) secrete hydrochloric acid. This is a very strong acid which kills most potential pathogens which might be ingested. Intrinsic factor is also secreted by the parietal cells; this is a glycoprotein which binds with vitamin B_{12} to allow this nutrient to be later absorbed in the small intestine. Without intrinsic factor this vitamin cannot be absorbed and pernicious anaemia will result. Gastric juice is a combination of these secretory products in a watery medium.

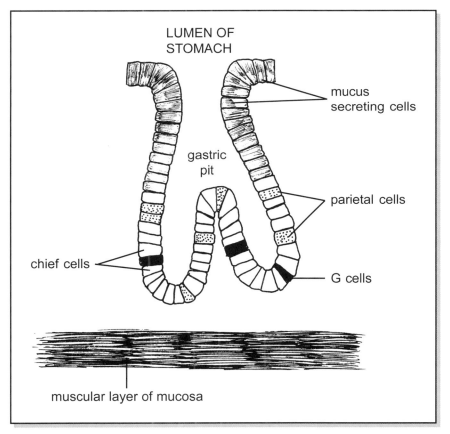

Diagram 8.10
Like diagram 8.9, this also shows a gastric pit, but at higher magnification. Tubular gastric glands, which secrete gastric juice are continuations of the gastric pits in the mucosa. Mucous neck cells secrete mucus, parietal cells secrete hydrochloric acid and intrinsic factor, chief cells secrete pepsinogen and G cells secrete the endocrine hormone gastrin directly into the blood. Gastric juice is an exocrine product and consists of a mixture of the secretions from the mucus, parietal and chief cells.

Gastric regulation

Nerve signals from the parasympathetic vagus nerve increase the secretion of gastric juice. In addition to this neuronal control, the presence of proteins in the stomach initiates secretion of gastrin from specialised mucosal G cells. Gastrin is an endocrine hormone which circulates in the blood and stimulates the chief cells to secrete more pepsinogen and the parietal cells to produce more hydrochloric acid. Protein in the stomach therefore stimulates the secretion of the digestive agents necessary for its own digestion. When there is no protein in the stomach the levels of pepsin and hydrochloric acid are comparatively low. This mechanism reduces the volumes of gastric juice when the stomach is empty so helps to protect the lining from the potential harmful effects of pepsin and hydrochloric acid.

Histamine is also produced by gastric mucosa. Parietal cells are able to detect this chemical via histamine type 2 (H_2) receptors. Histamine stimulates the parietal cells to secrete more hydrochloric acid. Drugs such as cimetidine and ranitidine reduce gastric acid by blocking the H_2 receptor sites on the parietal cells. This reduction in gastric acid can aid in the healing of peptic ulcers.

Mechanical and chemical digestion in the stomach

After a meal, slow peristaltic waves at the rate of about three per minute, pass down the length of the stomach from the top towards the pyloric sphincter. This muscular peristaltic activity helps to mix the gastric juices with the stomach contents. As a peristaltic wave nears the pyloric sphincter the sphincter will contract so that only a small volume of fluid, containing small food particles, will be squeezed through into the duodenum.

Once in the lumen of the stomach pepsinogen is converted into the active proteolytic enzyme called pepsin. 'Lytic' or 'lysis' means to break down, so a proteolytic enzyme will break down proteins. A protein is made up of a long chain of individual amino acid units joined together by peptide bonds. Pepsin

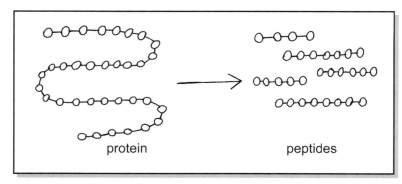

Diagram 8.11
Proteins are long chains of amino acid. Pepsin breaks these sequences down into smaller sequences of amino acids called peptides.

starts the process of protein digestion by breaking some of the peptide bonds. This results in shorter lengths of amino acid sequences called peptides.

Normally all enzymes end with the suffix 'ase'. However, pepsin was discovered before this convention was adopted. In young children the stomach also secretes rennin; this enzyme coagulates milk into a curd to prevent it running through the stomach before it has time to be acted on by pepsin.

Once chemical digestion has occurred the combination of gastric peristalsis and activity of the pyloric sphincter will move partly digested chyme into the small intestine. Chyme is the name given to the combination of partly digested food mixed with digestive juices. The rate of gastric emptying varies between 2-6 hours depending on the nature of the food contained. Liquids pass through the stomach much more quickly than more solid foods. Carbohydrates pass through the stomach fairly quickly but foods containing proteins take longer. Emptying is slowest after meals which contain a lot of fat. The rate of stomach emptying is limited by the rates at which the small intestine can process particular food types.

Absorption from the stomach

There is some absorption from the stomach into the blood. This is clearly limited by the large size of the undigested and partly digested food molecules; however water and alcohol will be absorbed as they are already small soluble molecules.

Vomiting is an important defence mechanism

Vomiting (emesis) is a natural defense mechanism to remove infected or poisonous food from the gut. Irritation or distension of the stomach sends nerve impulses to the vomiting centre which is located in the medulla oblongata of the brain stem. It is the vomiting centre which controls the vomiting reflex. Initially there is retrograde contraction of the small intestine. This antiperistalsis propels the contents of the small intestine back into the stomach. Once the material to be expelled is in the stomach there are forceful inspiratory movements with the epiglottis closed. This causes the diaphragm to press down and increase the pressure in the abdominal cavity. At the same time there is contraction of the abdominal wall muscles, effectively squeezing the stomach between the abdominal wall and diaphragm. There is contraction of the stomach and simultaneous relaxation of the lower oesophageal sphincter with antiperistalsis in the oesophagus. These effects cause gastric contents to be forcefully ejected through the mouth.

Liver and pancreas

These accessory organs of the digestive system produce juices and enzymes essential to the digestive process. Bile is produced and secreted by the liver. Although this is essentially an excretory product, largely derived from the destruction of old red blood cells, it also plays an active role in digestion. Bile from the liver passes out via the right and left hepatic ducts which unite to form the common hepatic duct. Freshly formed bile then travels along the cystic duct into the gall bladder where it is stored and concentrated.

When food containing fats arrives in the duodenum the gall bladder is stimulated to contract causing bile to pass down the common bile duct. The common bile duct joins with the pancreatic duct forming a common duct called the ampulla of the bile duct. This structure then communicates with the lumen of the duodenum. Reflux from the duodenum into the ampulla is prevented by the sphincter of Oddi.

In addition to the endocrine functions of the pancreas (discussed in chapter 7) it also produces digestive enzymes. The exocrine, secretory regions produce enzymes which drain via small pancreatic ducts into larger pancreatic ducts. The largest duct in turn leaves the gland to join the common bile duct at the ampulla. There is also a smaller accessory pancreatic duct which enters the duodenum separately. Pancreatic juice contains pancreatic amylase, pancreatic lipase, chymotrypsinogen and trypsinogen. Sodium bicarbonate is also produced which gives pancreatic juice an alkaline pH.

Diagram 8.12
The pancreas is described as an organ with a head, body and tail. Exocrine secretions include trypsinogen, chymotrypsinogen, pancreatic lipase and pancreatic amylase.

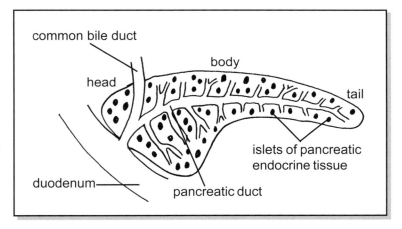

common bile duct

body

head

tail

islets of pancreatic endocrine tissue

duodenum

pancreatic duct

Regulation of the liver and pancreas

The arrival of chyme from the stomach into the duodenum and upper parts of the jejunum stimulates the release of an endocrine hormone called cholecystokinin (CCK). This is produced by specialised I-cells in the duodenal mucosa. As an endocrine hormone CCK circulates in the blood and stimulates the secretion of pancreatic digestive enzymes. It also causes contraction of the gall bladder, which leads to bile passing down the common bile duct into the duodenum. As in the stomach, it is the arrival of food which stimulates the release of the agents required for digestion of that food.

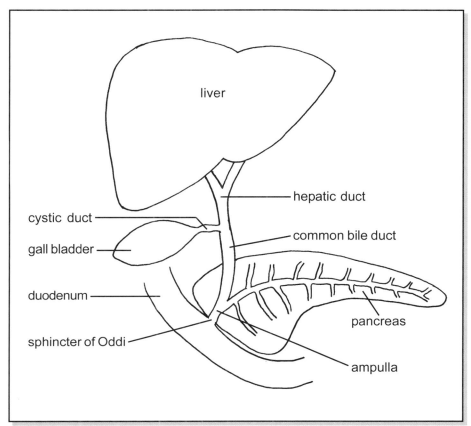

Diagram 8.13
The liver, biliary system, pancreas and ducts. The common bile duct and the
pancreatic duct merge within the tissues of the pancreas.

The small intestine is a muscular tube about six metres long which is arranged
in three segments. Firstly the pyloric sphincter regulates the passage of chyme
from the stomach into the first section of the small intestine which is the
duodenum. This first section is only about 25 cm long and forms a C shape as
it loops behind the transverse colon, adjacent to the head of the pancreas.
Anatomically it is high in the abdomen, above the level of the umbilicus. Chyme
leaving the stomach trickles into the duodenum. About half way along the
duodenum the sphincter of Oddi regulates the flow of bile and pancreatic juices
from the ampulla of the pancreatic and bile ducts. Bile is not a digestive enzyme;
its role is to emulsify fats into small globules. This emulsification greatly increases
the surface area of fats in the small intestine. As a result pancreatic lipase has a
larger surface area over which to access fat molecules, resulting in efficient digestion.
(Milk is an example of a fat emulsion). The duodenum is the most common site
for peptic ulcers, caused by peptic juices from the stomach.

After the duodenum, partly digested material passes on into the second section of the small intestine which is the jejunum. This section is about 2.5 metres in length and is mostly located in the upper left quadrant of the abdomen. The third and final section of the small intestine is the ileum. This section is about 3.5 metres in length and is mostly in the right lower quadrant of the abdomen. The ileum conveys material into the caecum which is the first part of the colon. Two flaps project from the distal end of the ileum into the lumen of the caecum. These flaps of duodenum are called the ileocaecal fold and act as a valve, allowing and possibly regulating the passage of material into the caecum and preventing reflux.

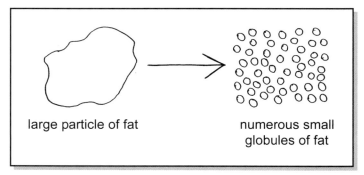

large particle of fat   numerous small
                                          globules of fat

Diagram 8.14
Fat before and after emulsification by bile. Emulsification greatly increased the surface area to volume ratio of fats. This means there is a large surface area over which lipase can access fat molecules to chemically digest them.

Chemical digestion in the small intestine

There are two sources of digestive enzymes active in the small intestine. Firstly, enzymes are produced in the pancreas. Secondly enzymes derive from cells which line much of the internal surface of the small intestine. These specialised lining cells are called enterocytes. As nutrients are absorbed and pass through these epithelial cells further digestion occurs. Enzymes located in the enterocytes include the carbohydrate digesting enzymes maltase, sucrase, lactase and a few protein digesting enzymes referred to as peptidases.

Digestion of proteins

Pancreatic juice enters the duodenum through the same duct as the bile. In the lumen of the bowel inactive trypsinogen is converted into trypsin by the action of enterokinase, an enzyme secreted by the mucosa of the small intestine. Once activated, trypsin in turn activates chymotrypsinogen which becomes chymotrypsin. This arrangement prevents conversion of proteolytic enzyme precursors into their active form before they reach the mucus protected gut lumen. Trypsin and chymotrypsin then both act to break down lengths of proteins and peptides into smaller peptide units. The three protein digesting enzymes mentioned so far, pepsin, trypsin and chymotrypsin, are all required to break down proteins because they all break the peptide bonds between different amino acids. The final phase of protein breakdown occurs mostly in, and near, the enterocytes. Peptidases from the enterocytes complete the breakdown of peptides into individual amino acids.

Digestion of carbohydrates

Some carbohydrate is broken down by salivary amylase; however, its action is blocked by the acidic environment of the stomach. Pancreatic amylase continues the break down of starch, which is a polysaccharide, into disaccharide sugars. Disaccharides are molecules made up of two monosaccharide units. The final digestion of these disaccharide sugars is completed by the carbohydrate digesting enzymes of the enterocytes. These contain maltase which breaks down maltose into two molecules of glucose. Lactase breaks down the milk sugar lactose into one molecule of glucose and one of galactose. Sucrase breaks down sucrose into one molecule of glucose and one of fructose. These processes result in all carbohydrates being digested down into monosaccharide single unit sugars. After being absorbed into the blood galactose and fructose are converted into glucose by the liver. This means the only sugar found in the systemic circulation is glucose.

Digestion of lipids

Lipid is another name for fat. Fats are first emulsified into very small globules by bile. Pancreatic lipase then breaks down lipid molecules into their component parts which are fatty acids and glycerol.

Intestinal juice

Between the individual villi are small pits called crypts of Lieberkuhn. These crypts are lined with a few goblet cells for the production of mucus. In addition there are a large number of enterocytes which secrete large quantities of water and electrolytes. These secretions, called intestinal juice, do not contain digestive enzymes but wash out of the crypt over the surface of the villi. This provides a watery medium for the absorption of the products of digestion from the lumen into the enterocytes of the villi.

Absorption of nutrients

Around 90% of absorption takes place from the small intestine, primarily in the jejunum and ileum. The remaining 10% of absorption from the gut takes place from the stomach and colon. In order for absorption to be efficient a large surface area is required into which the products of digestion can enter. The lining of the small intestine has circular folds. These project areas of mucosa into the lumen to increase surface area. The folds extend from about half to two thirds the way around the lumen and are up to 8 mm deep.

In addition the circular folds themselves have a highly infolded surface as they are covered with villi. These small projections, 0.5-1 mm high, further increase the surface area. Villi are lined with epithelial cells called enterocytes, the surfaces of

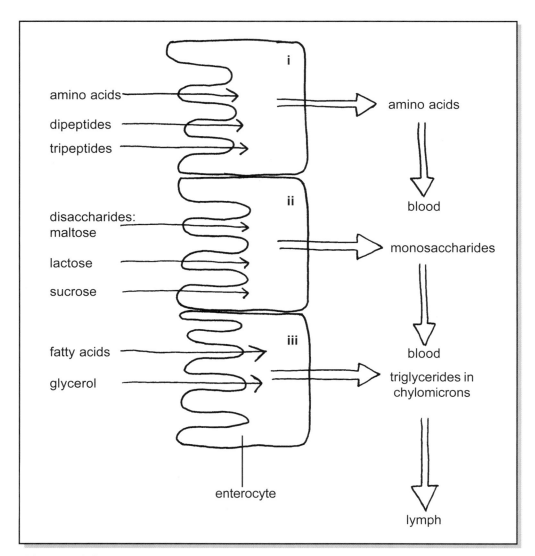

Diagram 8.15

The final phase of digestion occurs, via the action of intracellular enzymes, as nutrients pass through enterocytes. In reality a single enterocyte contains a range of enzymes but these are illustrated one at a time.

(i)   Action of peptidases.

(ii) Action of maltase, lactase and sucrase   .

(iii) Absorption of the products of fat digestion. Note fatty acids and glycerol are converted into triglycerides then packaged into chylomicrons within the enterocyte. This is necessary for them to be transported in the water based lymphatic fluid.

which are also highly infolded. Numerous small projections termed microvilli project from the surface of the enterocytes. Each individual cell has about 3 000 microvilli. Collectively the microvilli form a striated or brush border about one micrometre thick. These three levels of infolding massively increase the surface area for absorption, and so for the final digestion of food in the enterocytes. In an adult this detailed infolding provides an internal surface area of about 400m², which is about 200 times the surface area of the body.

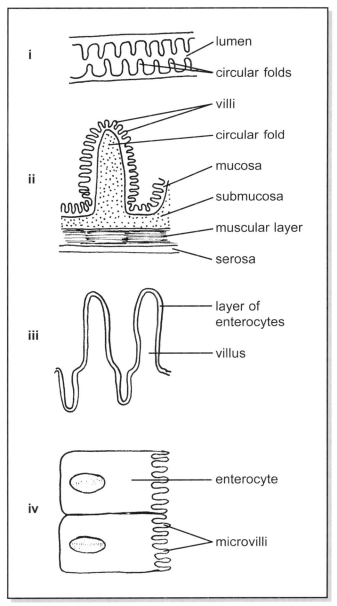

Diagram 8.16
These four diagrams represent progressively increasing powers of magnification. Three levels of infolding massively increase the internal surface area of the intestine.
(i)   Circular folds project into the lumen of the intestine.
(ii) Villi cover the circular folds.
(iii) An individual villus is lined with enterocytes.
(iv) Enterocyte surface area is increased by numerous microvilli.

Villi contain a central lymphatic vessel called a lacteal. Fatty acids are able to absorb readily into the enterocytes as they are lipid soluble. However, as they are lipid soluble they cannot be transported in the water based blood or lymphatic fluid without modification. Therefore, as fatty acids and glycerol pass through an enterocyte they are recombined to form triglycerides. These aggregate into globules and the enterocyte then coats them in water soluble protein so they can be transported in water. These combinations of fatty triglyceride based cores with protein coatings are called chylomicrons. These are too large to be absorbed into the blood capillaries so are absorbed through the larger pores of the lymphatic lacteal. From the lacteal in the villus, they drain with the lymphatic fluid into the central lymphatic system. From here they travel with the lymphatic fluid and eventually enter the blood via the left lymphatic duct which drains into the subclavian vein.

An arteriole feeds blood into each individual villus. This divides up into a capillary network which is subsequently drained into a venule. All of the products

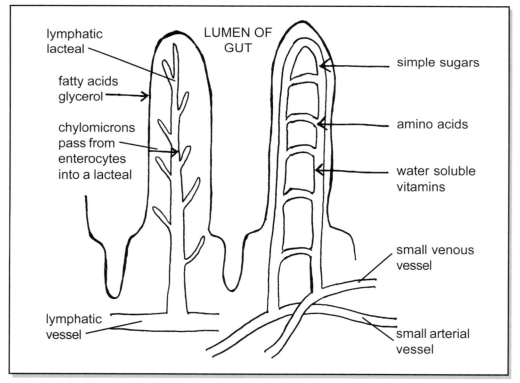

Diagram 8.17
Absorption of nutrients into the villi. Fatty acids and glycerol are absorbed into the enterocytes and converted into triglycerides. These are then packaged into chylomicrons which enter the central lymphatic lacteal. Water soluble nutrients, e.g. sugars and amino acids, enter the blood capillaries.

Essential science

Fat and water solubility

It is a common observation that fat and water do not mix. If cooking oil is poured onto water, it forms globules of fat. This occurs because the fat molecules will stick together and at the same time repel water molecules. If a water soluble molecule such as sugar is then added, this will dissolve into the water but not into the fat. In the same way if a fat soluble molecule such as vitamin A is added, this will dissolve into the oil but not into the water. Fat soluble molecules are described as being lipophilic (lipo relates to fat and philic means love), so these are literally 'fat loving' molecules. At the same time as being lipophilic, most fat soluble molecules are also hydrophobic (hydro means water and phobic relates to fear). Literally this means 'water fearing'. In practice this means fat soluble molecules repel water.

This is an important principle in physiology and pharmacology as only molecules with a fat soluble component will diffuse through cell membranes, which are mostly composed of lipids. Fatty cell membranes have hydrophobic properties so tend to repel water soluble molecules.

of digestion which are not absorbed into the lymphatic lacteal pass into the capillary blood of the villi. Veins draining the intestine combine to form the hepatic portal vein which carries blood directly to the liver.

Mechanisms of absorption

There are two mechanisms used to transfer the products of digestion from the gut lumen into the blood or lymphatic systems. The first is simple diffusion. Because the epithelium of the small intestine is thin, soluble molecules will diffuse from an area of high concentration to one of low concentration. This mechanism is however, dependent on the nutrient molecule being able to diffuse across the cell membranes of the cells which line the gut lumen. As cell membranes are largely composed of lipids, only small or fat soluble molecules may freely diffuse across. Fatty acids and glycerol are therefore able to be absorbed by diffusion. Most of the small molecules such as water, minerals and vitamins also simply diffuse into the villi.

As amino acids and sugars are water soluble they do not diffuse through the lipid based enterocyte cell membranes effectively. This means that these molecules must be specially transported if they are to be absorbed efficiently. This second process is called active transport. 'Active' implies the use of energy,

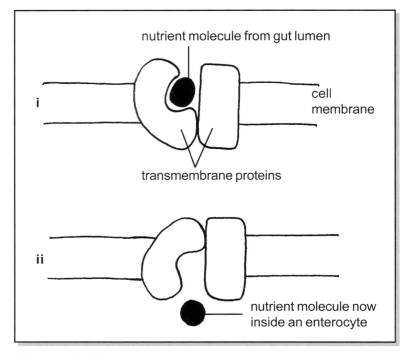

Diagram 8.18
Example of an active transport system. A water soluble nutrient enters the start of the transmembrane gate. Using energy derived from ATP, the protein then alters position to transport the nutrient through the cell membrane. After this the same protein will swing back again, ready to transport the next nutrient molecule. (This is also a good example of the importance of protein molecules being arranged into a particular shape.)

so this process uses ATP as an energy source to facilitate the movement. Enterocyte cell membranes contain specialised transmembrane proteins which act as a 'gate' into the cell through which sugars and amino acids may pass. Because this process is active it may work against the prevailing diffusion gradient.

Secretion and reabsorption

The GI tract secretes large volumes of fluids into the lumen to facilitate the processes of digestion and absorption. In addition to the fluid we drink, every day we swallow about 1.5 litres of saliva. Gastric secretions add 3 litres of fluid and bile about a further 0.5 litres. The pancreas secretes about 1.5 litres of pancreatic juice while total volumes of intestinal juice are around 2 litres per day. Even the colon secretes approximately 200 mls of fluid over a 24 hour period. The majority of secreted fluids are reabsorbed by the small intestine, although about 1.5 litres of fluid a day does enter the colon. Of this the colon reabsorbs all but about 100 mls which is excreted with the faeces.

Colon

Components of the colon

Anatomically, the colon is divided into several sections. The first part is the caecum; the appendix is a blind ended projection of this structure. Next, the ascending colon rises up the right side of the abdomen to the area of the liver; here it bends to the left at the hepatic flexure. Flexure just means bend, so this is the 'bend near the liver'. The transverse colon runs from right to left, near the top of the abdomen before turning down near the spleen at the bend called the splenic flexure. After this, the descending colon runs down the left side of the abdominal cavity and extends into the sigmoid colon which passes back in the direction of the anus. The rectum is between the sigmoid colon and the anus. Finally, the anus is a sphincter of muscle which regulates the exit of faeces from the rectum.

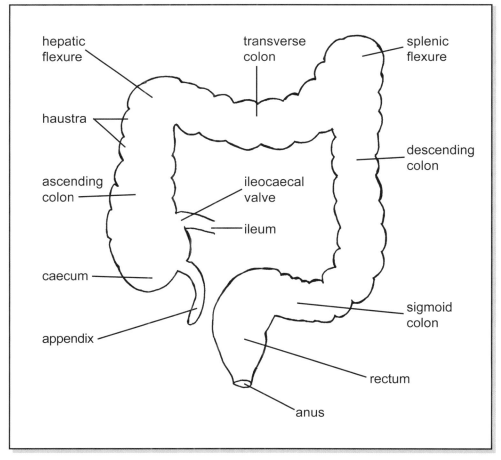

Diagram 8.19
Regions of the colon.

Absorption from the colon

As mentioned, about 1.5 litres a day of watery chyme enters the colon (or large intestine) from the ileum, via the ileocaecal valve. The colon then absorbs most of this water. This is important to prevent excessive water loss from the body. As well as preventing an inconvenient, near constant flow of watery faecal material from the anus, reabsorption is essential to prevent dehydration. Material that remains after the water has been absorbed becomes semi-solid faeces. Absorption of water from the colon is mostly by the passive process of osmosis.

There are a large number of bacteria living in the colon; these produce vitamin K which is also locally absorbed. Bacteria in the colon comprise the normal 'flora' of the large intestine and prevent colonisation with potentially pathogenic bacteria or fungi. This is why antibiotics may cause diarrhoea. Systemic antibiotics kill many of the bacteria and so disturb the natural balance between flora and the colon. Bacteria in the colon produce waste gases such as methane, hydrogen and hydrogen sulphide which give rise to flatulence. Typical volumes of gases expelled through the anus each day vary between about 0.5-2 litres.

Motility of the colon

Rates of peristalsis in the colon are generally slower than in the stomach and small intestine. The colon is arranged in a series of 'pouches' called haustra. As an individual pouch or haustrum is filling up it will relax to allow distension. However, once the wall is stretched to a particular point, contraction will be stimulated which passes the contents along to the next pouch or haustrum. In addition to this low grade level of activity, from time to time there is a dramatic increase in the rate of peristalsis. This occurs from about the middle of the transverse colon into the descending colon. In some people this mass peristalsis is stimulated by eating, the so called gastrocolonic reflex. In others it occurs at a particular time of day. This mass movement has the effect of moving the now faecal material down into the rectum. Mass movements involve active muscular contractions and may generate pressures within the colon as high as 100 mmHg. The rectum is normally empty, but as a result of mass movement it will rapidly fill up with faecal material which stretches the walls and brings about the desire to defaecate.

Arrival of faecal material in the rectum will cause the internal anal sphincter to relax. This internal sphincter is composed of smooth muscle and is involuntary. However, the external anal sphincter contains skeletal muscle and is under voluntary control. In defaecation the external anal sphincter is allowed to relax while the walls of the rectum contract. This muscular contraction will tend to increase the pressure in the rectum, causing the faeces to be expelled through the anus. Further pressure is exerted on the rectum by the downward movement of the diaphragm and contraction of the muscles of the abdominal wall. Pressure on the rectum is further increased if the person is in a squatting position. This is one reason patients find it difficult to defecate into a bed pan if they are lying flat.

Diarrhoea is an important defense mechanism

Inflammation of the lining of the intestine may be caused by infection with viruses, bacteria or protozoa. The natural response of the gut to such an infection is to secrete more intestinal fluids and increase the motility of the bowel. Large volumes of secreted fluid will physically flush disease causing organisms along the lumen of the gut. Increased motility will hurry the infection through, before it has time to increase in severity. Watery flowing stools will therefore act as a natural cleansing mechanism, flushing large numbers of bacteria or viruses out of the body. This is why drugs to prevent diarrhoea in infectious conditions are usually a bad idea; however, fluids and electrolytes should be replaced by eating and drinking. This replacement therapy is especially important in children who have small volumes of body water and may rapidly become dehydrated. This is why young children should be given oral rehydration salts and water as soon as they develop diarrhoea.

The appendix probably has a function

The appendix (or vermiform appendix) is a blind ended tube projecting from the caecum. There is an opening from the tube of the appendix into the lumen of the caecum. The walls of the appendix are rich in immunologically active lymphoid tissue. If the appendix becomes inflamed the condition is referred to as appendicitis. This is a common indication for the removal of the appendix in the surgical procedure of appendicectomy. Because people can live normal lives without an appendix the organ was believed to be vestigial (no longer having any function). However, in recent years the importance of the normal bacterial flora of the colon has been increasingly recognized. After an episode of diarrhoea many of the normal bacteria are flushed out of the colon and therefore lost. However, as the appendix is blind ended normal bacteria are preserved within the structure and will act as a seed population to re-colonize the rest of the colon.

CHAPTER 9

Liver

Introduction

The liver is the largest solid organ in the body with only the skin having a greater total mass. In men it normally weighs 1.4-1.8 kg and 1.2-1.4 kg in women. The liver is involved in many of the biochemical processes which are necessary within the body. This is why the liver is sometimes referred to as the 'chemical factory' of the body.

It is accurate to classify the liver as an exocrine gland as it produces approximately 500 mls of bile per day. This bile is secreted from the liver via the right and left hepatic ducts which merge to form the common hepatic duct. The cystic duct transports bile from the common hepatic duct into the gallbladder where it is stored and concentrated. The same cystic duct carries bile out of the gallbladder into the common bile duct. The pancreatic duct merges with the common bile duct before it communicates with the duodenum. This arrangement means that bile and pancreatic juices both enter the duodenum together via the hepatopancreatic sphincter (of Oddi) and major duodenal papilla. The major duodenal papilla is an elevation on the internal wall of the duodenum.

Blood supply

Unusually, the liver receives about 70% of its blood supply from the hepatic portal vein (HPV) which drains blood directly from the gastrointestinal tract. On average slightly over a litre of blood per minute passes into the liver from the hepatic portal vein. However, in order to support metabolism, liver cells also need a supply of oxygen rich blood which is supplied via the hepatic artery. After circulating through the liver, venous blood is drained into the inferior vena cava via three hepatic veins. The hepatic portal vein and the hepatic vein should not be confused. The HPV carries blood to the liver from the gut whereas the hepatic veins drain blood from the liver, back into the systemic venous return of the inferior vena cava.

Structure related to function

Position

The liver occupies most of the upper right quadrant of the abdominal cavity. Rounded upper surfaces fit snugly under the domed diaphragm while the lower surfaces are fairly sharp, giving a wedge shaped appearance from the side. In young children the relatively large size of the liver explains why their upper abdomens protrude.

The liver is arranged in four lobes

The liver is composed of four lobes. However, from the front only two lobes are visible, these are simply called the right and left lobe, the right being significantly

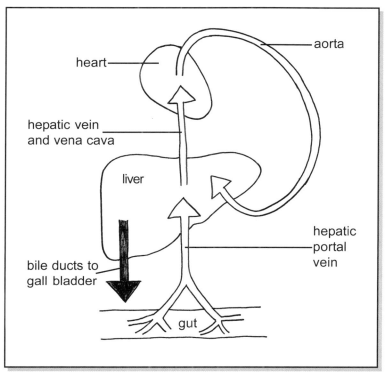

Diagram 9.1
Diagrammatic representation of the flow of blood to and from
the liver. The flow of bile to the duodenum is also indicated by
the dark arrow.

larger. From the back two additional smaller lobes can be distinguished, the
quadrate and caudate lobes. The right and left hepatic ducts drain bile from
their respective liver lobes.

The liver contains thousands of lobules

Within the lobes of the liver are numerous lobules, separated from each other
by connective tissue. Lobules are usually 5 or 6 sided and are cylindrical. At the
corners of the lobules are branches of the HPV, hepatic artery and bile ducts.
Collectively, these 3 vessels are referred to as a triad. A normal liver contains
between 50,000 to 100,000 lobule units which vary in diameter from 0.8 to 2
mm.

Lobules are the functional units of the liver. Individual liver cells are called
hepatocytes. In an individual lobule, hepatocytes are arranged around a central
vein, like spokes around a hub in a wheel. It is a radial arrangement of cells.
Typically the hepatocytes are arranged in a row, two cells thick. These two rows
of cells are described as a hepatic cellular plate.

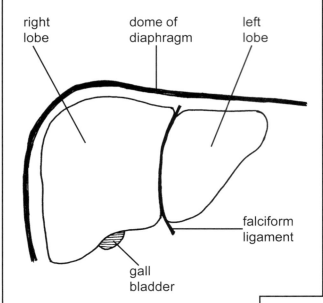

right
lobe

dome of
diaphragm

left
lobe

falciform
ligament

gall
bladder

Diagram 9.2
From the front the two principle lobes
of the liver can be clearly seen. They
are separated by the falciform
ligament. Note the position of the
gallbladder underneath the right lobe.
The liver is neatly tucked under the
dome of the diaphragm. Most of the
liver is protected from the front under
the fifth to the tenth right ribs.

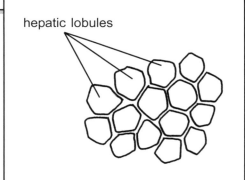

hepatic lobules

Diagram 9.3
A section of liver made up of lobules.

Sinusoids are the hepatic capillaries

In between two hepatic cellular plates are the blood sinusoids (i.e. the hepatic
capillaries). A sinusoid is essentially a type of blood capillary with very porous
walls, allowing more contact that usual between the blood and tissue cells. This
increased permeability of liver sinusoids is explained by the large pores found in
the cells which make up the endothelial wall. These large pores are referred to as
fenestrations, explaining why liver sinusoids are sometimes referred to as fenestrated
capillaries.

Unlike other capillaries, sinusoids receive blood from two sources. Firstly from
a branch of the hepatic portal vein and secondly from a branch of the hepatic
artery. This arrangement means venous and arterial blood mixes in the sinusoids

as it passes through the lobule. Hepatocytes are therefore supplied with nutrient rich blood from the hepatic portal vein and oxygenated blood from the hepatic artery. Hepatocytes lining the sinusoid are able to selectively absorb substances from the blood, carry out chemical processes, and then secrete the products back into the blood of the same sinusoid.

In the centre of each lobule are small tributaries of the hepatic vein. Blood from the sinusoids drains directly into this central lobular vein. This joins up with other lobular veins which eventually become one of the three large hepatic veins.

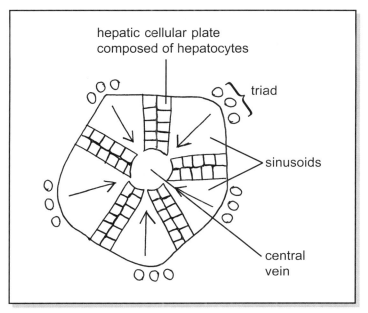

Diagram 9.4
Simplified view of the radial arrangement of hepatocytes and sinusoids in a liver lobule. Arrows indicate direction of blood flow through the sinusoids of the lobule.

Hepatic macrophage system

Liver sinusoids also contain macrophages called Kupffer cells (also called reticuloendothelial cells) in their walls. Like their counterpart macrophages in the spleen these liver macrophages also break down old red blood cells, recycling the amino acids and excreting bilirubin. In addition, liver macrophages perform an essential blood cleaning system by phagocytosing bacteria.

As blood drains from the capillaries of the gut some bacteria from the gut lumen are carried along in the flow. These bacteria are delivered into the sinusoids via the hepatic portal vein. Kupffer macrophages rapidly phagocytose any bacteria flowing through a sinusoid. This means the venous blood which eventually leaves the liver, joining the systemic circulation, has been cleansed of gut bacteria.

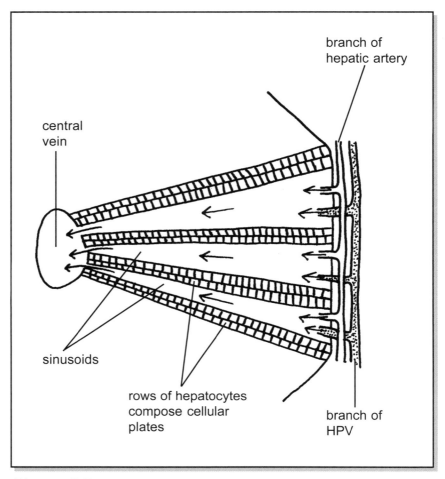

Diagram 9.5
Simplified view of a 'slice' of a lobule. Blood enters from small branches of the HPV and hepatic artery. Arrows indicate direction of blood flow (bile drainage vessels are not shown).

Canaliculi are the bile carrying channels

Between the two rows of hepatocytes are microscopic channels called canaliculi. Individual hepatocytes produce bile which they excrete from the cell into these canaliculi. These in turn drain into the small bile channels of the triads, which are tributaries of larger hepatic bile ducts. This arrangement means that bile flow in canaliculi is in the opposite direction to the blood passing through the sinusoids. The separation of the sinusoids (blood channels) and canaliculi (bile channels) prevents bile and blood mixing. Bile flows into progressively larger bile ducts which eventually unite to form the right and left hepatic duct, then the common hepatic duct.

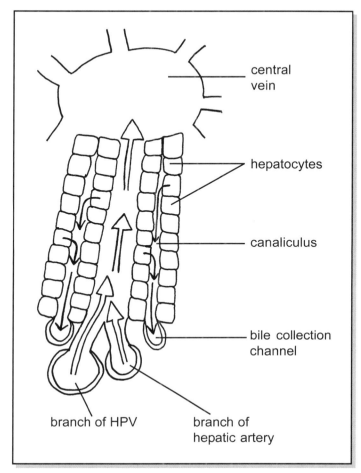

central vein

hepatocytes

canaliculus

bile collection channel

branch of HPV

branch of hepatic artery

Diagram 9.6
Cross section of part of a liver lobule. This shows two hepatic cellular plates with blood flowing through the sinusoid in between. Individual hepatocytes excrete bile into the canaliculi which then flows between the two rows of cells to be collected in a small bile duct. The three vessels of the triad are running in and out of the plane of the page. White arrows indicate blood flow and dark arrows bile flow.

Diagram 9.7
Transverse section of the two rows of cells which form a hepatic cellular plate. The canaliculus is actually formed between the two rows of cells. Bile produced in the individual hepatocytes is only excreted into the canaliculi. This means bile is only excreted from one side of the hepatocytes as the other side is in contact with the blood. Arrows indicate direction of bile flow.

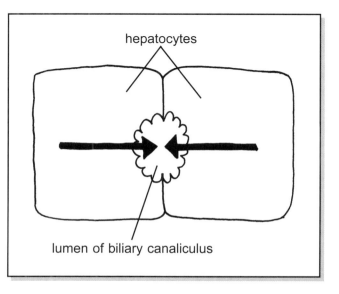

hepatocytes

lumen of biliary canaliculus

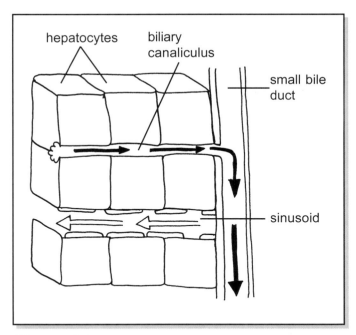

Diagram 9.8
In longitudinal section it can be seen how a canaliculus
is formed between two rows of cells. Dark arrows
indicate bile flow, white arrows blood.

The liver produces a lot of lymph

The pores (fenestrations) in the hepatic sinusoids (liver capillaries) are much larger
than in normal blood capillaries. This allows more water from the plasma than
normal to enter the tissue fluid which bathes the individual hepatocytes. In addition
the large size of the fenestrations allows the passage of proteins from the plasma
into the tissue fluid. This is in contrast to the capillaries in other parts of the body
which are essentially impervious to plasma proteins.

In the liver there is a larger space between the walls of the sinusoids and the
tissue cells than is normal in most other tissues. This space between the capillary
wall and the hepatocytes is called the perisinusoidal space (or the space of Disse).
Once formed from the plasma, tissue fluid circulates through the perisinusoidal
space of Disse, bathing the individual hepatocytes.

Microvilli from the hepatocytes extend into the perisinusoidal space to increase
the surface area with the circulating tissue fluid. This allows for free exchange of
substances between the tissue fluid and hepatocytes.

After circulating over the hepatocytes the tissue fluid is drained as lymphatic
fluid (lymph) into lymphatic vessels. From here the lymph drains into the main
systemic lymphatic vessels before being returned to the blood. About half of the
total volume of lymphatic fluid formed in the body is derived from the liver.

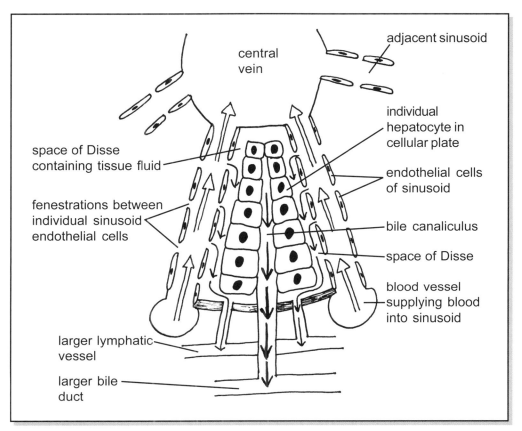

Diagram 9.9
Illustration of the flow of tissue fluid through the perisinusoidal space of Disse.
Tissue fluid which is high in protein is formed through the large fenestrations in the
endothelial cells of the sinusoids. This fluid circulates over the hepatocytes. This
allows substances from the tissue fluid to enter the hepatocytes. Substances which
have been formed by the hepatocytes are able to pass into the tissue fluid. After
circulating over the hepatocytes the fluid is drained into lymphatic drainage vessels
as lymph. White arrows indicate direction of blood flow. Small dark arrows indicate
direction of tissue fluid flow. Larger dark central arrows indicate direction of bile flow.

Bile

Bile is an alkaline fluid, with a pH of about 8. It is largely water but also contains
bile salts and bile pigments. Bile salts are important in the physical emulsification
of fats in the digestive process. They are produced from cholesterol, in the individual
hepatocytes, and secreted into the bile. Sodium chloride and bicarbonate are also
incorporated into bile.

Bilirubin is the principle bile pigment. When red blood cells reach the end of
their life they are broken down by macrophages, mostly located in the spleen and
liver. When the haemoglobin molecules are broken down, a yellow pigment called

bilirubin is left over. This bilirubin is extracted from the blood by liver cells. In the hepatocytes bilirubin is joined onto another molecule called glucuronic acid. This process is called conjugation which just means to 'join together'. Conjugation increases the solubility of bilirubin so it may be carried in solution in bile. While it is true that bilirubin is essentially an excretory product, bile pigments do colour and partly deodorise faeces.

If the liver is unable to excrete bile, bilirubin will dam back into the liver and ultimately into the blood. This can be seen initially in the whites of the eyes and later, if the condition becomes more severe, in the skin. This yellow discoloration, caused by the accumulation of bilirubin, is called jaundice.

Liver functions

In addition to the production of bile, the liver is involved in a wide range of biochemical and physiological processes.

Carbohydrate metabolism

The liver is important in the maintenance of blood sugar concentrations. When blood glucose levels are high, excess glucose is absorbed by the liver and converted into glycogen. This is stored, and then when blood sugar levels are low it is converted back into glucose and released. The liver will convert galactose and fructose (two other small sugar molecules) into glucose. Galactose and fructose may arrive from the gut, via the hepatic portal vein, and are always converted to glucose which is the only sugar found in the systemic circulation. Liver cells are also able to convert amino acids into glucose when there is a shortage in the blood. Maintenance of blood glucose levels is essential as the brain must have a constant supply of glucose to fuel its metabolic activity. If there is no glucose at all in the blood, brain function will cease, resulting in death.

Fat metabolism

Liver cells are able to process one type of fat into another which may be needed in various areas of the body. For example, some types of fat are needed for the production of cell membranes and organelles, as well as numerous biochemical processes throughout the body. In addition excess protein and carbohydrate is converted into fat for storage. This is why eating too much carbohydrate or protein also causes us to put on weight.

If there is alcohol in the blood hepatocytes are able to absorb fat for processing as normal. However, alcohol prevents the liver cells from secreting fat. This means that if there is alcohol in the blood every day, liver cells will start to accumulate fat. The increased amount of fat in the liver cells causes the liver to become fatty and bulky. If this is prolonged liver cells will start to die and be replaced by fibrous tissue leading to liver cirrhosis. If a person stops drinking while the liver is still at the fatty stage the condition is reversible. However, once cirrhosis, characterised by scar tissue formation, has developed the liver damage is irreversible.

Both high and low density lipoproteins are synthesised in the liver, these are the two forms of cholesterol found in the blood. These are secreted into the blood where they are involved in the transport of fats around the body.

Protein metabolism

Liver cells are able to change the form of some amino acids. Human proteins contain 20 different amino acids, which all need to be available for the processes of growth and repair. Of these 20 required amino acids, 10 can be produced in the liver from other amino acids; the other 10 cannot be converted. Therefore, the 10 which cannot be converted from others must be present in the diet if health is to be maintained. These 10 which cannot be produced in the liver are referred to as essential amino acids, because they must be part of the diet. Amino acids which can be produced in the liver by conversion are called non-essential, not because they are not necessary for normal physiology but because health may be maintained even if they are not part of the diet. The process of converting one amino acid into another is called transamination.

If more proteins are consumed than are required the excess amino acids are utilised for their energy yielding content. However, before proteins can be used to produce carbohydrates or fat they must first be chemically broken down. This breakdown of amino acids is called deamination and occurs almost exclusively in the hepatocytes.

Formation of plasma proteins, including clotting proteins

The liver forms all of the plasma proteins except the immunoglobulins (i.e. the antibodies). Albumin is the most abundant plasma protein and is produced by the hepatocytes and then released into the blood. This plasma protein is essential to maintain the osmolarity of the plasma which is needed to facilitate osmotic reabsorption of tissue fluids. Albumin also acts as a 'carrier' molecule, transporting some substances around the circulatory system. Some drugs are also transported bound to albumin.

Liver cells produce several of the clotting factors such as prothrombin and fibrinogen. If liver function is compromised, production of these plasma clotting proteins is reduced. This rapidly leads to haemorrhagic problems as the patients are no longer able to form blood clots. Angiotensinogen is a short protein molecule produced by the liver cells and is essential in the angiotensin-renin mechanism of blood pressure regulation.

Production of urea

Proteins are composed largely of carbon, hydrogen, oxygen and nitrogen. Fats and carbohydrates contain only carbon, hydrogen and oxygen. This means that when proteins are broken down, nitrogen is left over as a waste product. Nitrogen in solution forms toxic ammonia (NH_3) which must be rapidly removed from

Diagram 9.10
This diagram illustrates the function of the individual hepatocyte using protein synthesis as an example. Individual amino acids are absorbed from the blood flowing through a sinusoid. In hepatocytes the amino acids are chemically combined to produce a protein molecule which is then secreted back into the blood flowing through the sinusoid.

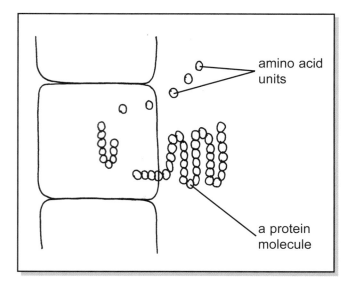

amino acid units

a protein molecule

the blood. Additional ammonia, produced by bacteria, is absorbed from the gut. Hepatocytes take up ammonia and chemically convert it into a much less toxic, highly soluble, nitrogen containing substance called urea. This is removed from the blood by the kidneys and excreted in urine.

In liver failure waste ammonia is not continuously removed so it accumulates in the blood. This effects the brain causing a condition referred to as hepatic coma which leads to death.

Storage of nutrients

The liver stores the fat soluble vitamins, A, D, E and K and it also holds reserves of vitamin B_{12}. These reserves may be extensive; enough vitamin A is stored to supply the body for 10 months with no dietary intake. Sufficient B_{12} is stored to prevent deficiency developing for several years. Iron is also stored in the liver cells in the form of a molecule called ferritin.

Breakdown of toxins and drugs

Liver cells are capable of recognising and chemically breaking down a wide range of toxins. Bacterial activity in the gut generates large amounts of toxic waste products which are transported to the liver by the HPV. These are broken down to less toxic substances which may be excreted by the kidneys, or incorporated into bile for excretion in the faeces.

Most drugs are recognised as 'toxins' by the liver and are broken down to metabolites. In the liver cells many drugs are oxidised or conjugated to increase their solubility in water. These processes are facilitated by numerous hepatic enzymes, the best known group of which are the cytochrome p 450 group. (You will certainly come across these if you study pharmacology.) Once the drug metabolites (break down products) are soluble they are usually excreted readily in the urine, although a few drug metabolites are excreted in bile. If there is liver failure drugs will not be broken down and can reach toxic levels.

Most hormones are also broken down by the liver after a period of time circulating in the blood. Liver failure can therefore result in increased plasma concentrations of such hormones as thyroxine, oestrogen and cortisol.

Generation of heat

As a result of ongoing metabolic processes in the liver, a lot of heat is generated. This makes an important contribution to body temperature, especially during periods of reduced muscular activity.

CHAPTER 10

Renal and Urinary Systems

Components

The urinary system consists of the organs and structures which produce, transport and store urine. Urine is produced in the kidneys and transported to the urinary bladder via the right and left ureter. From time to time the bladder is emptied and urine is voided from the body via the urethra. The urinary system describes the whole of the kidney, ureter, bladder and urethra system but the term renal is specific to the kidneys.

Diagram 10.1
Components of the urinary system.

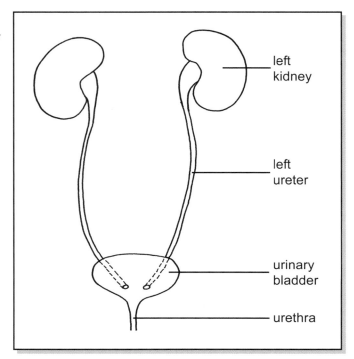

left
kidney

left
ureter

urinary
bladder

urethra

The kidneys

Normally more water and ions are ingested than are required to meet the requirements of homeostasis. Ions include potassium from fruit and sodium and chloride from salt. In order to prevent the body becoming overloaded with water and ions the excess must be excreted. The way water and ions are eliminated from the body is to incorporate them into urine which is then voided. This means the kidneys are responsible for regulation of the volume as well as the composition of body fluids.

In addition the kidneys excrete waste products from metabolic activity. Metabolic biochemical processes are carried out by all living cells. As a result of this biochemical activity, waste products are produced. If these are allowed to accumulate in body fluids they will soon reach toxic levels. The kidneys are able to isolate and concentrate waste products in urine, which is then excreted from the body.

There are two kidneys located high in the abdominal cavity, on the posterior abdominal wall. Kidneys are dark red bean shaped organs. The right kidney is a little lower than the left due to the presence of the liver above. Because of the domed nature of the diaphragm the upper part of the kidneys receive some protection from the lower ribs. In addition the kidneys are embedded in and completely surrounded by a protective layer of perirenal fat. Surrounding the perirenal fat is a further protective layer of connective tissue called the renal fascia.

Macroscopic renal structure

Surrounding the outer surface of each kidney is a layer of collagen rich fibrous tissue which comprises the renal capsule. This is a thin but tough layer of supportive connective tissue which contains many pain receptors (nociceptors). If swelling occurs within a kidney this capsule will be stretched causing pain. It also explains why it is so painful if we are poked in the kidneys.

The outer layer of the kidney itself is called the cortex. Under the cortex is a layer referred to as the medulla. The renal medulla is composed of structures called renal pyramids. Numbers of renal pyramids vary between individuals; there are normally 5 to 11 per kidney. Between the renal pyramids of the medulla are projections from the cortex referred to as renal columns. The inner area of the kidney is called the renal pelvis and is continuous with the ureter.

An arrangement of minor and major calyces connects the renal medulla with the renal pelvis. Calyces are essentially branches of the renal pelvis. Minor calyces form around the apex of the pyramids of the medulla and merge into larger calyces which then expand to form the pelvis.

At the centre of the concaved side of each kidney is the region called the renal hilum. A hilum is a relatively small area where blood vessels, nerves and lymphatic vessels enter and leave an organ. The inner surface of the hilum is called the renal sinus; this is a hollow area within the kidney which contains the renal pelvis. It is via the hilum that the arteries, veins, lymphatics, nerves and ureters enter and leave the kidneys. There are two adrenal glands, located one on top of each kidney; this is why these structures used to be called the suprarenal glands. Despite their position these endocrine glands do not have any direct anatomical connections with the kidneys. There is usually a thin layer of connective tissue separating the kidneys from the adrenal glands.

Renal blood supply

Blood is transported to each kidney via a short branch from the aorta called the renal artery. The renal artery rapidly divides into segmental arteries each perfusing a segment of the kidney. There are further rapid divisions of the branches of the renal artery until it breaks down into arterioles which are described as afferent. After blood has passed through the kidney, it is collected by a number of venous branches which unite to form a single renal vein. This vessel then returns blood directly to the inferior vena cava.

The kidneys have a large blood supply in relation to their size. Despite only comprising around 0.5% of body mass, in an average 70 Kg adult the kidneys receive about 1200 mls of blood per minute. This is more than 20% of total cardiac output at rest. Blood draining from the renal veins is not fully deoxygenated, indicating kidneys receive more blood than is required for purposes of oxygenation.

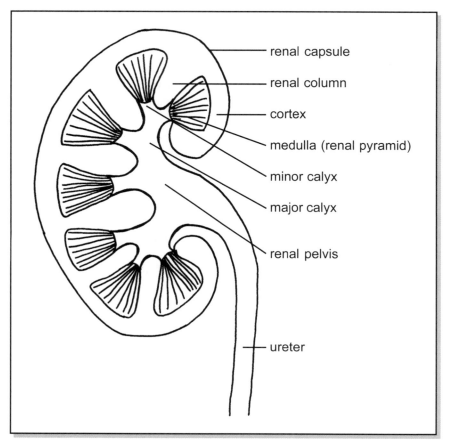

Diagram 10.2
Structure of a kidney.

Microscopic renal structure - the nephrons

Nephrons are the functional renal units; there are about one million in each kidney. Each nephron consists of a renal tubule and an associated vascular system. The start of the tubule is a structure called the glomerular (Bowman's) capsule which is located in the cortex of the kidney. Squamous cells comprise an outer or parietal layer of this capsule, while the inner or visceral layer is made up of specialised cells called podocytes. Between the two layers is a capsular space. Each nephron is supplied with blood from an afferent arteriole which opens

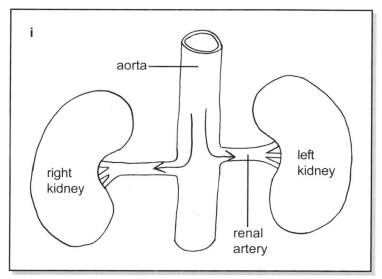

Diagram 10.3
Blood supply to and from the kidneys.
(i) Blood passes directly from the aorta into the two renal arteries which supply the kidneys.
(ii) Blood drains from the right and left kidney into the renal veins which drain directly into the inferior vena cava.

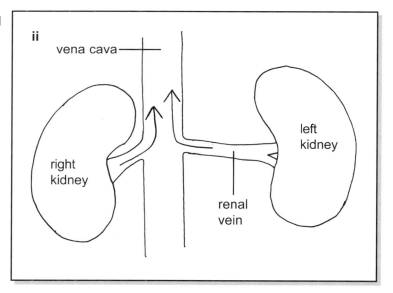

into a ball of capillaries called the glomerulus. Glomerular capillaries are located inside the glomerular capsule. The combination of the glomerulus and the glomerular capsule is referred to as a renal corpuscle.

The glomerular capsule is continuous with the next section of the renal tubule called the first or proximal convoluted tubule. Convoluted means coiled, the result of this coiling is that a greater length of tubule can be contained in a smaller area. From here the tubule forms a loop; often this is a long loop dipping right down into the medulla of the kidney. It is called the loop of the nephron (or loop of Henle). After looping down this rises again, back towards the cortex

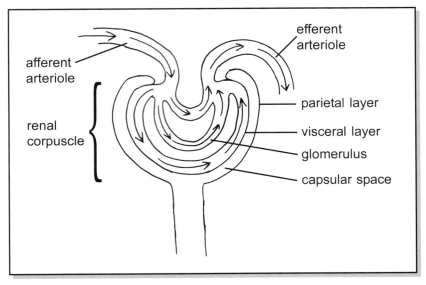

Diagram 10.4
A glomerular capsule and the glomerulus. The glomerulus is actually
a sphere of capillaries. Arrows indicate direction of blood flow.

where it is formed into a second or distal convoluted tubule before connecting
to a collecting duct.

Once blood has passed through the capillaries of the glomerulus it is drained
via a second, efferent, arteriole. This second arteriole then breaks up into a
second capillary bed, which wraps itself around the renal tubule.

Formation of urine

Endothelial-capsular membrane

Endothelial cells of the glomerular capillaries contain pores (or fenestrations)
which are too small to allow blood cells to pass through. However, smaller
dissolved components of the plasma may pass out of the capillaries via these
small spaces. The basement membrane of the capillaries is on the outside of the
endothelial cells which comprise the capillary wall. This membrane acts as a
further filter, preventing the escape of plasma proteins. Surrounding the
endothelial cells of the capillaries of the glomerulus and their basement membrane
are a form of specialised cells called the podocytes. Podocytes form the inner or
visceral layer of the glomerular capsule. These cells have fine extensions called
pedicels which wrap around the glomerular capillaries and form a physical sieve.
Between the pedicels of the podocytes is a thin membrane called the slit
membrane. This area between the pedicels form the filtration slits through which
filtered water and solutes may pass. A solute just describes a substance dissolved
in solution, in this case from the blood plasma.

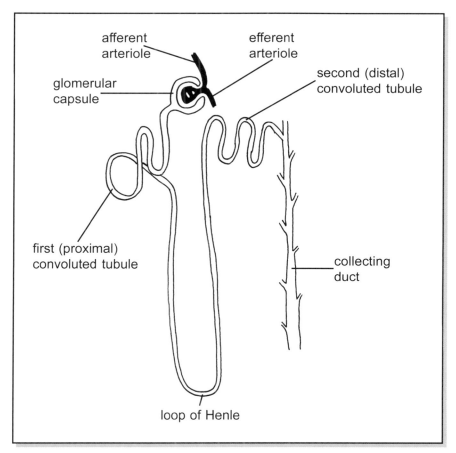

Diagram 10.5
Components of a renal tubule or nephron. The branched nature of the collecting duct indicates where other nephrons drain into the same duct. In reality the ascending part of the loop of the nephron (loop of Henle) makes contact with the afferent arteriole supplying the same nephron.

Collectively the endothelial cells of the capillaries, basement membrane and podocytes form the endothelial-capsular membrane. This is the dialysing membrane of the kidney. Dialysis is a physical process involving the separation of small molecules in solution from larger ones, through a separating (or dialysing) membrane.

Ultrafiltration from the glomerulus into the capsular space

The filtration function of endothelial-capsular membrane means that cells and large molecules are retained in the blood in the capillaries while smaller molecules are able to pass into the capsular space. This is a process of filtration on a small scale so it is called ultrafiltration. Blood cells, platelets and large plasma proteins

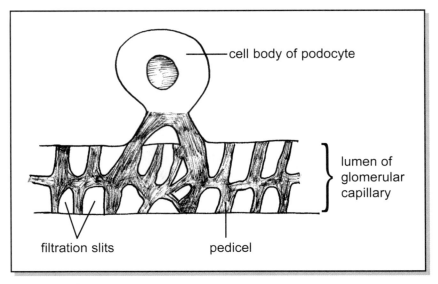

Diagram 10.6
An individual podocyte forms a physical filter around a length of
glomerular capillary. The branches of the podocyte form a very fine
physical sieve over the surface of the glomerular capillaries.

are retained while smaller molecules such as water, glucose, urea, amino acids,
sodium, potassium and creatinine pass into the filtrate.

Glomerular filtration rate refers to the volumes of glomerular filtrate formed
over a period of time. This is about 125 ml per minute which adds up to 180
litres per day. Filtrate is formed as a result of blood pressure in the glomerular
capillaries pushing water and solutes through the endothelial-capsular membrane
into the capsular space. Once in the capsular space filtrate is free to pass along
the rest of the renal tubule. The need for an adequate blood pressure to generate
filtrate explains why acute renal failure may be a complication of shock. In
shock there is a low systemic blood pressure; if the systolic BP falls below 80
mm Hg, glomerular filtration rate will start to decline.

Tubular reabsorption from the nephrons back into the blood

As glomerular filtrate passes through the nephron as much as 99% is reabsorbed
back into the blood. This is why the efferent arteriole breaks down into a network
of capillaries which carry on to surround the tubule. Water and solutes are
reabsorbed from the tubules into the surrounding capillary network and so are
returned to the blood. Blood containing reabsorbed material is then collected
in a venule which drains into a branch of the renal vein. Cell surfaces lining
much of the lumen of the renal tubules are infolded into microvilli which form
a brush border. This infolding greatly increases the internal surface area available
over which reabsorption may take place.

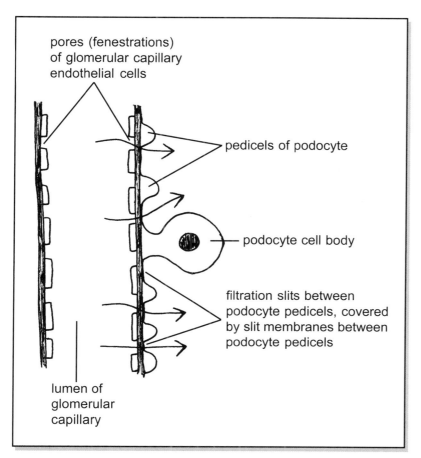

pores (fenestrations)
of glomerular capillary
endothelial cells

pedicels of podocyte

podocyte cell body

filtration slits between
podocyte pedicels, covered
by slit membranes between
podocyte pedicels

lumen of
glomerular
capillary

Diagram 10.7
The 3 layers of the endothelial-capsular membrane. Firstly there
are small pores within the endothelial cells. Secondly water and
solutes must pass through the basement membrane of the
capillary endothelial cells. Thirdly water and solutes pass through
the filtration (slit) membranes of the podocytes which cover the
filtration slits. Only after water and solutes pass through this
combined filtration system do they enter the capsular space as
glomerular filtrate. Arrows show direction of filtration. Through
these anatomical structures the physiological process of dialysis
takes place.

From the glomerular space, filtrate enters the renal tubule and passes around
the proximal convoluted tubule and on into the loop of the nephron. As filtrate
passes through the tubule, water and solutes are progressively reabsorbed. After
the distal convoluted tubule the fluid remaining in the nephron passes into the
collecting duct. Collecting ducts originate in the cortex where they are small.
However, as they pass down through the medulla they merge into progressively

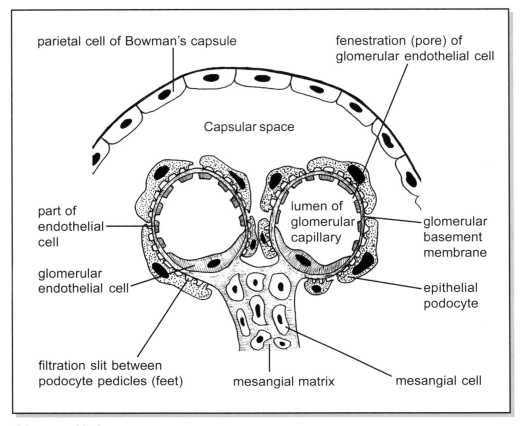

Diagram 10. 8
Overview of the structure and components of a renal corpuscle. Each of the one million glomeruli in each kidney is composed of a ball of capillaries. Ultrafiltration takes place from the lumen of the glomerular capillary into the capsular (Bowman's) space. From here the glomerular filtrate passes on into the nephron. The walls of the glomerular capillaries are composed of endothelial cells that contain pores (or fenestrations). Mesangial cells are located between the glomerular capillaries. Under the glomerular endothelial cells is the glomerular basement membrane (GBM), this forms a structural base for the glomerular capillary endothelial cells and also acts as a dialysing membrane. Glomerular capillaries are surrounded by podocytes; these specialised cells have numerous pedicels which are foot like extensions of cytoplasm which wrap around the capillaries forming filtration slits. A thin membrane called the slit membrane extends across each filtration slit.

larger ducts which eventually drain from the apex of the medullary pyramids into a minor calyx. Any glomerular filtrate which is not reabsorbed in the nephrons or collecting ducts is left as urine. Some reabsorption takes place from the collecting ducts; however, once urine is passed into a renal calyx no further reabsorption is possible. From a minor calyx urine passes on into the renal pelvis.

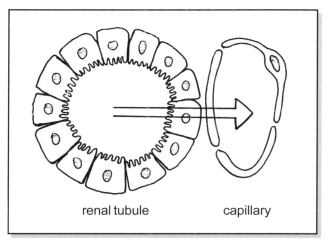

renal tubule   capillary

Diagram 10.9
Cross section of a renal tubule and adjacent capillary.
Reabsorption occurs from the renal tubules back into
the capillaries. Arrow indicates direction of flow.

Essential science – ions and electrolytes

When compounds containing sodium, potassium, chlorine, calcium, magnesium or phosphates dissolve in water they form ions. These ions have one or more positive or negative electrical charges, i.e. Na^+, K^+, Cl^-, Ca^{2+}, Mg^{2+}, PO_4^{3-}. Solutions which contain dissolved ions are good conductors of electricity and once dissolved in water these ions are described as electrolytes.

The concentration of electrolytes in the plasma and tissue fluids must be finely homeostatically regulated in order to allow the normal function of excitable cells. For example normal plasma concentrations of sodium are 135-146 mmol/L, potassium 3.5-5mmol/L, chloride 98-106 mmol/L, magnesium 0.7-1.1 mmol/L and phosphate 0.8-1.5 mmol/L. Excitable cells are the neurones and muscle cells which function by being polarised or depolarised and by changing between these two states. It is the relative concentration of ions across the cell membrane of an excitable cell which generates the electrical activity. In this sense electrolytes generate the electrical activity of the body. If there is deviation from normal concentrations of electrolytes the voltages across cell membranes will be altered meaning muscle and nerve cells will not function normally. It is therefore vital that the kidneys excrete or retain precisely the correct volumes of all of the electrolytes.

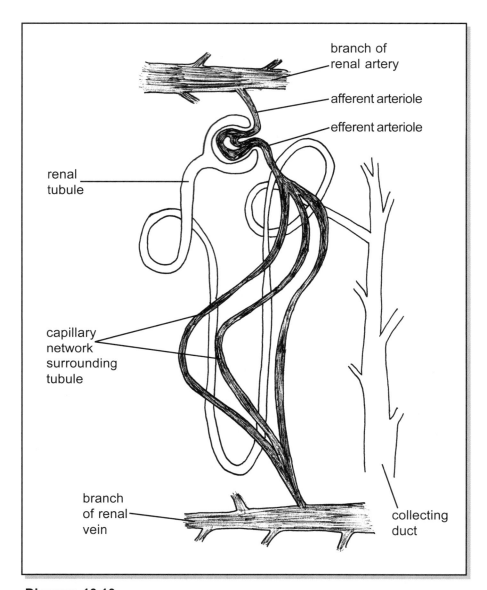

Diagram 10.10
The relationship between the tubule and capillary network. Capillaries wrap around the renal tubule to allow reabsorption to occur efficiently over short distances. Only 3 capillaries are illustrated. The name for the network of capillaries surrounding the nephron is the vasa recta.

Selective reabsorption and homeostasis

Reabsorption from the tubule is selective. Substances which the body needs such as glucose and amino acids are totally reabsorbed. In health, urine should contain no sugar or amino acids at all. Other substances are not fully reabsorbed, therefore enter the urine. This means the body can eliminate waste products

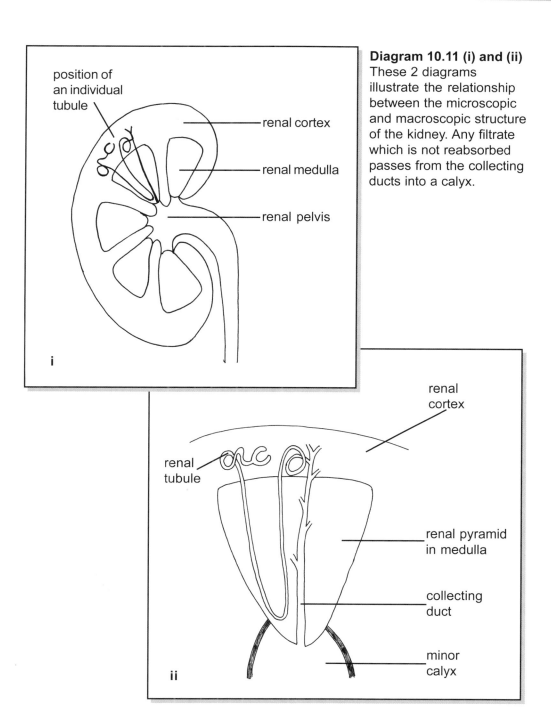

Diagram 10.11 (i) and (ii)
These 2 diagrams illustrate the relationship between the microscopic and macroscopic structure of the kidney. Any filtrate which is not reabsorbed passes from the collecting ducts into a calyx.

position of an individual tubule

renal cortex

renal medulla

renal pelvis

i

renal cortex

renal tubule

renal pyramid in medulla

collecting duct

minor calyx

ii

generated in metabolic processes. For example, as urea passes through the nephron, about 50% diffuses back into the blood leaving the other 50% in the filtrate to enter the urine. Creatinine is another waste product which is not extensively reabsorbed and so is found in urine.

Other substances are reabsorbed depending on the body's requirements at the time. For example, if we drink a lot it will be necessary to reabsorb less water from the nephrons. If less water is reabsorbed, more will remain in the tubules and pass into the collecting ducts. This will have the effect of increasing urine volumes and so excreting the excess water. Conversely if someone has not been able to drink for a period of time, the blood will become more concentrated and it will be necessary to conserve water. To achieve this more water will be reabsorbed from the nephron which will leave less in the tubules so less will pass into the collecting ducts. This will lower urine volumes, conserving water in the body. Regulation of water reabsorption is controlled by the antidiuretic hormone discussed in the chapter on the endocrine system.

In addition to water, there are other substances which are selectively reabsorbed depending on the body's current requirements. For example levels of sodium and potassium must be homeostatically controlled in the plasma. Regulation of sodium and potassium is essential as these elements dissolve in the plasma as ions forming the electrolytes. If we eat a lot of salty food (salt is sodium chloride) less sodium is reabsorbed, so more is excreted. The amount of sodium which is reabsorbed is controlled by the levels of the hormone aldosterone. As plasma levels of aldosterone rise so does reabsorption of sodium.

It is particularly important that serum potassium levels are finely controlled. If these rise or fall too much the electrical functioning of the myocardium may be affected causing cardiac arrest. Diets high in potassium will increase the amount of potassium found in the urine. Conversely if the diet is low in potassium less will be excreted in urine. Water soluble vitamins may also be selectively reabsorbed. If we eat too much vitamin C less is reabsorbed so vitamin C will be found in the urine.

The kidneys are also the principle route for excretion of drugs from the body. After taking a particular drug the metabolites will be found in the urine. A drug metabolite is a breakdown product of a drug. Drug metabolism usually takes place in the liver. Renal excretion explains why we need to be careful when giving drugs to patients with poor renal function. If the body cannot excrete a drug in the urine, it may build up to toxic levels.

Mechanisms of reabsorption

There are basically two mechanisms by which substances are reabsorbed from the renal tubules. The first is a passive reabsorption via the mechanisms of diffusion and osmosis. Water will move from areas of high water concentration in the first part of the tubule back into the blood, where the concentration of water is relatively lower. Other substances will also diffuse from filtrate back into the blood, down their diffusional concentration gradients. However, whenever reabsorption is required against a diffusion gradient, active transport mechanisms must be used. These are mostly membrane based systems which use energy to pump substances from the tubule, where they are at relatively low concentrations, into the blood where their concentrations are already relatively high.

Active transport explains why there is normally no glucose or amino acids at all in urine. It is true that in the proximal sections of the renal tubules there may be passive reabsorption of these nutrients, when the concentrations in filtrate are greater than those in the blood. However in the distal sections, much of the glucose and amino acids have already been reabsorbed. This will have increased the concentrations in the blood while reducing concentrations left in the filtrate generating a diffusion gradient from blood to filtrate. This means in order to reabsorb all the glucose and amino acids any remaining molecules must be pumped from the filtrate into the blood against their diffusion gradients. The presence of active transport mechanisms explains why the kidneys are relatively metabolically active. Many renal cells contain lots of mitochondria which generate all of the required energy.

Plasma is 'cleaned' 60 times a day

As plasma volume is only about 3 litres, the high volumes of glomerular filtration and selective reabsorption means that the entire plasma is cleansed of impurities and homeostatically regulated about 60 times per day. This allows for very fine, ongoing, homeostatic regulation of numerous constituents of the blood and prevents us feeling ill as a result of toxin accumulation.

Tubular secretion occurs directly from the capillaries into the nephrons

In the process of tubular secretion substances are transferred directly from the blood capillaries into the lumen of the tubules. In other words substances enter the lumen of the nephrons without going through the process of ultrafiltration

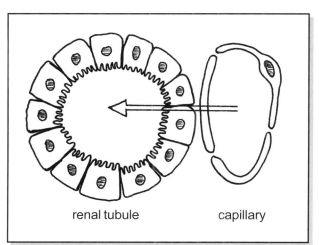

Diagram 10.12
Cross section of a renal tubule and adjacent capillary. Tubular secretion occurs from the capillaries into the renal tubule, in the opposite direction to reabsorption. Arrows indicate direction of flow.

renal tubule   capillary

in the glomerulus. Tubular secretion occurs in the opposite direction to the flow of material in reabsorption. Waste products such as ammonia are excreted in this way as are some drugs. Potassium and hydrogen ions are selectively secreted by tubular secretion depending on the body's current homeostatic requirements. If we eat a lot of bananas for example, serum potassium will start to rise. In this case, tubular secretion of potassium will be increased; this will result in more being excreted in urine. Substances secreted from the blood into filtrate will carry on through the renal tubule, into the collecting duct and enter a renal calyx as a component of urine. Active transport mechanisms are usually used to facilitate tubular secretion.

Essential science - acids and alkalis

The strength of an acidic solution is determined by the number of free hydrogen ions (H^+) in solution, stronger acids having more. An alkaline solution is able to absorb hydrogen ions, for example the hydroxyl ion (OH) can absorb an H^+ to form water.

In physiology it is vital to maintain plasma pH levels within finely tuned parameters. This is because all metabolic biochemical processes are facilitated by enzymes and enzymes are very sensitive to small changes in pH. If the pH falls or rises, enzymic function would be rapidly and potentially fatally affected.

The pH of the blood is partly controlled by regulation of the number of hydrogen ions in plasma. An increase in H^+ concentration increases acidity. When the pH of the blood falls and acidity rises, there will be more tubular secretion of hydrogen ions. This will reduce the H^+ concentration in the blood while increasing the concentration in urine. The effect of this will be that blood pH will rise back to normal as acidity reduces. As a result of the homeostatic regulation of pH by the kidneys, arterial plasma pH is finely tuned within a range of 7.35-7.45.

Urine

Normal urine

Typically urine is about 95% water and 5% dissolved substances or solutes. Because urine contains these solutes it is denser than pure water; a normal specific gravity of urine is about 1.010-1.035. Specific gravity describes the mass of a substance as a ratio to the mass of pure water. Solutes are derived from metabolic processes, the diet and sometimes from drugs, normally as metabolites.

Metabolism of amino acids by body cells results in the formation of waste nitrogen. This chemically combines with water to form ammonia which is toxic. In order to rapidly remove this toxic waste from the blood, the liver facilitates

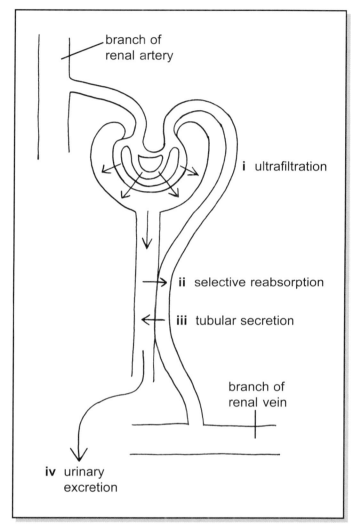

branch of
renal artery

i ultrafiltration

ii selective reabsorption

iii tubular secretion

branch of
renal vein

iv urinary
excretion

Diagram 10.13
Summary of the four
functions of a nephron.
(i)   Ultrafiltration from the
      capillaries of the
      glomerulus into the
      capsular space. From
      here the filtrate flows
      directly into the lumen
      of the renal tubules.
(ii) Selective tubular
      reabsorption, from the
      renal tubule back into
      the blood.
(iii) Tubular secretion
      from capillaries into
      the renal tubules.
(iv) Urine excretion, first
      into the collecting
      ducts then into a
      calyx. From here it
      passes into the renal
      pelvis and on into the
      ureters.

a chemical reaction which combines ammonia with carbon dioxide to form less toxic urea. As urea is very soluble in water it may easily be excreted in urine. Creatinine and uric acid are other nitrogen containing wastes. Levels of nitrogen excretion will increase if more protein is eaten as proteins contain nitrogen in addition to carbon, hydrogen and oxygen.

Other normal constituents, present in various amounts are sodium, potassium, magnesium, calcium, sulphate, chlorides and phosphates. Normal urine may also contain some ketones, especially if the person has not been eating much in the recent past. Ketones are breakdown products of fat metabolism.

Normal urine should be transparent; if it is cloudy this may indicate the presence of bacteria and white blood cells. Urine is normally a yellow to amber colour, the more concentrated the urine the darker the colour. The colour comes from a breakdown product of bile called urochrome. Urine is normally slightly acidic. Diets rich in protein tend to increase acidity and vegetarian diets cause an increase in alkalinity.

Urine volumes

The volumes and constituents of urine will vary significantly depending on the excretory needs of the time. Most adults produce between 1 and 2 litres of urine per day. It is a good idea to drink water from time to time during the day to maintain good urine volumes. This will mean urine produced is more dilute and will be passed more often. Dilute urine may reduce the risk of precipitation in the urinary tract. Precipitation i.e. formation of solids from solutions can lead to the formation of very painful and troublesome kidney and bladder stones. Larger urine volumes will also physically flush out the ureters, bladder and urethra reducing the probability of urinary infections. Urinary tract infections (UTIs) are common in females due to the short urethra and proximity of the anus. These infections commonly present as inflammation of the bladder, that is cystitis.

This flushing effect of larger urine volumes may also help to wash out potential carcinogens. The presence of cancer causing chemicals in urine may be caused by smoking. Some of the toxins from smoke pass from the lungs into the blood and are then excreted by the kidneys. This may explain why smokers are more at risk of renal and bladder cancers than non-smokers.

Tea, coffee and alcohol are all diuretics. A diuretic is any agent which will increase urine volumes. Diuretics result in larger volumes of urine than would be expected from the volume of fluids consumed. Diuresis therefore results in subsequent dehydration and production of smaller volumes of more concentrated urine. Dehydration caused by the diuretic effect of alcohol is one of the causes of a hangover. Drinking water as well as these other drinks will help to compensate for their diuretic effects.

Obligatory urine volume

The kidneys are able to alter the volumes of water excreted without altering the quantities of dissolved waste products excreted. When urine volumes are low, urea, creatinine, excess sodium and potassium can still be excreted as the kidneys are able to increase the concentration of urine. However, there is a limit to the kidneys ability to concentrate these wastes. This means that when urine volumes drop below a critical level, the body is no longer excreting all the waste material it needs to. Clearly this will result in waste accumulation and the development of toxic effects.

For an average adult the minimum obligatory urine volume needed to excrete the required solute load is between 300 and 500 mls. Any less and toxins will be retained. This gives a rationale for a common definition of acute renal failure, which is when less than 20 mls of urine are produced per hour for two consecutive hours. Clinically it is essential to differentiate between reduced urine production by the kidneys and retention of urine. In retention urine is still produced as normal but is prevented from being voided by some obstruction in the urinary tract. Conversely oliguria describes an abnormally reduced rate of urine formation and anuria means no urine at all is being produced.

Limits to the ability of the kidneys to concentrate urine have important implications if you are lost with limited supplies of fresh water. In this situation it would be best not to drink any of your water supplies until the kidneys are concentrating urine to their maximum ability. After this you should just drink enough to produce the obligatory urine volume. This will preserve water supplies, but prevent you from becoming toxic. If at sea it is always harmful to drink any sea water, as this is already more concentrated than the most concentrated urine the kidneys can produce. One litre of sea water needs two litres of urine volume to excrete the salt it contains.

Abnormal urine

Urinalysis, using dip sticks, should be performed on every patient admitted into a clinical situation. It is a quick, safe, cheap non-invasive screen for several possible disorders. The presence of protein, glucose or blood in urine is always an abnormal finding. Proteinuria (protein in the urine) may indicate damage to the glomerular membrane caused by disease or high blood pressure. Glucosuria indicates that the levels of glucose in the blood are too high suggesting the possibility of diabetes mellitus. Haematuria may derive from any part of the tract and may be caused by trauma or neoplasm, (possibly cancer) but more commonly infection. Contamination from menstruation is also common, and of course normal, just check the urine again next week after menstruation has finished. High levels of ketones may indicate the person has not been eating or has diabetes mellitus. In urinary tract infections it is also likely that the urine will contain nitrite as a result of bacterial activity and leucocyte esterase from white blood cells.

Water balance

Water is the most common substance in the body; in men it accounts for about 60% of body mass. In women water usually accounts for 50% of body mass. This difference is explained by women on average having a higher proportion of fat. Adipose tissue contains only about 20% water whereas other tissues contain proportionally more water.

As introduced in Chapter 1 body water is compartmentalised. About two-thirds of body water is intracellular, located in the cytosol of all the body cells. In an average adult this will represent about 28 litres. Extracellular fluid is mostly located in the interstitial space as tissue fluid, about 11 litres. In the blood there are a further 3 litres of extracellular water. Smaller amounts of water are also found in body cavities such as cerebrospinal, peritoneal, pleural, ocular and synovial.

Water in the body is only derived from three sources; drinking fluids, moisture in food and metabolic water from carbohydrate metabolism. Water is lost in four ways; through the skin as perspiration or transpiration, in the exhaled breath, in the faeces and of course in the urine. Volumes of water lost through the first three are variable, depending on environmental conditions and levels of activity. It is only the volumes of water lost in urine which can be regulated to allow for homeostatic water balance.

The hypothalamus controls thirst and ADH secretion

Loss of water from the body will lead to a loss of water from the blood. This will increase the concentration of salts and proteins in the blood so increasing plasma osmolarity. This change is detected by osmoreceptor cells located in the hypothalamus. In response to increased plasma osmolarity the hypothalamus generates the sensation of thirst which causes the person to seek out water to drink. These osmoreceptor cells also control the secretion of antidiuretic hormone (ADH) from the posterior pituitary gland. Increases in plasma osmolarity will increase secretion of ADH which will reduce urine volumes and therefore reduce water loss. Reductions in plasma osmolarity will reduce secretions of ADH, allowing larger volumes of urine to be formed.

Homeostasis of blood pressure

As the kidneys regulate the amounts of water and salts in the blood they are a major controlling influence in determining venous return to the heart. Venous return describes the volumes of blood which are returned to the heart by the veins. Venous return influences cardiac output (CO) which is a principle determinate of blood pressure (BP). An increase in CO will increase BP while a decrease in CO will lower BP. If the kidneys retain more water, venous return will be increased. If they excrete more water, venous return will be reduced. When more sodium is retained the osmotic pressure of plasma is increased which in turn attracts more water into the circulation, increasing plasma volume and so venous return. However, if more salt is excreted plasma sodium will be reduced, lowering the osmotic potential of the plasma and so lowering plasma volumes.

Juxtaglomerular apparatus (JGA)

There are two types of cells which comprise this apparatus and both cell types are very close to the glomerulus (juxta means 'beside'). Firstly, granular cells are immediately next to the afferent arterioles. Secondly the macula densa cells comprise part of the wall of the ascending loop of Henle in the distal tubule. As the ascending limb of the loop of Henle, containing the macula densa cells, passes close to this area both cell types are close to the glomerulus. If the blood pressure in the afferent arteriole is reduced the JGA cells respond by secreting the enzyme renin into the blood.

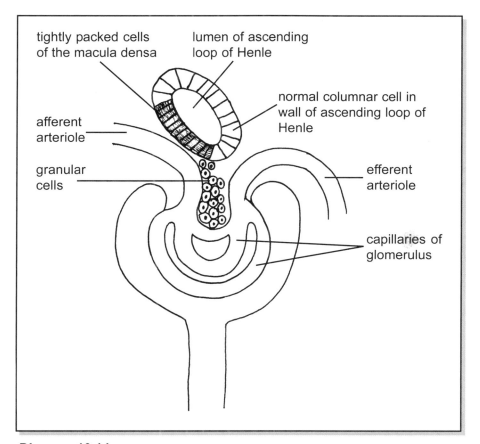

tightly packed cells
of the macula densa

lumen of ascending
loop of Henle

normal columnar cell in
wall of ascending loop of
Henle

afferent
arteriole

granular
cells

efferent
arteriole

capillaries of
glomerulus

Diagram 10.14
The two types of cells which comprise the juxtaglomerular apparatus
cells are both located close to the glomerulus. In each nephron the
ascending loop of Henle passes very close to the afferent arteriole
which supplies blood into the glomerulus. Macula densa cells are so
called because they are closely packed together in the distal loop of
Henle. Granular cells are actually modified smooth muscle cells
from the wall of the afferent arteriole. Together these two cell types
form the juxtaglomerular apparatus.

One of the proteins present in the blood is called angiotensinogen. This is a
short protein produced by the liver and is inactive; it just circulates in the blood.
However, when renin acts on angiotensinogen it converts it into another shorter
protein called angiotensin I. As angiotensin I passes through the lungs it is converted
into angiotensin II by an enzyme called angiotensin converting enzyme (ACE).
Angiotensin II is a powerful vascular vasoconstrictor; this will increase peripheral
resistance which will in turn increase blood pressure.

In addition to increasing BP by direct vasoconstriction angiotensin II also
stimulates the secretion of aldosterone from the adrenal cortex. This will increase

the amount of sodium reabsorbed from the renal tubules and so increase levels of sodium in the blood. As mentioned, increased levels of sodium increases the osmotic potential of the blood and so it attracts more water. This means more water is retained in the plasma increasing blood volumes. These increased volumes will increase venous return and so blood pressure. Conversely, lower amounts of angiotensin II will reduce aldosterone secretion leading to more sodium excretion. This will lower sodium levels in the blood leading to lowered blood volumes and so lower BP.

If the systemic blood pressure is increased the pressure in the afferent arteriole will also be increased. This will be detected by the JGA cells which will respond by reducing renin secretion. When less renin is present in the blood, more angeotensionogen will remain in inactive form. This renin-angiotensin-aldosterone mechanism allows the kidneys to regulate their own blood flow to an extent. When an organ regulates itself in this way it is called autoregulation.

If for any reason the kidneys over-secrete renin blood pressure will be raised. An abnormally high BP is termed hypertension. Renin excess probably explains most cases of chronic hypertension. You may have come across ACE inhibiting drugs; these inhibit ACE (angiotensin converting enzyme) and so inhibit the conversion of angiotensin I into angiotensin II. If there is less angiotensin II there will be less vasoconstriction and less secretion of aldosterone and so blood pressure will be lowered.

Renal endocrine functions

Activation of vitamin D

Vitamin D eaten in the diet, or generated by the skin when exposed to sunlight, is in the form of vitamin D_3 (cholecalciferol). This form of the vitamin is almost completely physiologically inactive. However in the kidneys it is converted into an active form called calcitriol. This form is 1000 times more active than the D_3 form. Conversion is actually facilitated by an enzyme produced in the proximal tubules. Activated vitamin D (i.e. calcitriol) increases calcium absorption from the gut and influences calcium metabolism in the bones by increasing bone deposition. This activation of vitamin D function by the kidneys explains why patients with chronic renal failure lose bone mass. Many people classify calcitriol as an endocrine hormone because it is generated in the kidney, passes into the blood and affects other target tissues.

Erythropoietin stimulates formation of erythrocytes

Erythropoietin is an endocrine hormone produced by the kidneys and is discussed in the endocrine chapter. Normally 90% of circulating erythropoietin is produced in the kidney; the remaining 10% comes from the liver. In chronic renal failure this remaining 10% is not sufficient to stimulate the formation of

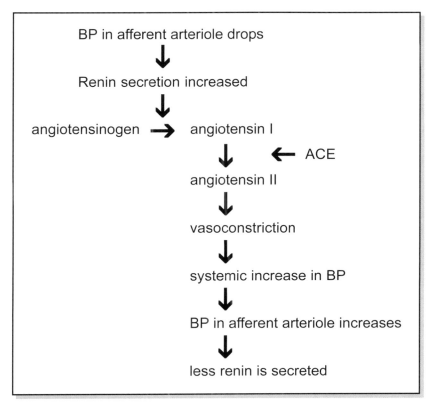

BP in afferent arteriole drops

↓

Renin secretion increased

↓

angiotensinogen → angiotensin I

↓ ← ACE

angiotensin II

↓

vasoconstriction

↓

systemic increase in BP

↓

BP in afferent arteriole increases

↓

less renin is secreted

Table 10.1
Regulation of blood pressure via the renin-angiotensin mechanism.
Renin converts inactive angiotensiongen into agniotensin I.

enough erythrocytes, resulting in the development of severe anaemia. Although erythropoietin is a large glycoprotein it is now available in injectable form. When given to patients with renal failure, the bone marrow is stimulated to produce normal amounts of red cells, curing the anaemia. In recent years this EPO (actually erythropoietin) has been used by cheating athletes to increase the number of red cells in their blood so increasing oxygen carrying and aerobic capacity. EPO is produced by fibroblast type cells in the interstitium of the renal cortex and outer medulla.

The urinary tract

The urinary tract begins in the kidneys when minor calyces join together to form major calyces which merge to form the renal pelvis. From here the urinary tract has a continuous surface down the ureters, through the bladder to the urethra. The inner lining of the tract is referred to as the mucosa. This is a mucous membrane, lined with a layer of mucus, and composed of transitional epithelium. Mucus lining protects the cells of the epithelium from the urine within the lumen of the tract.

Ureters transport urine from the renal pelvis to the urinary bladder

Each ureter is continuous with its renal pelvis. Urine drains from the funnel shaped renal pelvis into the ureters which transport it down to the bladder. Both ureters pass down for about 30 cm behind the peritoneum of the abdominal cavity i.e. they are retroperitoneal. The ureters pass behind the bladder before passing through the wall of the base of the bladder.

Ureteric lumen is lined with mucosa; this is a mucous membrane which secretes a layer of mucus to protect the transitional epithelial cells from irritants in urine. Under the mucosa is a muscular layer containing outer circular and inner longitudinal smooth muscle fibres. These facilitate peristaltic waves of contraction from the renal pelvis down towards the bladder. The peristaltic nature of the ureter is an important mechanism preventing urine from the bladder regurgitating back into the renal pelvis. It is important this does not happen as infection could ascend to the kidneys causing nephritis. Peristalsis of the ureters further allows the bladder to fill when we are lying flat or are positioned head down. The outer layer of the ureters is composed of fibrous connective tissue; this secures the position relative to other structures to prevent kinks.

Diagram 10.16
Cross section
of a ureter.

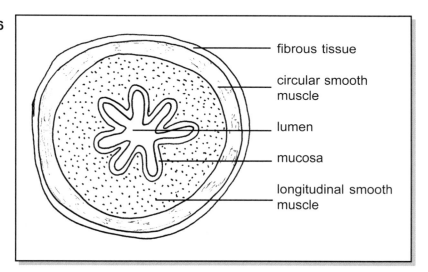

fibrous tissue

circular smooth muscle

lumen

mucosa

longitudinal smooth muscle

Prevention of reflux from the bladder back into the ureters

In addition to unidirectional peristalsis, reflux of urine from the bladder, back into the ureters is prevented by the ureters passing through the wall of the bladder over an elongated course. As the bladder fills up the length of the ureteric lumen which passes through the bladder wall is pinched off. This means that the fuller the bladder is, the more pressure it will impose on the distal sections of the ureters. The same effect will also firmly close off the ureters when pressures within the bladder increase during micturition.

Diagram 10.17 (i)
Prevention of reflux is aided by the lumen of the ureter passing through the bladder wall at a narrow angle. This means there is a flap of bladder wall over the ureteric lumen.

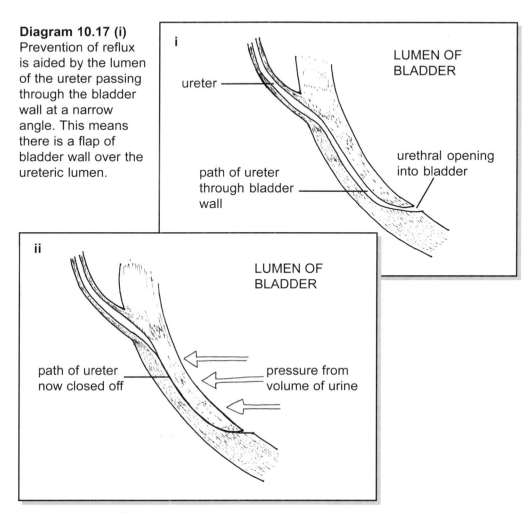

Diagram 10.17 (ii)
As the bladder fills, the pressure of urine pushes against the flap of bladder tissue overlying the lumen of the ureter. As urine volumes increase, there is more force closing off the flap and hence the lumen of the ureter. This prevents reflux of urine from the bladder back into the ureters. Some children are born with an abnormality of this ureteric valve which leads to repeated episodes of ascending infection into the kidneys which may result in permanent renal damage.

Urinary bladder

This anterior structure is located on the floor of the pelvic cavity when empty. However, as the bladder fills it may expand into the lower portion of the abdominal cavity. In women it is just in front of the vagina with the uterus lying immediately above. In men the urinary bladder is in front of the rectum. The bladder is essentially a muscular sack which stores urine until it can be voided. The two urethral openings enter through the bladder floor while in front of these is the internal urethral orifice. Between these three openings the lining of the bladder forms a smooth triangle called the trigone. Mucosa internally lining the rest of the bladder is arranged in folds when the bladder is empty which can unfold, allowing stretching as the bladder fills. The smooth muscle of the bladder wall is called the detrusor muscle.

The urethra drains urine from the bladder out of the body

Urine is drained from the bladder to the outside world via the urethra. In men the urethra is about 18-20 cm long. The first 3-4 cm of the male urethra passes through the tissue of the prostate gland. This is why the lumen of the urethra is compressed if the prostate gland enlarges; if this occurs the stream of urine becomes thin and difficult to initiate. The urethra passes through the penis to an opening at the end called the external urethral orifice.

In females the urethra is about 4 cm long and 6 mm in diameter. After leaving the bladder it travels in the anterior wall of the vagina. The urethral orifice is anterior to the vagina, about 2.5 cm inferior to the clitoris. When no urine is

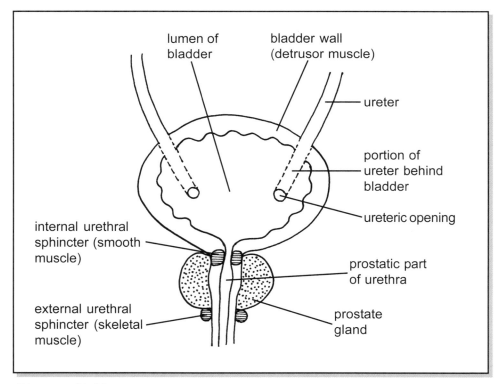

Diagram 10.18
The urinary bladder and start of the urethra in a man.

passing the urethra is a closed slit. This helps to prevent infection ascending into the bladder from the outside. Despite this, the relatively short length of the female urethra, and proximity to the anus, means that women are more prone to infections of the bladder (cystitis) than men. If cystitis does develop women should drink large volumes of water to flush bacteria out of the bladder and antibiotics may be needed for more serious infections.

Sphincters retain and allow the release of urine

In order to prevent urine dribbling out of the bladder all of the time it is necessary for sphincters to close off the lumen of the urethra. In both sexes there is an internal and external sphincter. Again in both sexes, the internal sphincters are under autonomic and the external under voluntary control. In females the internal sphincter is located around the neck of the bladder and in the first part of the urethra. The female internal sphincter is however, relatively weak compared to the male counterpart. In both sexes the external sphincter is partly provided by voluntary muscle fibres within the wall of the urethra. However these external sphincters are supported by external skeletal muscles. In women the external muscular support is provided by the pelvic floor muscles explaining why female continence of urine can be improved by pelvic floor muscle exercises. In men external muscular support is from the deep skeletal muscles of the perineum.

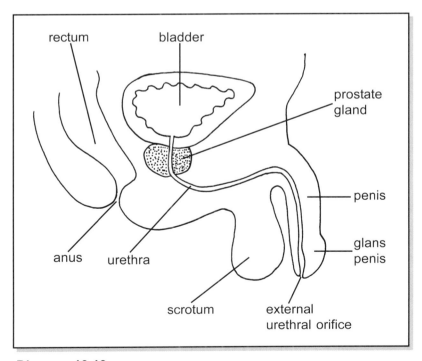

Diagram 10.19
Male urinary bladder and urethra.

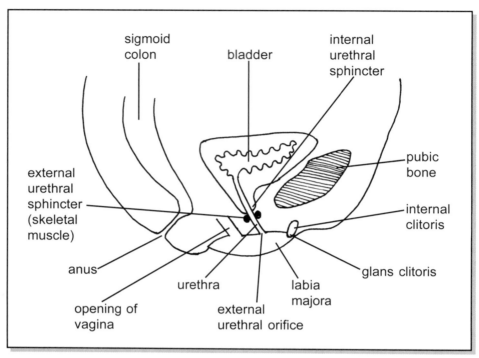

Diagram 10.20
Female urinary bladder and urethra.

Passing urine

Micturition is the emptying of the bladder; other terms for this process are urination or voiding. The process involves the co-ordination of the autonomic and voluntary nervous systems. As the bladder fills the wall stretches to accommodate the increasing fluid volumes. The sensation of fullness and the desire to empty the bladder is generated by sensory stretch receptors located in the bladder wall. Urine is commonly passed when about 280mls of urine have accumulated. The bladder can fill to 500mls or more but this causes an urgent desire to micturate.

In order to pass urine the detrusor muscle in the wall of the bladder contracts. This increases the pressure of urine stored in the bladder. At the same time there is contraction of the abdominal wall muscles which further increases pressure in the bladder. These activities are accompanied by relaxation of the sphincters between the bladder and urethra allowing urine to pass from the bladder out of the urethra.

The autonomic regulation of the bladder is controlled by the activity of the sympathetic and parasympathetic divisions of the autonomic nervous system. Stimulation by sympathetic nerves causes retention of urine by relaxing the detrusor muscle while contracting the internal sphincter. This is why it is sometimes difficult to pass urine when we feel anxious. Passage of urine is facilitated by parasympathetic stimulation which contracts the detrusor while relaxing the internal sphincter.

The external sphincter is under voluntary control which allows us to initiate and stop the flow of urine under control of our will. The activity of a voluntary external sphincter explains why people may be incontinent of urine if they become unconscious, such as during an epileptic fit. This is also why patients are asked to empty their bladder before being anaesthetised. All babies are incontinent of urine because the nervous connections to the external sphincter are not fully developed. When the bladder is distended to a certain point, a micturition reflex is stimulated. After the age of about 2 years, the nervous connections to the external sphincter are usually developed, allowing control of micturition to be learned.

CHAPTER 11

Skin

Introduction

Skin covers the entire outer surface of the body and is continuous with the membranes which line the various orifices such as the mouth, nostrils, anus and vagina. Skin thickness varies over different parts of the body from about 1.5 to 4 mm and has a total weight of about 4 to 5 kg. In an average adult it accounts for about 8% of body weight. This means, in terms of mass, the skin is the largest organ in the body. The second largest is the liver which is normally less than 3% of body weight. Clearly, skin surface area varies between individuals, but in most adults it covers about 1.5 to 2m². Skin is arranged in two distinct layers, the outer epidermis and under this the dermis.

Epidermis

This is the upper, surface layer of the skin and does not contain blood or lymphatic vessels. It is nourished and oxygenated by diffusion through the tissue fluid of the dermis.

Epidermal-dermal junction

The junction between the two layers of the skin is undulating with numerous projections from the epidermis dipping down into the dermis. Components of dermis which rise into the area of the epidermis are termed dermal papillae. This interlaced arrangement provides a great deal of resistance to shearing forces, preventing epidermis being rubbed away from dermis. When this does happen, e.g. as a result of persistent friction, a blister will form. A blister is a collection of fluid between the dermis and epidermis or between the layers of the epidermis. Using a light microscope the epidermal-dermal junction is marked by a basement membrane, but with the higher power of an electron microscope this is seen to be incomplete. This is why the junction between the epidermis and dermis is correctly referred to as the basement membrane zone.

The epidermis does not have any blood vessels passing through it. However there are capillary loops in the upper layers of the dermis immediately below the epidermis. This means that the tissue fluids of the upper dermis are well oxygenated and provided with essential nutrient molecules. Oxygen and nutrients diffuse into the lower layers of the epidermis to supply the metabolic needs of the epidermal cells. Waste products from the epidermis diffuse back into dermal tissue fluids prior to diffusing back into the dermal blood supply.

Epidermal turnover constantly renews the epidermis

Living epidermal cells are positioned on the basement membrane zone. This area is often called the germinative layer because there is ongoing mitosis in epidermal cells generating new tissue. Epidermal cells are correctly referred to as keratinocytes and approximately 10% of these are epidermal stem cells. These stem cells divide,

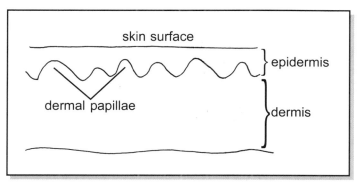

Diagram 11.1
There are two distinct layers in the skin as seen in this
cross section. Projections from the dermis called dermal
papillae increase the surface area between the dermis
and the epidermis. This arrangement fixes the two layers
of the skin together to prevent shearing injuries.

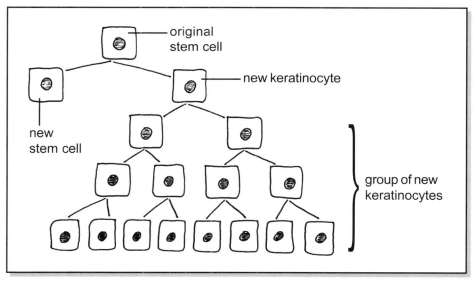

Diagram 11.2
A keratinocyte stem cell divides to produce a new stem cell and another
keratinocyte. The stem cell remains in the epidermis where it can divide in the
future. The new keratinocyte will then divide a few more times to generate a
group of young keratinocytes. Straight lines represent cell division by mitosis.

producing one further stem cell and another keratinocyte. Once formed, this
new keratinocyte is capable of a limited number of further mitotic divisions
giving rise to a group of young cells. Young keratinocytes are usually cuboidal to
columnar in shape.

As mitosis is ongoing, young cells push older ones upwards, away from the germinative layer on the basement membrane zone. Because epidermal cells are nourished and oxygenated from the tissue fluid of the dermis, they become progressively hypoxic the further they are pushed upwards. This means that only the cells near the bottom of the epidermis are alive, the outer layers are composed of dead cells.

This turnover of cells from the deeper layers of epidermis to the surface means the upper layer of the skin is constantly being regenerated. Complete turnover time for the epidermis is typically about 8 weeks; the best quoted figure is 52-75 days, depending on the individual and site on the body surface. Once dead, keratin rich cells, having completed their migration to the surface layer of the epidermis, are simply shed. You may have noticed an accumulation of white material on the skin surface when towelling yourself down after a shower. This is in fact a collection of dead keratinocytes. Much of the dust that accumulates in our houses is dead human epidermal cells.

Epidermis is a stratified, keratinized, squamous epithelium

These four terms concisely describe the epidermis. Stratified indicates that the epidermis is composed of several layers of cells. Stratification allows the skin to resist external forces. If some epidermis is removed it can rapidly be replaced from underlying cells.

As keratin is a hard, dry, horny protein it keeps the outer layer of epidermis fairly hard and able to resist friction and trauma. Hair and finger nails are both outgrowths of epidermal type cells and are composed mostly of keratin. Cells in the basal, germinative layer of the epidermis do contain some keratin. However, as the keratinocytes migrate upwards, proteins from the cell cytoplasm are progressively converted into keratin. There is also a change in the form of keratin present as the cells rise, resulting in progressive hardening. By the time dead keratinocytes reach the surface of the epidermis they are composed largely of hardened keratin.

Squamous refers to the flattened appearance of the upper skin cells. As the columnar and cuboidal keratinocytes are pushed away from the germinative layer they are subject to pressure from the skin surface. This means the cells are progressively flattened and adopt a squamous appearance. Epidermis is an epithelium because it is a lining tissue, in this case lining the surface of the body.

Epidermal lipids hold keratinocytes together and provide waterproofing

Above the basal germinative layer of the epidermis the keratinocytes secrete a variety of lipids including fatty acids, phospholipids and cholesterol. These help to hold the individual cells together, rather like cement holding bricks together in a wall. In addition, because the lipids are oily they repel water (remember lipids are hydrophobic) which is part of the reason skin is waterproof. It is also essential that the skin is waterproof to prevent excessive loss of water from the body into the environment. This is why burns patients can lose large volumes of water through their injuries possibly resulting in dehydration and hypovolaemia (low blood volume).

We all know it is important for us to wash our hands between patients at work. However, repeated washing with soap degrades the natural oils in skin and causes it to 'dry out' which in turn can lead to cracking and soreness. Bacteria may colonise these cracks in our skin, ironically making cross infection more likely. Moisturising creams may partly compensate for loss of natural skin lipids.

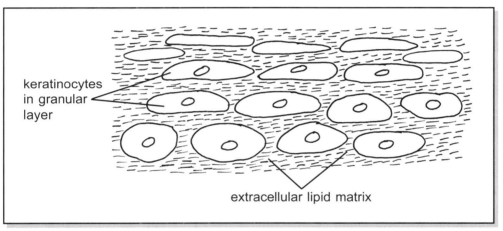

Diagram 11.3
Individual keratinocytes are held together by an extracellular lipid matrix which also provides waterproofing.

Synthesis of Vitamin D in the epidermis

One of the lipid based molecules found in the epidermis is called dehydrocholesterol. When this substance is exposed to sunlight it is converted into a form of vitamin D. Once this vitamin D has been synthesised in the skin it is transformed into a much more active form by the kidneys. In people who have diets deficient in vitamin D, this mechanism is essential to prevent deficiency. In children it has long been known that lack of vitamin D causes rickets resulting in abnormal bone formation. It is now also believed that deficiency of vitamin D in early life is a risk factor for diabetes mellitus type 1. In later life lack of vitamin D is a risk factor for cardiovascular disease.

Epidermal melanocytes produce melanin

Melanocytes are a specialised form of cell found in the epidermis which synthesise and secrete melanin. In order to aid distribution of melanin to the epidermis, melanocytes contain projections called dendrites. Melanin is the pigment found in the epidermis which gives skin colour. White people have small amounts of melanin. The darker a shade of brown or black a person, the more melanin is present. Red and yellow colours in human skin, characteristic of some races, are generated by a second form of melanin also synthesised in melanocytes. Albinos do not produce melanin meaning they have no melanin to give colour to their skin, hair or eyes. This condition of albinism is caused by a recessive genetic disorder.

Sunlight contains potentially harmful ultraviolet (UV) radiation; it is the function of melanin to absorb this, to protect underlying tissues. Exposure to sunlight therefore increases melanin synthesis rates and causes the skin to darken. However, the process of increasing melanin synthesis takes a few weeks to a few months to fully develop. Before there is sufficient melanin to protect the skin, the melanocytes are themselves prone to UV damage. After a winter in the UK melanin levels will be low. If we then fly off to a sunny country we will not have enough melanin to protect our skin against UV radiation. This can result in burning and damage to the DNA of the melanocytes. Some forms of DNA damage can lead to cancer, for example, malignant melanoma is cancer of melanocytes and can spread very rapidly.

Dermis

The dermis is a connective tissue which contains several types of structures such as hair follicles, sebaceous glands, sweat glands, nerve endings, blood and lymphatic vessels. The dermis also contains fibroblasts and extracellular matrix.

Fibroblasts secrete the intercellular components

Fibroblasts are found throughout the dermis and are the cells which produce the collagen and elastic fibres. In addition the dermis contains a protein based ground substance called proteoglycan which is also mostly derived from fibroblasts. An alternative term for ground substance is intercellular matrix. This intercellular matrix fills in the spaces between the dermal structures and tissue fibres. This has the effect of making the dermis a solid layer supporting all of the dermal components.

Collagen is a tough structural protein

There are several forms of collagen protein which often form long strands and occur in bundles. Collagen has high tensile strength which makes it very hard to snap. It is the presence of collagen which gives skin internal strength and prevents it becoming detached from underlying tissues. You may have noticed that elderly people are more prone to injuries where some skin is rubbed off. This occurs because old skin contains relatively less collagen than young skin. Collagen also provides a three dimensional structure which gives the skin 'body'.

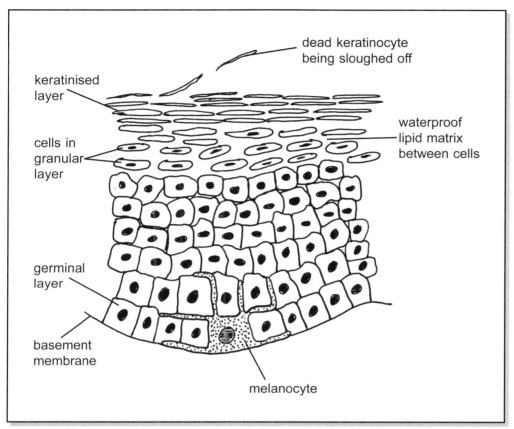

dead keratinocyte
being sloughed off

keratinised
layer

cells in
granular
layer

waterproof
lipid matrix
between cells

germinal
layer

basement
membrane

melanocyte

Diagram 11.4
Cross section of the epidermis. Cell division takes place in the germinal or basal
layer and older cells are gradually pushed upwards. As they move upwards the cells
die and there is progressive keratinisation. Dead keratin rich keratinocytes are shed
from the skin surface.

Dermal water

Collagen and matrix both attract water into the dermis. When a person is well
hydrated a sizable proportion of total body water is found in the dermis. In
dehydrated patients the skin loses its turgor (fullness, tension, resilience) meaning
that the skin feels thinner. When some skin is pinched up it does not recoil back
to its original position as quickly as in normal states of hydration.

Another common clinical observation is oedema. This occurs when there is
too much water in the tissues and may be caused by protein deficiency, lymphatic
obstruction, venous disease or heart failure. The skin becomes tight as it is expanded
by the increased fluid volumes below. If you press into an oedematous area with a
finger for a few seconds then remove your finger, a pit is left for a few seconds
afterwards. This is called pitting oedema.

Elastic fibres provide elasticity

Skin is very elastic to allow it to stretch and then return to its original shape. Elasticity is provided by elastic fibres running throughout the dermis. This essential property allows movement over joints and allows for increases in weight or pregnancy. Skin may also be stretched to a degree when closing wounds.

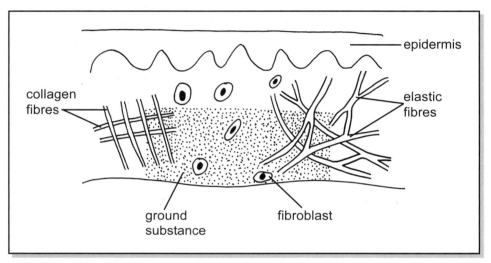

Diagram 11.5
Diagrammatic representation of the principle structural components of the dermis. Matrix (ground substance) fills in all of the spaces between the cells and structures found in the dermis.

Hair follicles house the hair shafts

Hair grows out of structures called follicles. These are downward projections of the epidermis, penetrating into the dermis and sometimes subcutaneous tissues. The outer layer of the follicle is composed of a fibrous sheath. Within this is a layer of epidermal tissue. At the base of the follicle is a layer of actively dividing epidermal cells forming an area called the hair bulb. There is a capillary loop in the dermis at the base of each hair bulb to oxygenate and nourish the actively dividing epidermal cells. As epidermal cells divide, older ones are pushed away from their dermal nutrient and oxygen source and so die. Further mitosis pushes the already dead, keratinized cells further up the follicle forming a hair shaft. Melanocytes at the base of the bulb produce pigmented melanin which gives hair colour.

The presence of epidermal protrusions down into the dermis and subcutaneous tissues, as found in hair follicles, has important implications for wound healing. If the epidermis and part of the dermis are lost due to trauma or a burn, epidermal tissue is able to regenerate from below, by mitosis of surviving keratinocyte germ

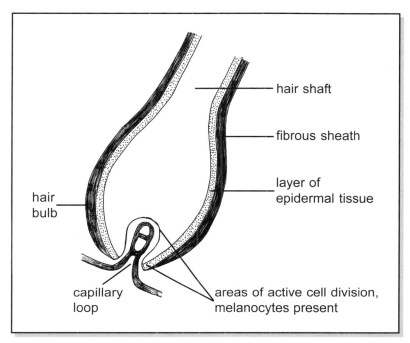

Diagram 11.6
The growing area of a hair in a follicle.

cells. This allows partial thickness wounds to heal without scarring. In this context partial thickness means that the wound extends part way through the dermis. The same principle of healing allows the donor site of a skin graft to heal rapidly with minimal or no scarring.

Hair

Hair of varying lengths and thickness grows from the entire skin surface except the palms, soles and lower surfaces of the fingers and toes. Hair follicles are well innervated with sensory nerve fibres. This means hairs increase the sensitivity of the skin to light touch stimuli. In the nose, hairs are able to trap inhaled foreign material such as insects. Eye lashes are very sensitive and may initiate reflex closure of the eyelids as a protective measure. Hair on the head helps to protect from sunlight.

The presence of hair near the skin surface generates a boundary layer of air. This is a layer of air which remains relatively static over the surface of the body. As air is an excellent insulator of heat, a boundary layer helps to prevent body cooling in cold environments. This mechanism works better in more hairy people. Hair erector muscles (also called arrector pili) are small bundles of smooth muscle connected to the fibrous capsule of the hair follicles. When these muscles contract they cause the hair to stand in an erect position. This occurs in response to cold and has the effect of increasing the depth of the boundary layer. Another consequence of this contraction is the production of numerous small indentations over the skin surface, often referred to as 'goose pimples'.

Distribution of hair growth is partly determined by the concentrations of oestrogen and testosterone in the blood. This gives rise to different distributions in body hair between men and women.

Sebaceous glands produce sebum

These glands are lined with specialised secretory cells which produce sebum. Once secreted, this passes along a small duct into a hair follicle. From here sebum moves towards the skin surface. There may be several sebaceous glandular units associated with a single follicle. Sebum is a lipid based oily substance which coats the hair and skin surface, helping to keep it moist and supple. Because it is oily, sebum aids in the waterproofing of skin. Around the time of puberty, in males and females, hormonal influences increase the size of sebaceous glands and sebum production. Excessive production of sebum may lead to impaction in the sebaceous ducts. This will cause stasis and subsequent infection and is the main cause of acne.

Sweat glands produce sweat

Glands which produce sweat are essentially long, unbranched tubes. The common form of sweat glands are correctly termed eccrine glands. Sweat is produced in the lower coiled part of the gland and passes up to the surface of the skin via a duct.

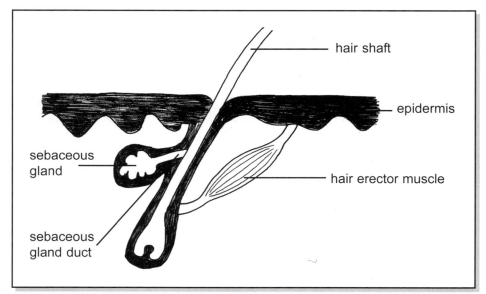

Diagram 11.7
Hair follicle showing the relationship between the hair, follicle, hair erector muscle, sebaceous gland and duct.

There are approximately 2-4 million sweat glands in the skin; numbers vary between individuals for genetic reasons. Races from hotter countries usually have more sweat glands than people from temperate zones. Like hair follicles, sweat gland ducts are lined with epidermal cells. Sweat is produced in response to a rise in body temperature; a mechanism which is controlled via the hypothalamus. Anxiety and other emotions also cause sweating because the glands are stimulated by the sympathetic nervous system. This is why we can get a 'cold sweat' when anxious.

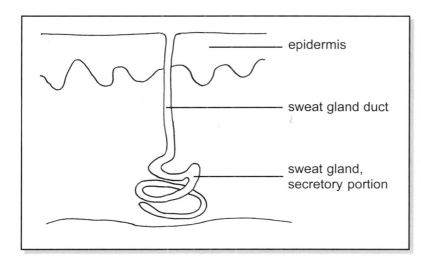

epidermis

sweat gland duct

sweat gland, secretory portion

Diagram 11.8
Sweat gland. Sweat is produced in the secretory portion of the gland in the dermis; products are then transported through the epidermis in a duct to the skin surface.

Sweat is a clear odourless fluid. In addition to water it contains salt (sodium and chloride ions) with some potassium, urea, and other trace substances. In extreme circumstances the body's sweat glands are capable of producing 10 litres of sweat per day resulting in potentially significant losses of salt and water.

There is a second form of larger sweat gland called apocrine glands. These are found primarily in the axilla, groin and around the genitalia. Apocrine ducts open into hair follicles. These glands start to function at puberty in males and females, under hormonal influences. Once on the skin surface some of the components in apocrine sweat are degraded by bacteria. It is these break down products that causes unwashed arm pits and groins to smell. Some people have suggested that these smells, or other breakdown products that we cannot consciously smell, act as pheromones, generating sexual interest in potential partners. You can make your own mind up on that one.

Nerve endings facilitate tactile sensation

The skin is the principle organ of tactility (the sense of feeling). There are four main types of sensation that the skin detects; light touch, pressure, temperature and pain. The skin is also capable of detecting more complex sensations such as vibration, tickle and itch. Sensations are generated by peripheral sensory receptors. These convert a tactile stimulus into a series of nerve impulses which are relayed to the sensory areas of the brain via sensory neurones. The brain interprets these electrical impulses to generate the appropriate sensations which we then experience.

Specialised structures called Messner's receptors, located just under the epidermis, are sensitive to touch. When touch is detected they generate a sensory nerve impulse. There are also a few touch receptors just above the basement membrane in the lower area of the epidermis; these are called Merkel-cell receptors. These same Merkel type detectors also innervate hair follicles so we can detect touch from hairs. Touch receptors are particularly common in the fingertips, eyelids, lips, penis and clitoris. The combination of touch receptors allows for skin to be superbly sensitive to the lightest of touch. For example, it is possible to detect a 10 nanometre indentation in the skin over the fingertips.

Sensations of pressure are generated by large receptors deep in the dermis and hypodermis. These are referred to as Pacinian corpuscles. Pressure awareness allows us to hold objects with an appropriate degree of force. This is important to stop us from dropping tools or crushing eggs.

Thermoreceptors respond mostly to changes in temperature. For example, when getting into cold water it feels cold at first, then we get used to it. This is because once the temperature is no longer changing we are not so aware of it. There are two types of temperature detectors in the dermis. Cold receptors detect a drop in skin temperature and warm receptors detect an increase. Because these receptors are located throughout the dermis, we can detect the temperature of localised areas of skin surface, as well as overall ambient temperature. Thermoreceptors are probably specialised free nerve endings in the dermis. They do not have an anatomically recognisable receptor like touch and pressure receptors have.

Pain is detected by specialist neurones which only respond to pain. These are free nerve endings in the dermis and are correctly referred to as nociceptors. Pain detection is nociception, the detection of the noxious. Fortunately, pain receptors only generate an impulse in response to trauma or to being cut. Pain is essential to prevent the tissues of the body being damaged. It also promotes rest if an area of the body has been damaged, for example, we do not go running on a sprained ankle. Perhaps the value of pain can be most clearly seen when it is absent. People with Hanson's disease (leprosy) often burn their hands picking up hot cooking pots, because they cannot feel the pain. A similar situation may occur in peripheral sensory neuropathy, a long term complication of diabetes. Because these patients cannot feel pain from their feet they suffer from pressure effects that lead on to tissue damage and infection.

Dermal blood vessels

Small arteries deep in the dermis sub-divide into numerous small arterioles. These arterioles in turn perfuse large numbers of capillaries. Capillaries drain into venules which drain into small veins. The amount of blood flowing through

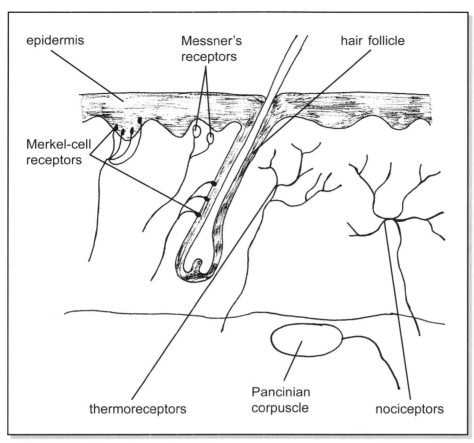

Diagram 11.9
The sense of tactility, detection of touch, pressure, temperature and pain.

the dermis may be controlled by increasing or reducing the volumes flowing through the capillary beds. Before each bed of capillaries there is a ring of muscle, located in the arteriole wall, called the pre-capillary sphincter. If the pre-capillary sphincter contracts, this will reduce the lumen of the arteriole and so limit the volume of blood passing into the capillary bed. However, if the sphincter relaxes, the arteriole will get wider which will increase the flow of blood through the dermal capillaries. Contraction of the pre-capillary sphincter causes peripheral vasoconstriction and relaxation causes vasodilation.

Dermal capillaries also form, and largely reabsorb, tissue fluid, this is essential to provide a diffusional medium for both dermal and lower epidermal cells.

Dermal lymphatic vessels

The dermis is drained by lymphatic capillaries which drain into larger lymphatic vessels as discussed in chapter 3.

Hypodermis is the layer below the dermis

Below the dermis is a subcutaneous layer sometimes referred to as the hypodermis. This varies in thickness over different parts of the body and between individuals. It contains mostly adipose tissue with varying amounts of connective fibres.

Age related changes

Overall skin condition deteriorates with age affecting the epidermis and dermis. As is probably the case with all body tissues, two factors contribute to age related changes; chronological and environmental factors. Chronological factors occur as a result of ageing but show considerable variation between individuals. Chronological reasons why some people appear to 'age better' than others are not fully understood but are probably mostly related to genetic make up.

Environmental ageing of skin is primarily a consequence of chronic exposure to ultraviolet light from the sun, referred to as photoageing. You may have noticed in older people that the quality of the skin over areas such as the buttocks or lower back, which are infrequently exposed to sunlight, is in better condition than skin covering the face, neck and backs of the hands. UV exposure probably causes the formation of cross bonding between individual strands of collagen, which will result in tangled dermal collagen, contributing to wrinkles. A secondary factor in skin related ageing is probably quality of diet or the presence of malnutrition.

Older skin is more prone to wrinkling and loss of elasticity. Wrinkle lines are caused by contraction of underlying muscles. On the face they are called lines of expression and as a result of age related loss of skin elasticity they become permanent. This can be partly explained by a reduction in the numbers of fibroblasts in the dermis. As these cells normally produce collagen and elastic fibres, the amount of these structural components of connective tissues will be reduced. In addition to loss of elasticity, reduced production of collagen and elastic fibres will result in reduced tensile strength and 'body'. These factors partly explain the formation of droopy skin such as 'bags under the eyes'. Loss of these tissue components also partly explains increased skin thinning with ageing.

In older skin there is a flattening of the junction between the dermis and epidermis. As epidermal cells are nourished from dermal tissue fluid, the epidermis becomes relatively hypoxic and malnourished. These factors contribute to a reduction of up to 50% in keratinocyte replication rates. Because the epidermis contains fewer keratinocytes there is reduced production of epidermal lipids, resulting in dry skin. Flattening of the epidermal-dermal junction also increases the probability of shearing and blister formation.

Slower rates of wound healing in the elderly are partly caused by an age related reduction in dermal vascularity. Reduction in the numbers of peripheral sensory receptors reduces skin sensitivity. Melanocyte populations are reduced by 10-20% in older people with a resulting sensitivity to sunlight and predisposition to burning. Another obvious age related change is in hair distribution. There may be a thinning of scalp hair in men and women. Men tend to grow thicker hair on their eyebrows, ears and from their noses. Women start to grow hair above the upper lip and face. Never mind - we all grow old unless we die first. Perhaps the key is to accept age related changes with dignity.

Skin colour is an important clinical observation

In addition to assessment of skin turgor and general condition there is a great deal that we can learn through observation of skin colour and tone.

Pallor

Pallor describes the absence of normal colour in the skin. In health there are volumes of red blood perfusing the capillaries close to the skin surface. This gives skin a normal rosy tint in white people. If the volumes of blood perfusing the superficial capillaries are reduced the skin will look a pale colour (i.e. pallor). This sign may therefore be seen in any condition where there is peripheral vasoconstriction. Cold may induce pallor. Sympathetic activity is another cause which may occur during anxiety, acute pain or anger. Pallor is also a sign of more serious conditions such as shock which is a state of abnormally low blood pressure. In patients with darker skin there are still changes in skin tone which represent pallor and these can be recognised with experience. Anaemia may also lead to a degree of pallor. This may be more accurately assessed by looking at the degree of pallor in the mucous membranes, such as the lips or lower eyelid.

Flushing

Flushing is caused by increased perfusion of the peripheral capillaries as a result of peripheral vasodilation. This increases the volumes of red blood passing close to the skin surface. Increases in body temperature will generate vasodilation and flushing. Clinically, localised redness caused by flushing is a key clinical feature of inflammation.

Cyanosis

Cyanosis describes a bluish discoloration of the skin, mucous membranes and nail beds. The cause is the presence of increased proportions of reduced haemoglobin in the peripheral capillaries. Reduced haemoglobin is haemoglobin which has become deoxygenated. Clinically, cyanosis typically becomes apparent when the oxygen saturations drop below about 86%.

Cyanosis may be central or peripheral. Central cyanosis may be observed in the chest, neck, lips or tongue and indicates a reduction in the levels of oxygen in the systemic arterial blood, as might be caused by suffocation, lung or heart disease. Peripheral cyanosis may be seen in extremities such as the fingers, toes and tips of the nose or ears. This is caused by slowing of the blood flow through a peripheral area. This gives more time for the oxygen in the red cells to diffuse into the tissues, resulting in reduced haemoglobin in the capillaries. Peripheral cyanosis occurs in conditions where there is peripheral vasoconstriction such as exposure to cold, shock, heart failure or peripheral vascular disease.

Jaundice

Jaundice describes a yellowish discolouration of the skin, mucous membranes and sclera of the eye. The cause is increased amounts of the pigment bilirubin in the blood. Bilirubin is a normal breakdown product of haemoglobin which is incorporated into bile by the liver. In liver disease the liver may no longer be able to perform this incorporating function resulting in an accumulation of bilirubin in the blood. Common causes of liver disease are drinking too much alcohol and viral hepatitis. Jaundice may also develop if the normal flow of bile from the liver to the duodenum is obstructed by gallstones or a tumour in the pancreas.

CHAPTER 12

Thermoregulation

Introduction

Life can only exist within narrow temperature ranges. Some animals, e.g. fish and reptiles, vary their body temperature depending on environmental conditions. These animals are described as 'cold blooded' or poikilothermic. However, in higher animals and humans, body temperature must be finely controlled within a fairly narrow temperature range. As previously discussed, cellular biochemistry is essential for life. All intracellular biochemistry is catalysed by enzymes which only work within narrow ranges of temperature. If the body becomes too hot or too cold enzymic activity will be reduced and physiological functions will no longer work efficiently. Eventually both hyper or hypothermia will lead to death. Humans are biologically classified as homoiothermes because we maintain a constant body temperature. This means that if body temperature starts to rise cooling mechanisms must be employed. Likewise, when body temperature falls there must be mechanisms available to conserve heat and increase body temperature.

Mechanisms of heat gain

Metabolic processes generate heat

Heat is gained by the body as a result of metabolic processes. All energy chains, i.e. sequences of energy conversions, end as heat so whenever fuels are used heat will be generated. Metabolic activity in an organ will therefore result in heat being produced. For example, the liver is a large metabolically active organ and so produces a lot of heat. Heat is also generated by the use of energy in organs such as the brain, heart, intestines and kidneys. Muscles produce a lot of heat when actively contracting. When muscles are contracting only about 20% of the energy they use is converted into movement, the remainder is converted into heat.

Rate of heat generation is determined by the metabolic rate of the body. This does vary between individuals and may partly explain why some people are more tolerant of cold or heat than others. Increased levels of thyroid hormone in the blood will stimulate metabolic rate whereas reduced thyroxine levels will allow metabolic rate to fall. After a meal the metabolic rate of the body is increased for a few hours increasing total heat production. Only a small part of this effect is due to the energy required to physically and chemically digest the food. Most of the additional energy used after eating is as a result of the metabolic processing of food after it has been absorbed. When people die they are no longer carrying out metabolic processes so body temperature drops until it is the same as the surrounding environment.

Heat gain from the environment

Heat may be gained from warm environments or from infrared radiation, which is emitted by the sun and other hot objects. Hot food and drink may also result in limited heat gain in the body.

Heat retention in the body

Most of the body is insulated by a layer of subcutaneous adipose tissue which is an excellent insulator of heat. The thicker this layer, the more it will retain heat within the body. People with a thinner adipose layer lose heat more rapidly. This principle also explains why obese people are often heat intolerant.

Overall body volume (i.e. body size) is another factor in heat retention. Larger bodies will lose heat more slowly than smaller bodies. This is explained by the surface area to volume ratio. Larger bodies will have a lower surface area to volume ratio, which means that compared to their mass they have a relatively small surface area through which to lose heat. Smaller bodies have a greater surface area compared to their volume. More heat will therefore be lost through this relatively large surface area. In children the surface area to volume ratio is high, so they can lose heat to the environment much more quickly than adults.

Mechanisms of heat loss

Heat may be lost via a combination of three physical processes; conduction, convection and radiation.

Conduction

In conduction heat passes from warm objects to cooler ones via direct contact. This explains why people can become hypothermic very quickly when immersed in cold water. Because water is in direct contact with the body, heat will pass directly from the body into the water. Conduction works particularly efficiently in the case of water because it is a good conductor of heat with a thermal conductivity 25 times greater than dry air. This also explains why both heat and cold are felt more severely when the humidity in the air is high. Humidity describes the water content of the air.

One reason we wear clothes is to keep warm. Clothes work because a layer of air is trapped near the surface of the skin. This thin layer is warmed up by the body and because air is trapped next to the skin surface further heat loss is reduced. Air is a particularly poor conductor of heat, so as long as we can trap some air next to the skin it will insulate us from heat loss.

Cooling due to evaporation may be considered as heat loss via conduction. When water is on the surface of the body it starts to evaporate. Evaporation and vaporization both describe the process of a liquid changing into a vapour. When water changes from a liquid into a vapour it requires a large amount of energy in order to do so. This energy is called the latent heat of vaporization; latent meaning hidden. The latent heat required is extracted from the surface of the body explaining why evaporation from the body surface has an overall cooling effect. Some heat is also lost from the body as water evaporates from the moist lung surfaces during breathing.

Convection

Natural convection occurs when air near the surface of the body is warmed. When air is warmed the molecules which it is made up of vibrate more vigorously than they do when cold. Because they are vibrating more rapidly they take up more space when warm than they do when cold. The result of this is that the density of warm air is less than cold air. (This principle is most clearly seen in a hot air balloon where warm air provides lift.) Warm air near the surface therefore rises away from the body to be replaced by more dense, colder air from below.

Heat loss due to wind chill may be considered as forced convection. Wind will blow away warmed air from near the body surface which will be replaced by cold air. More heat will then be conducted out of the body to warm up this new cold air. Fanning will cool us down as a result of convection and increased rates of sweat evaporation.

Radiation

All hot objects radiate heat, mostly in the form of infrared radiation. Heat is therefore transferred away from the body in the form of radiation. The hotter an object the more heat it will radiate. Human skin is a very efficient emitter of radiation, resulting in heat loss from the body surface. Quantities of heat lost in this way are essentially the same for all skin colours. Because our clothes also possess some heat they too emit radiation into the environment. Clothes only radiate heat away from the body as a function of their surface temperature. Because clothes trap air, and so insulate the body, the surface temperature of clothes is much lower than the surface temperature of the body. This means we lose less heat by radiation when we are dressed than when undressed.

In a warm sunny environment we may gain more heat from solar radiation than we lose via radiation from the body surface. In this situation total heat gain would be less if we wear a covering layer over the skin. This is why clothes can also help to keep us cool in very sunny conditions. Again, the tendency for the skin to absorb heat from the environment is independent of skin colour. However, the big advantage of dark skin is that the increased amounts of melanin present protect the person from ultraviolet radiation, sun burn and sun damage.

Body temperature

Normal body temperature varies a little between individuals. Mine is normally about 36.4°C however, up to 37°C is considered normal. Occasionally individuals have temperatures, which are normal for them, of as low as 36°C to as high as 37.5°C. Individuals with persistently high body temperatures are uncommon; the vast majority of times you record a temperature of 37.5°C it will be an indication of an infection or tissue damage. If the environment is very cold then core temperature may start to drop. People are particularly prone to lowering their

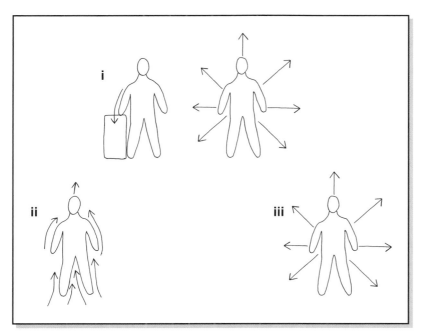

Diagram 12.1
Physical processes resulting in heat loss from the body. Arrows
indicate direction of heat flow.
(i)   Conduction, including heat lost by direct contact and as a
      result of evaporation.
(ii) Convection.
(iii) Radiation.

body temperature if they are immobile or wet as well as cold. If the core
temperature drops below 35°C this may be described as hypothermia.

During physical exercise body temperature may rise to 38°C and vigorous
exercise may elevate this as high as 40°C. However, these rises soon trigger cooling
responses from such mechanisms as sweating. Whenever total heat gain exceeds
heat loss body temperature will start to rise. This can occur in very hot environments
or when cooling mechanisms are unable to function.

Wearing a lot of clothes prevents heat loss to the environment and reduces
evaporation of sweat. For example, soldiers have become hyperthermic while
exercising in full kit on hot days. Like hypothermia, hyperthermia is a life
threatening condition and must be corrected as a matter of urgency.

Core temperature

This is the temperature of the body core, in the main organs. Core temperature
remains relatively constant over long periods of time, although it usually varies
slightly through a 24 hour period. It is normally about 0.5°C below average early
in the morning and as much as 1°C higher in the evenings. When the environment

is cool or warm, core temperature will remain constant as a result of various homeostatic mechanisms discussed shortly. In ovulating women, temperature may drop slightly for about 24 hours after ovulation. Typically, temperatures are about 0.5°C higher during the second half of the menstrual cycle. These changes are not accurate enough to use as a guide to contraception but may be used to aid conception.

Peripheral temperature

Temperature on the surface of the skin or in the hands and feet may be well below core temperature, especially in cold environments. This is normal. Arms and legs have a large surface area in comparison to their volume, so have the potential to lose a lot of heat. This is useful in warm environments to increase heat loss but a potential problem in cold conditions. These factors explain why considerable proportions of the arms and legs are at or near core temperatures in hot environments, but well below in cold conditions. A comfortable skin temperature is usually about 33°C.

Temperature detection within the body

In the body there are peripheral and core temperature receptors. Peripheral thermoreceptors are mostly located in the dermis but there are also some in the mouth and urogenital mucosa. Core temperature is detected by deep-body sensors located in the vena cava, oesophagus and stomach. These two groups of receptors send messages to the brain which give us our sensory awareness of temperature. This is the main determinant of how hot, cold or comfortable we feel. Humans are not very tolerant of temperature change; we start to feel cold or hot with only a few degrees of ambient temperature change. Ambient refers to conditions in the immediate environment.

The main area of the brain detecting blood temperature is the hypothalamus. A thermosensitive area of the hypothalamus compares the temperature of the blood passing through it with a set level. Neurones in the hypothalamus 'know' what this set body temperature should be. If blood temperature drops below this level, the hypothalamus initiates homeostatic mechanisms to increase body temperature. When blood temperature rises it initiates mechanisms to lower body temperature. The hypothalamus has often been likened to a thermostat, detecting temperature and instigating warming or cooling mechanisms.

When core temperature rises

This situation initiates body cooling mechanisms.

Behavioural change

When too hot, people tend to become lethargic and inactive which will reduce heat gain from muscular activity. We also go into the shade which reduces gains from external radiation. If available we may choose to stand in a cooling breeze,

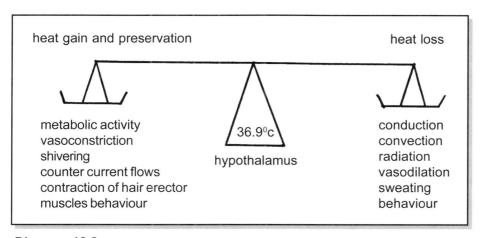

heat gain and preservation		heat loss
metabolic activity vasoconstriction shivering counter current flows contraction of hair erector muscles behaviour	36.9⁰c hypothalamus	conduction convection radiation vasodilation sweating behaviour

Diagram 12.2
Diagrammatic representation of the function of the hypothalamus which maintains a balance between heat gain and loss to maintain thermal homeostasis.

or arrange to be fanned. During sleep warm people naturally adopt a 'spread out' posture to maximise surface area over which heat can be lost by radiation and convection. Increasing and decreasing clothing is an option usually available.

Peripheral vasodilation

When body temperature rises the hypothalamus causes peripheral pre-capillary sphincters to relax. This allows dilation of the arterioles, resulting in increased blood flow to the superficial capillaries. Warm blood flowing near the surface of the body will lose heat to the environment by conduction and convection as long as air temperature is below body temperature. Peripheral vasodilation can lead to a ten-fold increase in subcutaneous blood flow.

Increase in blood temperature also causes a superficial peripheral venodilation (widening of the lumen of veins) in the arms and legs. Blood therefore returns to the heart via superficial peripheral veins near the skin surface, allowing more time for heat loss to the environment.

Sweating

This is a very efficient cooling mechanism and is the only physiological mechanism which will still work when the environment is warmer than the skin temperature, i.e. where the air temperature is more than 37°C. Water deposited on the body surface extracts the latent heat of vaporization in order for it to evaporate. A lot of heat is required to evaporate water; for example, is takes almost six times more heat energy to vaporize water at 100°C than it does to raise the temperature of the same amount of water from 0 to 100°C. This means a lot of heat is extracted from the body surface to evaporate a relatively small volume of sweat.

Even in very hot environments people can usually maintain normal body temperature as long as they have plenty of water to drink which will allow them to continue to produce sweat. If a person in a hot environment becomes dehydrated and can no longer sweat freely they may rapidly become hyperthermic. Dehydration is a risk in hot environments as sweating can result in fluid losses as high as one litre per hour.

Ambient humidity is another factor in how efficiently sweating works. In low humidity sweat will evaporate quickly resulting in a rapid cooling effect. Conversely, in humid environments sweat will not evaporate efficiently. This will result in sweat remaining on the body surface without evaporating. As less evaporation has occurred, less latent heat of vaporization will be extracted, so cooling rates will be reduced. These variable rates of evaporation also explain why we feel dry in low humidity but 'sweaty' in high humidity.

Failure to lower body temperature will cause hyperthermia

Cooling mechanisms only work within a limited range of ambient conditions. If the environment continues to get hotter, or heat loss mechanisms are inhibited, then body temperature will start to rise and hyperthermia will develop. Any temperature above normal is technically a hyperthermia; however, this is not usually a major problem up to about 40°C. At temperatures above this level, the brain has a reduced capacity to function normally and the individual will progressively lose the ability to think in a coherent way. If the body temperature rises above 41°C the condition should be urgently treated.

Death from hyperthermia becomes a serious risk at about 45°C. This is because essential intracellular enzymes denature and no longer function. Denaturing means enzymes change their physical shape and so are no longer able to catalyse essential biochemistry. This process of enzyme denaturing occurs because enzymes are composed of complex protein molecules. These protein molecules fold in highly specific ways to generate precise three dimensional structures. If the temperature of the enzyme based protein molecule is increased this can interfere with some of the chemical bonds between the constituent amino acid sub-units of the protein. If chemical bonds are broken the overall shape of the protein molecule is lost meaning it can no longer function as an enzyme. As a result of this enzyme deactivation essential biochemical reactions in the cell no longer take place.

Fever

Infections are caused when transmissable agents such as bacteria or viruses enter body tissues. When systemic infection is present white blood cells will release cytokines which act as pyrogens. A pyrogen is any substance which initiates a pyrexia or fever. The thermoregulatory centre of the hypothalamus is designed to detect the presence of pyrogens. When detected the hypothalamus increases the 'set point' for body temperature. Initially the body temperature will be normal but the person will feel cold. Heat generating and conserving measures will be initiated, resulting in an increase in body temperature above the norm.

The reason the hypothalamus increases body temperature is to optimise the function of the immune system which works best at an increased pyrexial temperature, probably about 39°C. This increase in body temperature enhances white cell (leucocyte) function, stimulates the production of some white cells and enhances phagocytosis. All of these immune boosting effects increase the efficiency with which the infecting bacteria or viruses can be eliminated. From this it can be seen that pyrexia is a normal protective response to infection and perhaps we should be less hasty in our use of antipyretics in older children and adults. Once the infection has been overcome, cooling mechanisms will return body temperature to normal.

Young children, below the age of 2 years are not able to regulate their body temperatures as effectively as older children and adults. If they develop a pyrexia, their core temperature may rise dramatically, leading to hyperthermia, brain injury and potentially death. This is why it is vital to monitor febrile (i.e. pyrexial) children carefully and to reduce their body temperatures when required. Most fevers in children are caused by infections and body temperature can be lowered by keeping the child cool and by using drugs such as paracetamol or ibuprofen.

Pyrexia may also be caused by tissue damage in the absence of infection. This is partly explained by damaged body cell membranes releasing fatty based

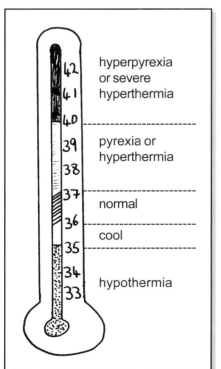

Diagram 12.3
A guide to the classification of body temperature in the clinical setting. Pyrexia describes an increase in body temperature caused by the release of pyrogens. Hyperthermia describes increased body temperature caused by hot environments or failure of cooling mechanisms.

molecules which are converted into prostaglandins which then function as pyrogens. This effect may be seen after an infarction when the blood supply to part of the body is occluded. You may also see this effect after trauma or surgery.

When core temperature falls

This situation initiates body warming mechanisms. Some mechanisms conserve heat which is already in the body while others work by increasing heat production using thermogenesis. This literally means 'the beginning of heat' and describes any process in which heat is produced.

Behavioural change

When too cold, we often try to warm up by a voluntary increase in metabolic activity, waving our arms or jogging on the spot. We try to avoid further cooling from wind chill by avoiding moving air currents. Cold sleeping people naturally curl up to reduce the surface area available over which heat loss from convection and radiation may occur. We put on more clothes and seek out warm environments.

Arterial vasoconstriction reduces blood flow to the periphery

In order to preserve heat in the physiologically essential core organs, blood supply to the cold peripheries such as hands and feet is reduced. Arterial supply of blood is restricted by reduction of arterial lumens. This is why we get cold hands and feet in cold environments. In humans, reduction of arterial blood supply to cold extremities is a very efficient mechanism. Reduction in blood perfusion can be so pronounced that the temperature in extremities may drop to 0°C. When this happens the tissue freezes. As a tissue freezes, ice crystals form in the cytosol of the cells. The expansion of these crystals results in rupture of cell membranes, disrupting tissue integrity at the cellular level. Tissue necrosis (necrosis means death) caused by this freezing mechanism is called frost bite and often necessitates amputations. Interestingly this same process of tissue destruction on freezing explains why people who are frozen after death, in the hope of being brought back to life in the future, never will be.

When the body is cold, it is essential to minimise heat loss through the skin. This can be done by reducing skin temperature. Pre-capillary sphincters in the arterioles supplying blood to dermal capillary beds contract when it is cold. This results in peripheral vasoconstriction, greatly reducing the perfusion of the skin. Blood which would normally perfuse the capillaries is transferred directly from small arteries to small veins via shunt vessels. Reduction of superficial blood flow explains why cold people look pale.

If people are injured in cold conditions, vasoconstrictive mechanisms can help to reduce blood loss. This is why people with external significant haemorrhage should not be warmed up until they are in a situation where the

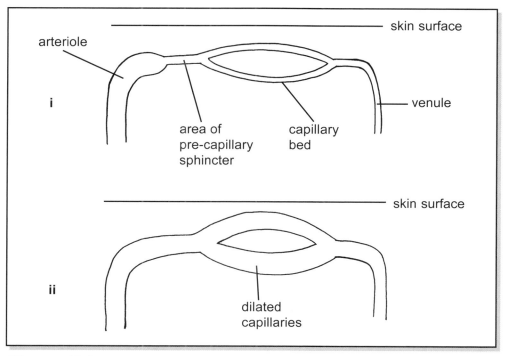

Diagram 12.4
Body temperature is partly regulated by varying the perfusion of superficial capillaries.
(i) When the body is too cold, pre-capillary sphincters constrict reducing the volumes of warm blood flowing near the body surface.
(ii) When the body is too hot, pre-capillary sphincters dilate increasing the volumes of warm blood flowing near the body surface.

bleeding vessels can be ligated. Conversely, if part of the body is warm and well perfused, bleeding may be more severe than it would be in a cooler environment. The inflammatory response is also reduced in cold conditions as it involves vasodilation.

Venoconstriction

In order to conserve heat, superficial veins also constrict. This obliges blood, returning from the periphery, to return to the heart via the deep venous systems of the legs and arms. As warm blood is kept away from the cold surface, less heat will be lost from the skin surface.

Venoconstriction of peripheral veins also preserves heat via a second mechanism as deep veins often run close to arteries. This closeness allows for a counter current heat exchange mechanism to operate. Counter current systems operate when two fluids flow near each other in opposite directions. In conduction heat always passes from hot areas to cold ones therefore as warm arterial blood passes down the limb, heat is directly transferred to the cooler venous blood. This means

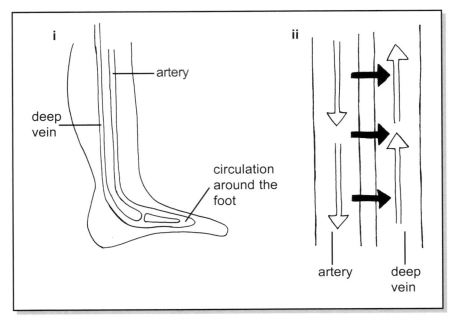

Diagram 12.5
(i)   Anatomical arrangement of deep blood vessels which facilitates counter current heat exchange between an artery and a vein.
(ii) Close up view of an artery and a deep vein. White arrows indicate the direction of blood flow and dark arrows indicate heat transfer.

returning venous blood is warmed and the arterial blood cooled. Blood entering a cold extremity is therefore already cooled while blood returning to the warm core is already warmed. This allows cold peripheries to remain perfused and oxygenated while minimising heat loss from the blood.

Contraction of hair erector muscles

Contraction of these muscles causes the hair to 'stand on end'. This will increase the thickness of the boundary layer of insulating air, increasing the insulation of the body, so conserving heat. This effect on the skin is sometimes likened to 'goose flesh'. While this effect is highly effective in hairy animals it only has a small effect in humans.

Shivering generates a lot of heat

As a person cools there is initially an increase in skeletal muscle tone; this does not cause shivering but does generate some additional heat. As a person continues to cool there is rapid involuntary contraction of skeletal muscles, mostly of the upper half of the body. This shivering is initiated and controlled by the hypothalamus. Shivering can triple metabolic rate and therefore is an effective means of thermogenesis.

Metabolic (non-shivering) thermogenesis

Hypothermia is a particular risk in the newborn. In cold environments neonates should be quickly dried and wrapped up next to the mother's body. However neonates also contain their own emergency heat generating mechanism. In various areas of the body there is brown fat, or brown adipose tissue. The brown colour is caused by the enormous numbers of mitochondria the fat cells (adipocytes) contain. This specialised tissue is able to rapidly metabolise fatty acids to generate heat. There is debate as to how long this metabolic heating mechanism remains active and while it may well persist into childhood it is thought to have little or no role in adult thermoregulation.

In cold environments people will increase their rate of non-shivering thermogenesis via the mechanism of increased activity of the sympathetic nervous system. Enhanced sympathetic activity releases norepinephrine (noradrenalin) and epinephrine (adrenalin) which both increase metabolic activity and hence heat generation. Over time exposure to cold will also increase the levels of metabolism stimulating thyroid hormone. Arctic explorers lose a large percentage of body fat over a few months. While part of this is because they are physically active it is also because energy reserves have been burned up to support the increased metabolic rate. So, one way to lose some weight is to turn off the central heating.

Failure to maintain body temperature will cause hypothermia

Heat gain and conservation mechanisms only work within a limited range. If the environment continues to get colder, or heat gain mechanisms are inhibited, then body temperature will start to fall and hypothermia will develop. When a person becomes hypothermic, their metabolic rate will suffer a corresponding drop. At a temperature of 27°C the metabolic rate is 2.5 times lower than at 37°C. Therefore any reduction in body temperature will reduce metabolic heat gain, and so lower body temperature further. The drop in body temperature will cause a further drop in metabolic rate, setting up a downward spiral leading to death from hypothermia. If a hypothermic patient is not shivering they are at serious risk as this indicates that their main compensatory mechanism has already failed.

If you are ever in a situation where hypothermia is a possibility, it is important not to go to sleep, as this will allow the vicious downward spiral to start. However, if you keep awake you can generate heat by voluntary muscular activity and so maintain metabolic rate and core temperature. Sleep is a particular temptation in developing hypothermia because the lowered temperature reduces the metabolic activity of the brain which makes us feel sleepy. People who have been rescued from hypothermic coma report that apart from feeling cold for a time they just felt drowsy and went to sleep. This would seem to indicate that death from hypothermia is not as unpleasant as some other mechanisms of death.

Because living hypothermic patients may be comatose and cold they may appear to be dead. In cases where death is suspected in hypothermia the patient should be warmed up before death is pronounced. Sometimes when patients are warmed up they recover. There is a reliable saying in Accident and Emergency practice, 'no one is dead until they are warm and dead'. In other words only pronounce death once you have returned body temperature to normal.

The body is economical in using water or energy reserves

It is interesting to note that the body tries to maintain a normal body temperature using the most economical mechanisms possible in terms of energy use and water loss. This means there will be vasodilation as an initial response to increasing body temperature. Only if temperature continues to rise will water reserves be used to produce sweat. In the same way when body temperature drops there will be initial vasoconstriction with shivering only being used if temperature drops further. In this way energy reserves such as glycogen and fat are conserved as much as possible. This economical use of body reserves means we can survive for longer while we look for sources of water and food.

Alcohol and anaesthesia

Apparently an order of Swiss monks used to send St. Bernard dogs to the aid of people trapped in snow drifts. Around their necks were tied small barrels of brandy. When cold people drink alcohol they feel warmer. This is because alcohol is a peripheral vasodilator so increases dermal capillary blood flow. This warm blood will stimulate dermal warmth thermoreceptors; however, excessive amounts of heat are lost to the cold environment at the same time. Alcohol therefore reverses the natural vasoconstrictive response to cold. Most of the unfortunate people supplied with brandy by the well meaning monks and dogs would therefore rapidly become hypothermic and die.

A similar problem may arise in surgical patients. General anaesthesia may reduce vasoconstricting tone, allowing warm blood to perfuse the subcutaneous tissues. Heat will then be lost from this blood into the environment resulting in a drop in core temperature. This is one reason why hypothermia is a recognised complication of surgery and anaesthesia.

CHAPTER 13
Musculoskeletal System

Functions of bones

The skeleton supports the softer tissues of the body providing rigidity and a structural framework. This framework supports the weight of the body and maintains an upright posture. Bones also provide the attachment points for tendons and skeletal muscles thereby facilitating movement. Many delicate components of the body are protected by overlying bony structures. For example, the cranial bones of the skull protect the brain and the vertebrae protect the spinal cord. The ribs protect the heart, lungs and major blood vessels. Large blood vessels and nerves in the limbs often run deep within or under the soft tissues medially to lateral bones. This means these important structures are protected from blows or falls applying forces from the outside.

Red bone marrow is the site of red and white blood cell production. Platelets are formed from a type of white blood cell which develops in red bone marrow. Red bone marrow is found in the ends of the long bones of the arms and legs. It is also found in flat bones including the sternum, ribs, pelvis, skull and vertebrae. If the bone marrow is damaged by radiation or drugs the body will not be able to produce new blood cells or platelets. Yellow bone marrow is found predominantly in the shafts of long bones. As yellow bone marrow consists mostly of adipose cells (adipocytes) its main function is to store fat in the form of triglycerides. Minerals such as calcium and phosphorus are stored in bone and can be mobilised and released into the blood if needed to maintain homeostasis.

Long bone macroscopic structure

Most long bones have a wider portion at either end called the epiphyses. These are joined by the shaft of the bone which is termed the diaphysis. Between an epiphysis and the diaphysis is a section termed the metaphysis. In children's growing bones the metaphyses house the growth plates which consist of cartilage. As newly produced cartilage is replaced by bone the length of the bone shaft is increased. In adult bones all of the cartilage in the growth plates has been replaced by bone leaving an epiphyseal line.

Where the end of an epiphysis articulates with another bone the surface is covered with articular cartilage. This is a thin but very smooth layer of hyaline cartilage which reduces friction between two bone ends within a joint.

The rest of the bone surface which is not lined with articular cartilage is covered by periosteum. This covering layer is composed of tough connective tissues that are adherent to the bone surface. Bone forming osteoblasts are also found in the periosteum. These cells can cause the bone to grow in width if mechanical forces are consistently applied through the bone. This mechanism allows bones to strengthen and thicken in response to exercise and weight bearing. However, no amount of exercise will cause bones to grow in length once the growth plates have sealed. If a bone is fractured, osteogenic stem cells from the periosteum divide and differentiate into osteoblasts which secrete collagen to provide the structural framework for the regenerating bone. Periosteum also contains many nociceptors (pain receptors); you will be reminded of this every time you bash your shin.

Within the diaphysis (bone shaft) is a cylindrical space called the medullary cavity. This means that long bones are hollow which greatly reduces their weight. Yellow bone marrow is contained within this space. Lining the medullary cavity is a membrane called the endosteum; like the periosteum this contains bone forming osteoblasts needed for bone formation and repair. Red bone marrow is contained within the spongy bone which fills the epiphyses of the long bones.

Bone tissue

Bone, or osseous tissue, consists of about 25% collagen fibres and 50% crystallised mineral salts with the remaining 25% being water. Collagen fibres provide structure, flexibility and high tensile strength. Mineral salts are deposited onto

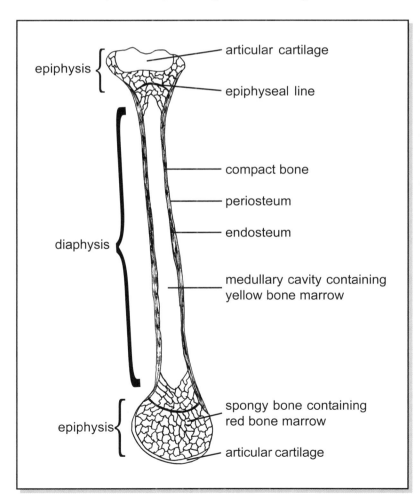

epiphysis

articular cartilage

epiphyseal line

compact bone

periosteum

endosteum

diaphysis

medullary cavity containing yellow bone marrow

epiphysis

spongy bone containing red bone marrow

articular cartilage

Diagram 13.1
The components of a long bone illustrated in a cross section of an adult humerus. Periosteum lines the outside of the bone and the endosteum lines the inside of the medullary cavity.

this collagen matrix where they crystallise causing the tissue to harden. This crystallisation process is termed calcification. There are two forms of bone tissue; compact and cancellous (also called spongy bone).

Compact bone

This is the form of dense bone, found under the periosteum of all bones, forming the bone cortex. It is very strong but also relatively heavy. As bone is a living metabolically active tissue it needs a good blood supply. The copious blood supply of bone is clearly illustrated if there is a fracture. Broken ends of bone bleed leading to an internal haematoma (collection of blood). If a substantial bone such as the femur is broken, large volumes of blood may be lost into the tissue spaces. Up to one litre of blood may be lost from a fractured femoral shaft.

Blood vessels travel through tunnels within the bone referred to as canals. Arteries, veins and lymphatic vessels from the periosteum pass through perforating (also called Volkmann's) canals into the compact bone. These transverse perforating canals connect with the central Haversian canals. Further perforating (Volkmann's) canals carry blood vessels into deeper central Haversian canals.

Some blood vessels also enter the central Haversian canals from within the medullary cavity. In long bones relatively large blood vessels enter and leave a bone via a nutrient foramen (literally window). Through such a foramen a nutrient artery carries blood into the medullary cavity and a nutrient vein transports blood back out to rejoin the systemic venous circulation. Some bones such as the tibia only have one nutrient artery; others such as the femur or scapula have several. Within the medullary cavity the nutrient artery divides with branches passing up and down the cavity. Large branches of a nutrient artery will divide into progressively smaller arterial vessels and supply blood to the inner areas of the compact bone.

Central canals (also called Haversian canals) run longitudinally through compact bone. These central canals carry blood and lymphatic vessels together with nerves. Blood vessels divide to form networks of fenestrated capillaries located within the canals of the osteons (Haversian systems). Fenestrated means the capillaries have numerous small pores to allow gases, nutrients and metabolic waste products to freely pass between the blood and tissue fluids. This allows oxygen and nutrients to diffuse into the tissue fluid within the central Haversian canals. Surrounding the central canals are rings of calcified collagen fibres which form the bulk of the compact bone tissue. These rings of extracellular calcified tissue form thin plates of bone called lamellae.

Osteocytes live in small spaces called lacunae situated between the lamellae. Osteocytes have thin projections which lie in microscopic spaces called canaliculi. As well as interconnecting the lacunae, the canaliculi connect with the central canals. This arrangement means there are continuous spaces within the compact bone connecting the lacunae with tissue fluid in the central canals. This microscopic interconnection of spaces within bone means there is an intricate fluid filled system

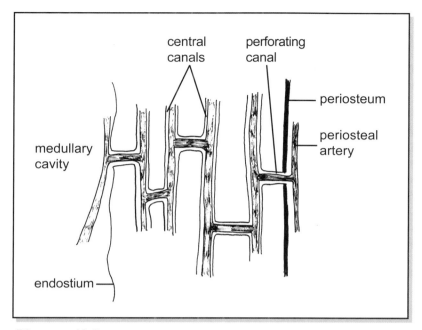

Diagram 13.2
Blood vessels pass from the periosteum through perforating
Volkmann's canals to supply blood to capillary systems within the
central Haversian canals. These Haversian canals run through the
compact bone up and down the length of a long bone. Other blood
vessels enter central Haversian canals from branches of a nutrient
artery within the medullary cavity. (In reality the perforating and
central canals carry veins, lymphatics and nerves as well as
arterial vessels.)

for the transport of oxygen and nutrients to osteocytes and extracellular tissues
together with the removal of waste products. Oxygen diffuses down a diffusion
gradient from the central canal out to the osteocytes. In the same way carbon
dioxide diffuses down a diffusion gradient from the osteocytes to the central canal.

This concentric arrangement of osteocytes around a central canal means that
any individual osteocytes are not too far from the blood capillaries supplying oxygen
and nutrients. In addition, as the osteons follow the lines of force running through
a bone the arrangement also provides great strength. Tubes and cylinders are strong
structures and are often used by engineers in situations which require structural
strength combined with flexibility.

The combination of a central canal, the vessels it contains, the surrounding
lamellae, osteocytes, lacunae, canaliculi and tissue fluids form units called osteons
(also called Haversian systems). Although the structure of the compact bone appears
rigid and permanent it is not. Bone is constantly being remodelled during life
with osteons being built, reabsorbed, and replaced.

Diagram 13.3
Canaliculi connect the central canal with the osteocytes located in the lacunae. Canaliculi therefore provide the avenue of communication between osteocytes and the blood supply of the central Haversian canals. Essential nutrients and oxygen diffuse through the canaliculi from the central canals to the lacunae while carbon dioxide and metabolic waste products diffuse through the same channels from the osteocytes in the lacunae back to the central canals. From this it can be seen that compact bone is not solid but extremely porous.

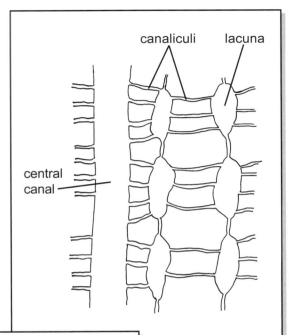

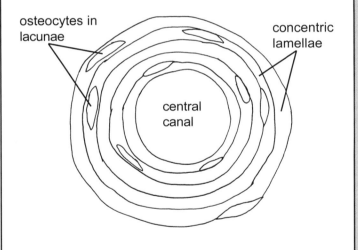

Diagram 13.4
Cross section of a single osteon (or Haversian system). This diagram shows the lamellation of bone when viewed under a microscope; the strata of individual lamella are seen as concentric rings around a central canal. Each lamella is a thin plate or layer of bone consisting mostly of calcified collagen. Within the rings are the spaces called lacunae which house the osteocytes. Lacunae and the central canals are interconnected by numerous canaliculi which are not illustrated in this diagram.

Diagram 13.5
Cross section of a long bone showing the position of the osteons (Haversian systems) in the compact bone of the cortex. Osteons run up and down the length of the bone. The size and

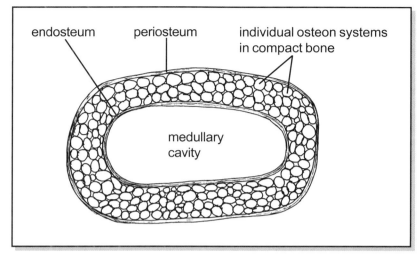

shape of osteons varies but an average unit is about 0.2-0.3mm in diameter and several millimetres long. Immediately below the periosteum and encircling the medullary cavity are layers of circumferential lamellae. These superficial layers do not have the circular osteon pattern.

Cancellous (spongy bone)

Cancellous bone has a honeycomb, sponge like appearance and is therefore often described as spongy bone. However, unlike a sponge it is hard and rigid as it is composed of the same tissue as compact bone. The difference is that spongy bone contains larger spaces and less solid matter. Spongy bone is made up of an irregular three dimensional lattice of thin columns of bone called trabeculae. Like compact bone there are lacunae containing osteocytes, interconnected with canaliculi but these are not arranged in osteon systems.

Spongy bone is light compared to compact bone so reduces the overall weight of the skeleton, allowing for faster movements. It provides spaces between the bony columns for red bone marrow. Trabeculae are arranged along lines of force operating through a bone so they make bones much stronger, transmitting forces through the bone. Spongy bone containing red bone marrow is found in the epiphyses of long bones and in short, flat and irregular shaped bones. Red bone marrow contains the stem cells which give rise to all of the red and white blood cells.

Bone cells

Like other connective tissues, bone consists of cells and the extracellular substances they synthesize and secrete. Osteogenic (bone beginning) cells are found in the lower part of the periosteum, endosteum and lining the central canals within bone which carry blood vessels. These osteogenic cells are stem cells which divide to produce populations of osteoblasts. In connective tissues a blast cell is one which secretes extracellular matrix. Osteoblasts therefore synthesize and secrete the collagen matrix. Osteoblasts are similar to fibroblasts in that they secrete collagen and an associated amorphous matrix ground substance. (Amorphous means the matrix does not have a regular shape or structure.) As osteoblasts secrete collagen they eventually become surrounded and encased by their own product. When this happens they are then termed osteocytes (bone cells). Osteocytes live within the bone and are responsible for bone metabolism, i.e. using oxygen and nutrients to maintain bone structure.

Another cell type associated with bones are osteoclasts. These are very large cells which form when several monocytes merge together. They may therefore be considered to be a large form of bone specific macrophage. Osteoclasts secrete enzymes capable of digesting the protein which forms collagen. They also secrete acids which dissolve calcium salts. This means they are capable of breaking up bone extracellular matrix. This process is termed resorption and while it may sound drastic is part of the normal growth, maintenance and repair of bone.

Bone mass and exercise

When mechanical stresses are applied through a bone it becomes thicker and stronger. There will be increased production of collagen matrix and deposition of mineral salts. In this way bones are able to adapt to the demands placed upon them. Exercise and weight bearing will strengthen bones in adult life; however, it is particularly important for children to exercise and place reasonable stresses on their bones before the epiphyseal growth plates close. Adequate amounts of bone stressing exercise in childhood builds up bone mass and reduce the probability of developing osteoporosis in later life.

Conversely, when no mechanical stresses are applied through a bone there is a decrease in the volume of collagen fibres and demineralization occurs. In other words the amount of mineral salts in the bone decreases. This will happen if a bone is not stressed for a period of time; for example, if a limb is in a plaster cast for a number of weeks there can be a reduction in bone mass. The same effect occurs if a patient is on bed rest or limbs cannot be exercised as a result of paralysis.

Bone growth

Throughout childhood bones grow in length from the epiphyseal growth plates. Growth in these plates is the only mechanism by which bones grow in length. An epiphyseal plate is a zone of cartilage in an area called the metaphysis which is the area between an epiphysis and the diaphysis. Cartilage cells (chondrocytes) within the epiphyseal plate undergo mitosis producing lots of new cells. Ongoing cell division of chondrocytes pushes the slightly older cells towards the diaphysis (bone shaft), causing the whole bone to grow in length.

Chondrocytes secrete an extracellular cartilage matrix. As the now maturing chondrocytes are pushed further away from the diaphysis by ongoing mitosis, the surrounding matrix calcifies. This process of calcification describes the deposition of calcium salts into the extracellular cartilage matrix.

As the matrix around the chondrocytes calcifies the living cartilage cells are cut off from their oxygen and nutrient supply and so they die. Osteoclasts then dissolve the calcified cartilage and osteoblasts from the diaphysis migrate into the space. These osteoblasts secrete an extracellular collagen rich matrix which is then calcified to form new bone. The addition of this new bone increases the length of the diaphysis (i.e. the bone shaft). During this process of bone growth new chondrocytes are formed at the epiphyseal end of the growth plate while old ones are replaced by bone at the diaphyseal end. These two ongoing processes mean the width of the epiphyseal growth plate remains relatively constant as a bone grows in length.

When men are about 21 and women about 18 the epiphyseal plates close. The chondrocytes stop dividing and the whole area is replaced with bone. An ossified epiphyseal line is left indicating no more bone elongating will occur. As increase in bone length can only occur through the activity of the epiphyseal plate. Any injury to this area in children must therefore be recognised and properly treated. Failure to correctly manage fractures involving the growth plates may result in premature fusion of the epiphysis and diaphysis resulting in growth failure. Dislocation across the growth plate may result in deformed growth.

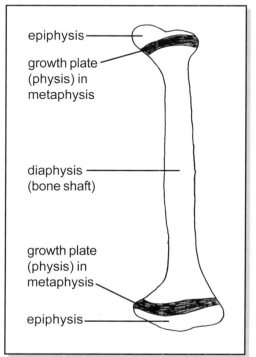

epiphysis

growth plate (physis) in metaphysis

diaphysis (bone shaft)

growth plate (physis) in metaphysis

epiphysis

Diagram 13.6
The growth plates are located between the epiphysis and diaphysis.

Classification of bones

Bones are often described as being long, short, flat or irregular, and sesamoid. Long bones are longer than they are wide consisting of two end parts joined by a shaft. Examples include the femur, tibia, fibula, humerus, radius and ulna. Despite being relatively short the hand bones (metacarpals), foot bones (metatarsals) and the phalanges of the fingers and toes are also classified as long bones.

Short bones do not have a shaft and are often described as cube or box shaped; examples include the carpal bones of the wrist or the tarsal bones of the ankle. Most flat bones are broad and thin, often with a curved surface. Flat bones include the bones of the skull, scapulae, sternum and ribs. Irregular bones have complex shapes so do not fit into any of the previous categories. Examples of irregular bones include the vertebrae, calcaneus (heel bone), some facial bones and the pelvic bones. Sesamoid (shaped like sesame seeds) bones are found within tendons. The only true examples are the two patellae or knee caps. However, bones usually described as sesamoid are also found within some large tendons of the legs and feet.

The skeleton

The human skeleton consists of all of the bones in the body; the arrangement of bones has bilateral symmetry, being the same on both sides. Traditionally the skeleton is described in two divisions, the axial and appendicular skeleton. The axial skeleton is composed of the skull, vertebral column (back bones), ribs and sternum (breast bone). In addition, the hyoid bone in the upper neck and the auditory ossicles of the middle ear are included within the axial division. All remaining bones are part of the appendicular skeleton; these are all of the bones in the limbs as well as the pelvis, clavicle and scapulae.

The axial skeleton consists of 80 bones; there are 8 cranial bones with 14 facial bones. The vertebral column consists of 26 separate bones and there is 1 sternum with 12 pairs of ribs. Within the ears are 6 auditory ossicles (the middle ear bones) and there is 1 hyoid bone in the neck.

The cranial bones form the cranial cavity of the skull; they protect and enclose the brain. There is 1 frontal bone, 2 parietal at each side with 2 temporal bones beneath these. At the back of the skull is the occipital bone with 1 sphenoid and 1 ethmoid bone towards the front.

The vertebral (spinal) column is made up of a series of individual vertebrae, together with tough connective tissues. As well as providing support for the body the vertebral column surrounds and protects the spinal cord and large spinal nerves passing down to the lower areas of the body. Counting from the top, the first 7 bones are the cervical vertebrae, found in the neck. The top one is C1, the second C2 the third C3 and so on down to C7. In addition C1 is called the atlas and C2 the axis. Next there are 12 thoracic vertebrae, passing behind the thoracic cavity. Again counting from the top there is T1, T2, T3, T4, through to T12. Below the thoracic spine are the 5 large lumbar vertebrae. These pass behind the abdominal cavity and carry the weight from the upper parts of the body; these are L1, L2, L3, L4 and L5. Below this is the sacral bone, but this is composed of 5 fused bones, S1 through to S5. Finally the small coccyx is counted as 1 bone but consists of 4 fused bones.

Everyone working with injured people must always ensure they do not damage the spinal cord or large spinal nerves after an injury. This is particularly important if the patient is unconscious as they are unable to report pain. A fractured vertebra may not be displaced and so no damage to the spinal cord will have occurred. However, if the patient is moved without paying full attention to vertebral alignment after trauma, the fractured components of a vertebra may displace, cutting through the spinal cord. If this occurs the patient will not be able to move their body or receive any sensation from below the level of the injury ever again.

In the appendicular skeleton each side of the body has 1 clavicle (collar bone) and 1 scapula (shoulder bone). In each arm there is 1 humerus (upper arm), 1 ulna (forearm), 1 radius (forearm, in line with the thumb), 8 carpals (wrist bones), 5 metacarpals (hand bones), and 14 phalanges (finger bones). In each leg there is 1 femur (upper leg), 1 patella (knee cap), 1 fibula (thinner bone in lower leg), 1 tibia (shin bone), 7 tarsals (ankle bones), 5 metatarsals (foot bones) and 14 phalanges (toe bones). The pelvic girdle consists of 2 bones. This gives a total of 126 bones in the appendicular skeleton with a whole body total of 206. Men and women have exactly the same bones as each other.

Joints

Joints are arrangements of connective tissues between two bones or between cartilage and bones. There are three types of joint which connect bone to bone; these are fibrous, cartilaginous and synovial joints. Fibrous joints are usually described as being fixed, cartilaginous as slightly movable and synovial as freely movable.

Fibrous joints

In a fibrous joint the two bones are held together by collagen rich, fibrous connective tissue. Collagen rich tissue has a high tensile strength making these joints very difficult to pull apart. Fibrous joints are therefore strong and permit little or no movement between the joined bones.

Fibrous tissues hold the various bones of the skull together across narrow joints called sutures. The ends of the flat skull bones are irregular and interlocking making these joints rigid and strong with no movement between adjacent bones. At birth there are two areas of the cranial cavity covered by tough membranes as opposed to bones. These gaps between the skull bones are described as the anterior and posterior fontanel (or fontanelle). Bone growth covers the relatively small posterior fontanel by the age of about 2 months while the larger anterior fontanel remains palpable until 18 to 24 months.

Other fibrous joints have a larger gap between the bones with more fibrous tissue present. For example, between the tibia and fibula as well as between the radius and ulna is a sheet of tough fibrous connective tissue. This connective tissue holds the two bones firmly together but does allow a slight degree of movement. A third type of fibrous joint holds the teeth into the jaw bones. A tooth is firmly held into a socket by the dense fibrous connective tissue which forms the periodontal ligament.

Diagram 13.7
At a fibrous joint two bones are held together by strong fibrous connective tissues, for example the bones of the skull are joined along suture lines. These joints are usually described as fixed.

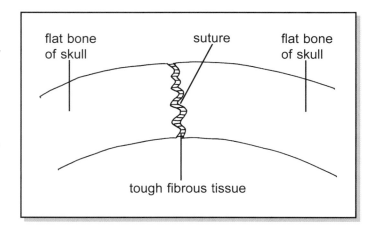

Cartilaginous joints

In a cartilaginous joint two bones are joined together via some cartilage. The first ten ribs attach to the sternum via cartilage. There is a pad of cartilage between the pubic bones at the front of the pelvis called the pubic symphysis. Between the bodies of adjacent vertebrae there are intervertebral discs. These discs have an outer ring of collagen and fibrocartilage called the annulus fibrosus. The centre of an intervertebral disc is called the nucleus pulposus and is filled with a gelatinous substance which allows movement between two vertebrae. If part of the outer annulus fibrosus is torn due to an injury, some of the inner pulposus may track out along the line of weakness. This protruding material may then press on the spinal cord or large nerves causing severe pain. This abnormal condition is usually referred to as a slipped disc but more accurately is described as a disc protrusion. Although each intervertebral joint will only allow a little movement the back is flexible as there are 23 articulations with discs. In addition to the intervertebral discs adjacent vertebrae are held together by numerous reinforcing ligaments. During bone growth in childhood the epiphyseal growth plates also constitute cartilaginous joints.

Synovial joints

Synovial joints form freely movable articulations between two bones. The characteristic feature is the presence of a joint or articular cavity between the

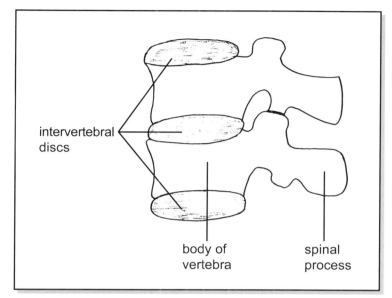

Diagram 13.8
Intervertebral discs form cartilaginous joints between adjacent vertebrae. These joints are usually described as slightly movable.

intervertebral discs

body of vertebra

spinal process

articulating bones. A joint capsule firmly connects the two articulating bones together. The outer layer of a joint capsule is composed of dense bundles of collagen fibres which form a tough fibrous tissue. Often the fibrous tissues of the joint capsule are arranged in parallel bundles forming ligaments. Such ligaments and fibrous tissues firmly join one bone to another providing stability and preventing the joint from dislocating. The fibrous tissues of the joint capsule are attached to the periosteum of the articulating bones. The inner layer of a joint capsule is termed the synovial membrane. This membrane surrounds the joint and lines the part of the articulating bones not covered with articular cartilage. Synovial membrane is vascular and produces synovial fluid from components in the plasma. Once produced synovial fluid fills the articular cavity. Although the volume of synovial fluid is small it is at a slight negative pressure which greatly improves joint stability.

Synovial fluid is similar in appearance and texture to the white of an uncooked egg. It provides a high degree of lubrication within the joint cavity. As the surfaces between the articular cartilage are well lubricated the joint is able to move freely and quietly. Synovial fluid also acts as a transport medium, transporting oxygen and nutrients to the articular cartilage. Phagocytic macrophages are present in synovial fluid to remove debris generated by normal wear and tear on the articular surfaces. Any infecting bacteria will also be phagocytosed by these macrophages.

The ends of the bones within a synovial joint are covered by a layer of articular cartilage. This is very smooth to reduce friction within the joint and the two opposing surfaces are also lubricated with synovial fluid. On radiographs of joints a wide gap appears to separate the adjacent bones. This is because cartilage covering the articulating surfaces is more transparent to x rays than bone.

Diagram 13.9
A generalised synovial joint. These joints are usually described as freely movable.

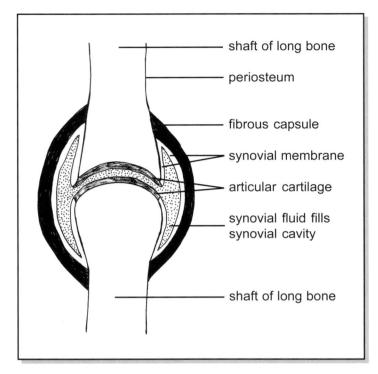

shaft of long bone

periosteum

fibrous capsule

synovial membrane

articular cartilage

synovial fluid fills synovial cavity

shaft of long bone

Types of synovial joint

Ball and socket joints

In these joints a ball shaped head fits into a concaved socket or depression. This allows free movement of the first bone with a rounded head within the socket of the second bone. The shoulder is a ball and socket joint, but the clearest example is the hip joint between the head of the femur and the acetabulum of the hip bone.

Hinge joints

In hinge joints the shape of the articulating bone ends only permit uniaxial movement, i.e. movement in one plane. The hinge joint between two articulating bones therefore only allows the back and forth movements of flexion and extension. In this sense the joint is analogous to a simple hinge on a door which allows opening or closing but not any other movements. Hinge joins include the elbow, knee and interphalangeal joints of the fingers.

Pivot joints

In pivot joints the rounded or pointed surface of one bone articulates in a ring formed by the combination of a second bone and a ligament. These joints allow rotational movement only, so are another example of a uniaxial joint. For example, the odontoid (also sometimes called the dens) process of the second cervical vertebrae (i.e. of the axis) projects through a hole (vertebral foramen) in the first cervical vertebrae (i.e. the atlas). The head moves from side to side as the atlas rotates over the odontoid process. This arrangement is called the atlanto-axial joint. Another example of a pivot joint is between the radius and ulna to allow rotation of the hands, turning the palms up or down.

Condyloid joints

A condyle is a rounded projection on a bone. In a condyloid joint such a condyle articulates within an elliptical shallow socket. For example, there is a condylar process on the upper part of the mandible which fits into the mandibular fossa. This is an elliptical depression in the temporal bone of the skull. These structures form the temporomandibular joint which allows the mouth to open and close facilitating chewing and speaking. Other examples of condyloid joints include the wrist (between the radius and the carpal bones), knuckles (between the hand and fingers) and between the occipital bone and the atlas.

Saddle joints

In a saddle joint the two bone ends resemble reciprocally shaped saddles (as used in horse riding). Saddle joints allow a greater freedom of movement than condyloid joints. Saddle joints are found between the metacarpal bones of the thumb and the trapezium (one of the wrist carpal bones) and in the sternoclavicular joints between the sternum and clavicles. This saddle arrangement allows the thumb to touch all of the other finger tips in the movement of opposition. This is vital to allow humans to grip and manipulate small objects between finger and thumb.

Gliding joints

These are also sometimes described as planer joints; they have flat or slightly curved articulating surfaces. Movement occurs as one surface glides over another, but the overall amount of movement is limited. Gliding joints are found between the carpal bones of the wrist and between the tarsal bones of the ankle. Other examples are between the ribs and transverse processes of the thoracic vertebrae and between the scapula and the clavicle.

Problems with joints

Joint problems are commonly encountered in clinical practice. As people age there is a tendency for articular cartilage to be lost in the degenerative process of osteoarthritis. This is more common in weight bearing joints, especially if the person is overweight. It is also more likely to develop after there has been trauma to a joint. Osteoarthritis should not be confused with rheumatoid arthritis which is an autoimmune disease. Autoimmune diseases develop when the immune system attacks the body's own tissues; in this case the synovial membrane is affected first with later progressive destruction of the articular cartilage. Both of these joint disorders are very painful.

As a result of trauma a joint may be dislocated. The connecting ligaments are damaged or torn allowing the joint surfaces to separate. One surface of the joint will be physically knocked away from the other resulting in pain and loss of articulation. A subluxation is a partial dislocation where there is a separation of the articulating surfaces but the bone ends remain connected to each other.

Skeletal muscles

Skeletal muscles are so called because they are attached to bones. They are composed of bundles of muscle fibres. Within these fibres are arrangements of sliding

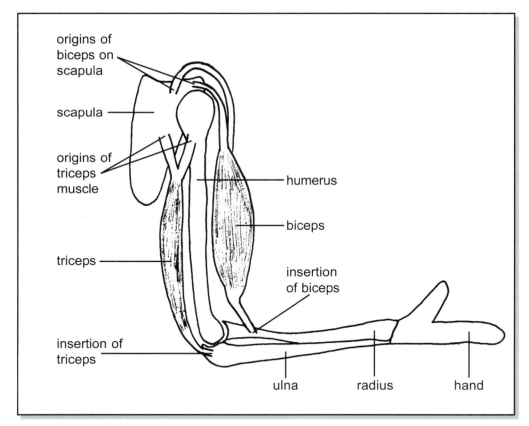

Diagram 13.10
Anatomy of the arm. The biceps muscle is at the front of the arm with the triceps behind. The biceps muscle has two origins on the scapula and an insertion on the radius. The triceps has origins on the scapula and humerus with its insertion on the ulna. An extension of the biceps tendon also binds with the fascia of the forearm muscle to spread the load.

filaments. These filaments are composed of proteins which are capable of contraction. During contraction a muscle becomes shorter and fatter. A muscle is enclosed within a sheath of tough fibrous tissue called the muscle fascia. At the ends of a muscle the fascia is continuous with the muscle tendon, which in turn connects to the periosteum surrounding a bone. When a muscle contracts it pulls on the tendons which in turn exert pulling forces on the bones. During movement bones function as levers and the joints as fulcrums, a fulcrum being a fixed point around which a lever acts. As muscles are metabolically active they have a good blood supply.

Functions of skeletal muscles

Skeletal muscles contract to produce body movements and can also stabilise the body in a particular position for a period of time. It is the skeletal muscles which maintain body posture, holding structures in the correct positions. This is possible because when a muscle is not actively contracting it is not fully relaxed. At any one time a few muscle fibres will be contracting giving rise to muscle tone. This means even an essentially relaxed muscle will exert a certain amount of force to maintain posture. Active muscular contraction uses a lot of energy and so produces heat. This is an important aspect of thermogenesis. When a person is very cold there is rhythmic, involuntary muscular contraction; such shivering produces a lot of heat to warm the body. Muscle tone and contraction, especially in the legs, squeezes deep veins promoting venous return of blood back to the heart. Skeletal muscle is also found in the diaphragm, which together with the intercostal muscles are essential for breathing movements. Glycogen is stored in skeletal muscles. In times of starvation, muscles will release amino acids to supply essential physiological needs.

Movement

Tendons and ligaments

Tendons and ligaments are both composed of collagen rich dense connective tissue. This gives both types of structure great tensile strength. A ligament is a structure that connects bone to bone whereas a tendon is a structure which connects muscle to bone. Tendons may be cordlike or form flattened sheets as in the abdominal muscles.

Ligaments often form part of the fibrous joint capsule, connecting with the periosteum of the two joined bones. Additional ligaments outside the joint capsule increase the strength and stability of a joint. Some ligaments are also found within a joint capsule, for example the ligament of the head of the femur connecting to the acetabulum. Within the knee joint capsule are the two cruciate ligaments, so called because they cross over within the joint. Ligaments within a joint capsule give the joint enhanced strength and stability.

Bursae

Bursae are essentially little bags of fluid; they are found around bony prominences such as the knees, elbows and shoulders. A bursa is a closed sac-like structure composed of walls of connective tissue, lined internally with synovial membrane which secretes synovial fluid. The synovial fluid provides lubrication between the two sides of the bursa to facilitate movement. They also provide cushioning and lubrication for moving parts such as tendons. Bursitis is a painful condition in which a bursa is inflamed.

Origin and insertion of muscles

Typically when a muscle contracts one bone remains close to its original position. This gives a fixed point for the muscle to pull against. The muscle will then pull on a second bone, bringing it closer to the first bone. The attachment of a muscle tendon to the first relatively stationary bone is called the point of origin. Where a muscle tendon connects to the second more mobile bone is called the point of insertion. Muscles therefore apply forces into bones through points of origin and insertion. In most cases the point of origin is proximal while the point of insertion is distal. It is these forces, applied as a result of skeletal muscular contraction that cause bones and therefore parts of the body to move.

Diagram 13.11
Movement of the arm. When the biceps muscle contracts the triceps muscle relaxes. This has the effect of flexing the arm, drawing the hand towards the shoulder. The origins of the biceps remain in the original position while the insertion moves upwards. In order to extend the forearm the biceps muscle relaxes while the triceps muscle contracts. The origins of the triceps on the scapula and humerus remains relatively stationary while the insertion on the ulna moves to straighten the arm.

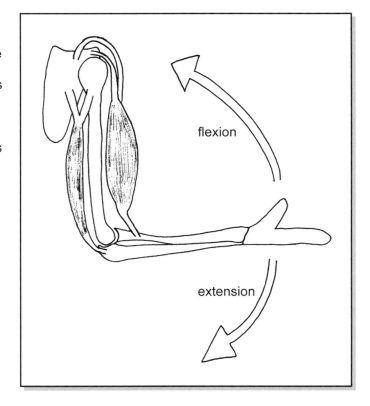

Antagonistic pairs of muscles

Muscles can only contract, once in a contracted position they are completely unable to elongate again, unless they are stretched by the action of an opposing muscle. It is for this reason that muscles are arranged in groups and pairs. When two separate muscles produce opposite movements they are described as an antagonistic pair. For example to flex the forearm the biceps muscle contracts, stretching the triceps muscle as it does so. Conversely to extend the arm the triceps muscle contracts, stretching the biceps muscle. Contraction of each muscle of an antagonistic pair therefore generates opposite movements. All movement of the skeleton and therefore of the body occurs as a result of coordinated contraction of groups and pairs of muscles.

Rigor mortis develops after death

Several hours after death all of the skeletal muscles go into a state of contraction causing the body to become stiff and rigid. This contraction occurs as adenosine triphosphate (ATP) is no longer synthesised in the dead muscle. In normal physiology some ATP is required to facilitate normal muscle relaxation. About 24 hours after death a body will become flaccid again as muscle proteins start to denature. Both rigor mortis and the subsequent flaccidity will develop more quickly in higher temperatures.

CHAPTER 14

Male Reproductive System

Scrotum

Scrotum is a term which simply means bag. This container is composed of loose skin, fibrous and connective tissues with some subcutaneous smooth muscle. Although the scrotum looks like one pouch from the outside, internally it is divided into two sacs by the scrotal septum. This dividing septum is composed of connective tissues and also contains some smooth muscle fibres. Each scrotal sac contains one testis, one epididymis and the testicular end of the spermatic cord.

Optimum sperm production in the testes requires a temperature 3°C below normal body core temperature. This explains why the testes are located in the scrotum, external to the pelvic cavity. In cold conditions the subcutaneous and septal smooth muscles contract to draw the testes close to the warm body. Conversely in warm environments these muscles relax and the testes descend further away from the warm body cavities. This explains why testicular examination is easier to perform in warm conditions or after a warm bath.

Testes are the male gonads

The testes (also called testicles) are paired glands located in the scrotum. As the testes are the male gonads they are equivalent to the ovaries in females. In fetal life the testes develop in the abdomen and usually descend into the scrotum before birth.

Each testis contains a surrounding capsule of dense white fibrous tissue called the tunica albuginea. This fibrous structure folds inwards to form numerous septa which divide each testis into 200-300 lobules. Within each lobule there are one to three (occasionally more) tightly coiled tubules forming closed loops which open at the top to allow sperm to exit. These are the seminiferous tubules of which there are a total of 400-600 per testis. Each individual seminiferous tubule would be 70-80 cm in length if straightened out. These seminiferous tubules are the site of sperm production, a process correctly termed spermatogenesis. Between the seminiferous tubules, within the lobules, there are groups of interstitial cells called Leydig cells. These are the cells which produce and secrete the male hormones collectively referred to as androgens.

Spermatogenesis is the process of sperm production and occurs in the seminiferous tubules

Sperm are also referred to as spermatozoa. Sperm cells are produced from a population of stem cells called spermatogonia. These cells are found on the basement membrane of the seminiferous tubules and have been present in the testis since the individual was an embryo. These spermatogonia are therefore the germ cells, the cells which pass genetic information on from one generation to the next. As spermatogonia differentiate to produce sperm cells they undergo meiosis, the form of cell division which reduces the number of chromosomes from 46 per

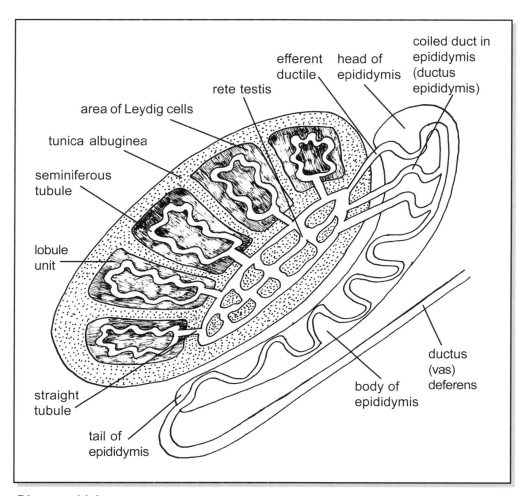

Diagram 14.1
The testes contain lots of very fine tubes called tubules. In reality each testis contains 200-300 lobules each of which usually contain 1-3 seminiferous sperm forming tubules. Seminiferous tubules drain newly formed sperm through the short straight tubules into the rete testis. From the rete testis there are 12-20 efferent ducts through which sperm may pass to reach the epididymis. The epididymis is essentially a single long tubule. Again the level of tight packaging is impressive; if the ductus epididymis were uncoiled it would be 6 metres long.

cell to 23. All gametes, sperm and ova, must contain 23 chromosomes so that when fertilization occurs the newly formed zygote contains 46 chromosomes. Meiosis also ensures that half of the formed sperm contain an X chromosome and half a Y. This is vital to ensure that the next generation contains about the same number of girls as boys. If a couple are trying to conceive it is important for the man to have good nutrition and to avoid toxins such as cigarette smoke in order to promote good quality sperm.

Spermatic cord

Spermatic cords (one per testis) suspend the testes in the scrotum and passes through the inguinal (groin) canal into the pelvic cavity. They are covered by a sheath composed of fibrous and connective tissues with smooth muscle fibres. Within this sheath are located the ductus (vas) deferens, transferring sperm towards the urethra. A testicular artery carries blood rich in oxygen and nutrients to the testes and epididymides. Testicular veins transport deoxygenated blood back from the testes towards larger veins in the pelvic cavity. These testicular veins will also transport testosterone, formed in the Leydig cells of the testes, into the systemic circulation for distribution to all body tissues. Lymphatic vessels within the spermatic cords transport lymphatic drainage fluid from the testes and epididymides into larger lymphatic vessels. The spermatic cords also contain autonomic nerves to control peristalsis of the sperm ducts and to provide sensation.

Sperm (spermatozoa) are the male gametes

The numbers of sperm produced are huge; about 300 million are produced each day by the testes. Located in the head of each sperm cell, the nucleus contains the 23 chromosomes. At the front of a spermatozoon is a structure called the acrosome, this contains enzymes the sperm cell will need to pass through the cervical mucus and to break down the outer covering of the ovum. The body of the sperm is packed with mitochondria; these are needed to generate the energy required for locomotion of the sperm towards the ovum. Locomotion is enabled by contractile bundles of microscopic filaments running from the neck through the tail. Unlike women who stop producing viable gametes at menopause, men go on producing sperm into old age.

Sperm and seminal fluid ducts

Straight tubules and rete testis

Seminiferous tubules produce spermatozoa and some fluid which acts as an initial transport medium for the young sperm. Once formed sperm cells pass out of the seminiferous tubules and travel through a series of very short passages called the straight tubules. These straight tubules connect with a network of ducts called the rete testis which form a collecting chamber for the sperm. From the rete testis there are 12-20 connecting tubules (i.e. the efferent ductiles) through which the sperm travel to reach the epididymis.

Epididymis

The connecting efferent ductiles from the rete testis enter the head of the epididymis. These efferent ductiles are highly coiled within the head of the epididymis and all join to form one single tubule called the ductus epididymis. This is a single, highly coiled tubule which thickens towards the end as it passes

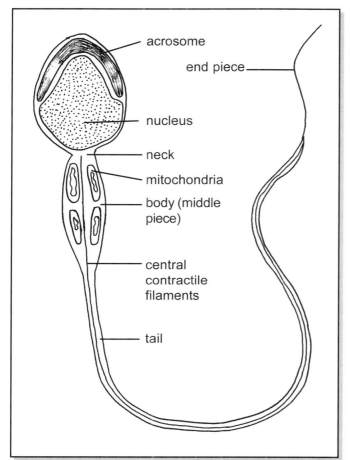

acrosome

end piece

nucleus

neck

mitochondria

body (middle piece)

central contractile filaments

tail

Diagram 14.2
A single sperm cell (or spermatozoon) consists of a head, neck, body (or middle piece) and tail.

through the body of the epididymis down towards the tail of the epididymis. The ductus epididymis is tightly coiled and would be 6 metres long if uncoiled. In the tail of the epididymis the ductus epididymis becomes continuous with the ductus deferens. This allows sperm to exit the ductus epididymis and enter the ductus deferens.

Sperm mature within the tubules of the epididymis over a period of about 14 days. If not ejaculated sperm may be stored in the epididymis for up to several months. As the walls of the ductus epididymis contain smooth muscle fibres they are able to contract during sexual arousal to propel sperm into the ductus deferens prior to ejaculation. Any sperm that are not ejaculated are eventually broken down in the ductus epididymis and the contents reabsorbed.

Ductus (vas) deferens

The ductus deferens (also called vas deferens) is the tube which receives sperm from the ductus epididymis. After leaving the epididymis the ductus deferens ascends in the scrotum within the spermatic cord before passing into the pelvic cavity. From here it loops over the side of, and then behind the urinary bladder. Towards the end or terminal section, the ductus deferens widens into a section called the ampulla. Walls of the ductus deferens are muscular in order to generate peristaltic contractions during sexual arousal. These peristaltic waves of contraction propel sperm from the epididymis towards the ejaculatory ducts prior to ejaculation. The ductus deferens ends where it merges with the duct from the seminal vesicle to form the ejaculatory duct. Like the epididymis, the ductus deferens can store viable sperm for several months. However, if ejaculations are frequent sperm may only be in the ductus deferens for a few days.

Ejaculatory ducts

The two ejaculatory ducts (one on each side) are formed by the joining of the ductus deferens and the duct from the seminal vesicle. These ejaculatory ducts pass through the prostate gland and terminate as they open into the prostatic urethra. Just before ejaculation occurs, the ejaculatory ducts eject sperm and seminal vesicle secretions into the prostatic urethra.

Urethra

In men the urethra is about 20 cm long. This length makes it difficult for bacteria to pass from the outside environment up the urethra to the bladder and is one reason why cystitis is less common than in women. The urethra is divided into four sections. Firstly the short preprostatic part is surrounded by a cuff of smooth muscle which acts as a sphincter. Secondly, the prostatic urethra is the section of urethra which passes through the prostate gland. Thirdly, the membranous urethra is a short and narrow section, connecting the prostatic urethra with the spongy (penile) urethra. Fourthly, the spongy urethra extends from the bulb of the penis to the external urethral orifice at the end of the penis. This fourth section is described as spongy as it is surrounded by erectile tissues.

Flow of fluids through the urethra is regulated by two sphincters. Firstly the internal urethral sphincter is a cuff of smooth muscle fibres so is under autonomic control. This internal sphincter contracts to retain urine within the bladder and relaxes to allow urination. Also, during ejaculation this internal sphincter will contract to prevent retrograde movement of semen into the bladder. At the end of the prostatic urethra there is a second sphincter. This is composed of skeletal muscle allowing for a degree of voluntary control. This sphincter will relax to allow a flow of urine or the passage of seminal fluid from the prostatic urethra.

In addition to the mucus secreted into the urethra by the two bulbourethral glands during sexual arousal, the urethra is routinely lubricated and protected by mucus secreted by numerous minute urethral glands. These small glands drain directly into the spongy urethra.

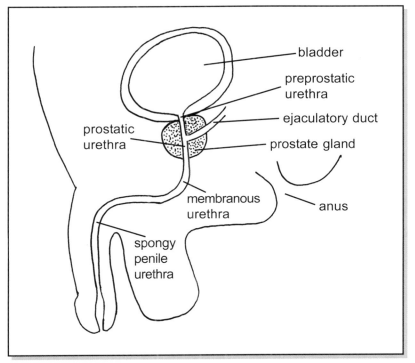

Diagram 14.3
The urethra is described in four sections; preprostatic, prostatic, membranous and penile.

Glands associated with the seminal fluid ducts

Seminal vesicles (seminal glands)

These two glandular structures are about 5 cm long and lie behind the base of the bladder. They are blind ended pouches which are internally lined with secretory epithelial cells which produce a viscous fluid. This fluid eventually forms 60% of the volume of the semen which is ejaculated during sexual intercourse. Fluid from the seminal vesicles is alkaline which helps to neutralize the acidic environment of the vagina. Without this effect the acidic vaginal environment would inactivate and kill most of the sperm. Fluid from the seminal vesicles also contains the monosaccharide sugar fructose. This is used by the mitochondria in the sperm to produce the energy required for sperm motility. Prostaglandins in the fluid stimulate sperm motility and may stimulate muscular contraction in the female reproductive tract. This female muscular contraction probably aids the passage of sperm from the vagina towards the ovum high in a uterine tube. Seminal vesicle fluid also contains clotting factor proteins. These clotting proteins help semen to coagulate in the vagina after ejaculation. Once the semen has coagulated it is less likely to run out of the vagina, increasing the numbers of sperm retained.

Prostate gland

The prostate gland secretes a milky fluid which contributes about 25% of the total volume of semen. Components in prostatic fluid contribute to sperm viability and motility and have an antibiotic effect to kill bacteria. Individual glandular units within the prostate gland open independently into the prostatic urethra via several prostatic ducts. Immediately prior to ejaculation fluid from the prostate gland mixes with fluid from the seminal vesicles and sperm from the testes.

The size of the prostate gland increases slowly from birth to puberty. It then grows rapidly in size up to the age of about 30 years. In some men it starts to increase in size again after the age of about 45 years. Sometimes the enlargement is so great that the gland compresses the prostatic urethra running through. This will lead to difficulty passing urine causing urinary retention. This disorder is benign and so is called benign prostatic hyperplasia. Cancer of the prostate also occurs and is the single most common cancer diagnosed in men in the UK.

Bulbourethral (Cowper's) glands

These are two small glands located on either side of the membranous urethra. They have ducts which open into the spongy urethra. During sexual arousal they secrete mucus which lubricates the urethra to facilitate the smooth passage of sperm and seminal fluid. These secretions will also lubricate the end of the penis to some extent. As bulbourethral secretions are alkaline the sperm are protected from any residual acids in the urethra which might be present from urine.

Semen is ejaculated during sexual intercourse

Semen is a thick, cloudy, sticky fluid composed of a mixture of sperm with seminal fluid. Seminal fluid is a mixture of the secretions from the seminal vesicles, prostate and bulbourethral glands. There are also some fluid secretions from the seminiferous tubules. Collectively seminal fluid provides sperm with nutrition, a transport medium and protection from the acidic vaginal environment. In a typical ejaculation there will be 2.5-5 mls of semen, containing about 100 million sperm per ml.

Vasectomy

A highly effective means of male sterilization is vasectomy where a small section of the ductus (vas) deferens is removed from the spermatic cord, before it enters the pelvic cavity. The ends of the ductus deferens are then closed to prevent any more sperm passing from the testis to the urethra. If this is done on both sides no sperm can travel from the testes to the ejaculatory ducts meaning ejaculated fluids contain no sperm. After vasectomy men need to be told that they will have substantial reserves of sperm in the length of the vas deferens so may remain fertile for some time after the procedure.

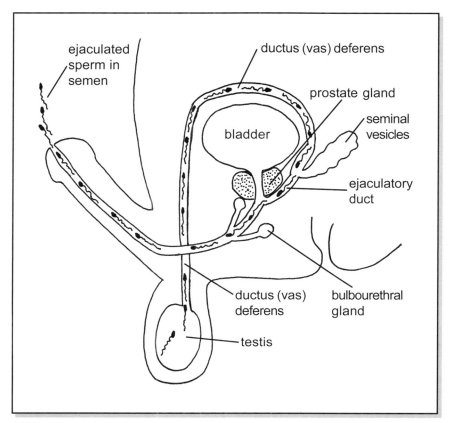

Diagram 14.4
Pathway of sperm from the seminiferous tubules where they are formed
to the urethra where they are ejaculated.

Penis

This structure has three components, a root, body and the glans penis. The body
of the penis is composed of three cylindrical areas of tissue, each being surrounded
by an individual sheath of fibrous tissue. On either side of the penis the cylindrical
masses of tissue are called the corpora cavernosa. Between these two structures is
a third smaller cylinder of tissue called the corpus spongiosum. The urethra runs
through the corpus spongiosum. The whole body of the penis is surrounded by a
layer of fascia and skin.

The root of the penis is the internal component, situated within the perineum.
At the end of the penis the corpus spongiosum enlarges to form the glans penis.
At the tip of the glans penis is the external urethral orifice. Covering the glans
penis is a retractable loosely fitting area of skin called the foreskin. Sometimes the
foreskin is too tight or repeated infections may develop under it. In this case it is
sometimes surgically removed in the procedure of circumcision.

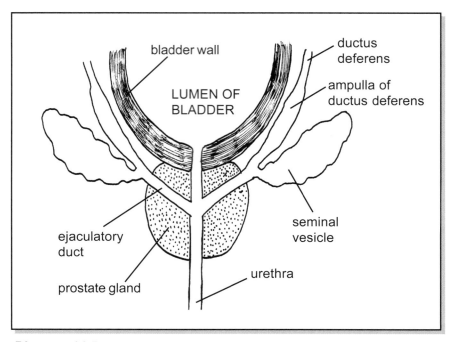

Diagram 14.5
Sperm, together with some fluid produced by the seminiferous tubules pass along the ductus deferens. Much larger volumes of fluid are added by the seminal vesicles. Together the sperm and fluid from the seminal vesicles pass into the ejaculatory ducts. These ejaculatory ducts pass through the prostate and join the prostatic urethra. More fluid is secreted by the prostate gland directly into the prostatic urethra. During ejaculation the whole mixture is propelled out of the urethra as semen.

Erection

Within the corpora (singular, corpus) cavernosa and corpus spongiosum are numerous blood sinuses which are small spaces that can fill up with blood. These small vascular spaces are surrounded by smooth muscle and elastic tissue. Collectively the corpora cavernosa and corpus spongiosum comprise the erectile tissues of the penis. Surrounding the body of the penis and the individual compartments of erectile tissue are layers of fibrous connective tissue. During sexual arousal stimulation of the parasympathetic nervous system leads to sinuses within the erectile tissues filling up with blood, increasing the size and stiffness of the penis. This increase in the volume of blood retained within the penis is facilitated by dilation of arterial vessels with constriction of venous drainage. These changes cause the penis to become erect which is necessary for penetration of the vagina. Impotence describes the inability to achieve an erection. This may occur for psychological reasons but may also develop as a result of degeneration or disease processes in the arterial vessels.

Emission and ejaculation

Ejaculation describes the powerful ejection of semen from the external urethral orifice. Prior to ejaculation there are peristaltic contractions in the epididymides, ductus deferens, seminal vesicles, ejaculatory ducts and prostate to propel semen into the prostatic urethra. Peristaltic activity in these structures is initiated and regulated by activity of the sympathetic nervous system. The process whereby sperm and seminal fluids are ejected into the lumen of the urethra is termed emission. Once in the urethra the sperm and seminal fluid mix to form semen. Next there are further rhythmic contractions in the genital ducts and urethra, coordinated with contraction of muscles around the bases of the penile erectile tissues. These muscular contractions compress the erectile tissues contributing to the pressure increase within the urethra which propel the semen out of the urethra. Emission and ejaculation are associated with the sensory experience of orgasm and may occur during sexual activity, masturbation or nocturnally during sleep.

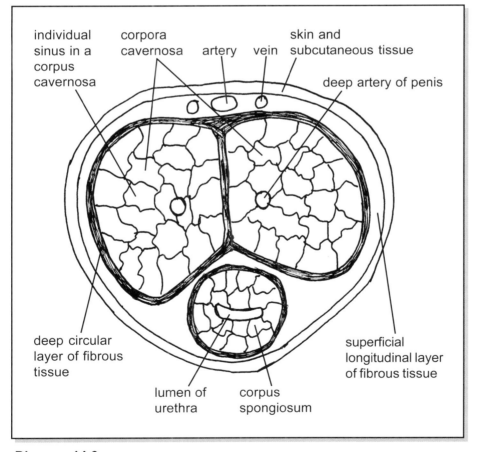

Diagram 14.6
Cross section of the body of the penis.

Testosterone

The interstitial cells of Leydig secrete several androgens but by far the most abundant one is testosterone. At puberty testosterone and sperm production are stimulated under the influence of anterior pituitary gonadotrophic hormones, i.e. luteinizing hormone (LH) and follicle-stimulating hormone (FSH). In men FSH (working together with testosterone) stimulates spermatogenesis and LH stimulates testosterone secretion. (Despite these different functions in men, these two hormones retain the same names as they do in women.) After puberty testosterone levels remain high up until the age of about 50 years when they start to gradually reduce.

In fetal life the Y chromosome causes the early genital tissues to produce testosterone. If this stimulation from the Y chromosome does not occur a baby girl will develop. It is this fetal testosterone which causes the development of the penis, prostate gland, seminal vesicles, male genital ducts and scrotum as well as other male body characteristics. Testosterone also causes the testes to descend into the scrotum in late fetal life. From shortly after birth and throughout boyhood the levels of testosterone in the blood are very low. With puberty testosterone stimulates the enlargement of the primary male sexual characteristics which are the penis, testes and scrotum. It also stimulates the development of male secondary sexual characteristics which distinguish men from women.

Male secondary sexual characteristics

Testosterone causes the growth of male distribution pubic hair. It also causes facial hair and usually the growth of chest hair. Hair growth on other surfaces such as the arms and legs is also stimulated. Enlargement of the larynx, together with thickening of the vocal cords causes the tone of the voice to deepen resulting in the voice 'breaking' with puberty. Testosterone increases the thickness of the skin over the entire body. Production of sebum by the sebaceous glands is also stimulated. The combination of skin thickening and increased sebum production can lead to acne around the time of puberty. Testosterone stimulates protein formation and muscle development. As a result most men have a 50% greater muscle mass than women.

In conjunction with muscle development there is an increase in bone mass with stimulated syntheses of bone collagen and additional deposition of calcium. Both of these factors lead to bone growth and thickening. Testosterone probably also increases red cell concentration, fluid and electrolyte retention and basal metabolic rate. Testosterone in combination with genetic factors is the cause of male pattern baldness. Testosterone stimulates the brain in both men and women to increase interest in sex, explaining the arousal of sexual interest at adolescence. It is also interesting to note that men have significant amounts of oestrogen in their blood. Most of this is formed by converting testosterone into oestrogen in the liver.

CHAPTER 15

Female Reproductive System

Introduction

Externally the female genitals consist of the labia majora, labia minora, clitoris, vestibule, vestibular glands, vaginal orifice and hymen. Collectively this area is described as the vulva. The internal organs of the female reproductive system are located in the pelvis the principle structures involved are the vagina, uterus, two uterine (also called Fallopian) tubes and ovaries.

External structures

Labia

The labia majora are two large longitudinal folds composed of skin, fibrous and adipose tissue. Labia refers to lips and majora means larger. These structures are covered by pubic hair and contain a large number of sebaceous and sweat glands. These structures are normally in contact with each other, closing off the vulva.

The labia minora are two smaller folds of skin lying within the labia majora. Minora means smaller. These structures do not have pubic hair or contain fat like the labia majora but they do contain sebaceous glands. Oily sebum produced by these glands helps to lubricate the area and forms a barrier against infection. The longitudinal cleft between the labia minora is termed the vestibule. Posteriorly in the vestibule is the opening of the vagina. Anteriorly in the vestibule, but posterior to the clitoris, is the urethral orifice. There are two vestibular (Bartholin's) glands, one located on each side of the vaginal opening. These glands have ducts which secrete mucus into the vestibule to keep the vulva moist.

The clitoris is very sensitive

This structure is located at the anterior junction of the labia minora. The clitoris is homologous to the male penis and is a small cylindrical mass of erectile tissue. The external exposed part of the clitoris is the glans. Many sensory nerve endings are located within the clitoris. In appropriate emotional situations the clitoris is the principle sensory structure which stimulates an orgasm. Orgasm describes the climax of the pleasurable sensations associated with sexual activity.

In some cultural situations little girls have part, or all, of their clitoris cut off in a practice described as female genital mutilation (FGM). This causes immediate extreme pain with serious potential complications such as haemorrhage, infection and psychological trauma. There may be longer term complications such as fibrosis and an inability to enjoy sex. This practice is of course an outrage against womanhood and humanity which as health care professionals we strive to eradicate.

Hymen

This is a thin layer of mucus membrane which occludes the opening of the vagina in young girls. However, it must be incomplete to allow menstrual flow and may be completely disrupted if tampons are placed into the vagina. It may also be disrupted by exercise or gymnastics.

Perineum

This is the area inferior to the pelvic floor between the thighs and buttocks in both males and females. The anterior part is called the urogenital triangle and contains the roots of the external genitalia in men and the openings of the urethra and vagina in women. Posteriorly the anal triangle contains the anus. (The mons pubis is the anterior area, covered with pubic hair, above the female genitalia.)

Internal structures

Vagina

This is a fibromuscular tube consisting of fibrous and muscular tissues. Muscular tissue is elastic and will allow for expansion. The vagina extends from the vestibule through the pelvic floor into the pelvis. The anterior wall of the vagina is typically about 7.5 cm in length and the posterior wall about 9 cm. Normally the vagina is collapsed so the anterior and posterior walls are in contact with each other. During sexual intercourse the penis will separate these normally closed walls. As the vagina forms a communication between the uterus and the outside world, menstrual flow may pass through the vagina to be voided. During the process of birth the baby passes down through the vagina as it is the only exit from the uterus. In order to cope with the traumas of sexual intercourse and child birth the walls of the adult vagina are lined with a stratified squamous epithelium. In order to allow expansion this epithelial lining of the vagina is arranged in a series of folds or rugae. Despite having no glands which secrete mucus the vagina is kept moist by secretions from the cervix. From puberty to the menopause the vagina is heavily colonized with bacteria which ferment glycogen to form lactic acid. This acid environment protects the vagina from other potentially infecting bacteria or fungi.

Uterus

This pear shaped hollow muscular organ lies in the pelvic cavity between the bladder to the front (anteriorly) and the sigmoid colon behind (posteriorly). During pregnancy, the uterus is the place where the developing fetus is situated from the time of implantation to delivery. The uterus is divided into three areas, the fundus, body and cervix. The fundus is the domed part above the opening of the uterine tubes. Below this is the body of the uterus which is continuous with the uterine tubes. The cervix has a narrow central channel which connects the body of the uterus with the vagina. The lower part of the cervix projects into the vault of the vagina.

There are three layers of tissue composing the wall of the uterus. The outer layer is termed the perimetrium. The portion covering the fundus of the uterus is composed of peritoneal membrane. Above this layer of peritoneal membrane is

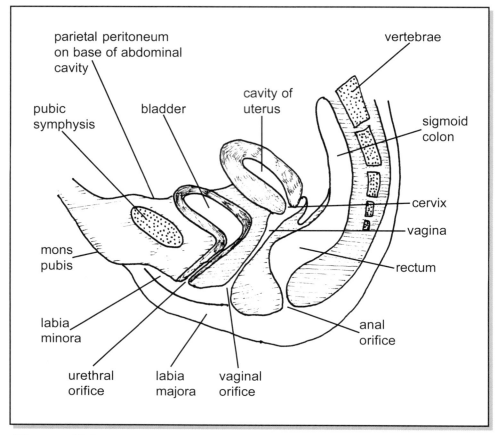

Diagram 15.1
Principle structures of the female pelvic cavity. The pubic symphysis is a joint composed of cartilage between the two hip bones; in late pregnancy this cartilage becomes more flexible to ease delivery. Behind this is the urethra and bladder, then the vagina and uterus, then the sigmoid colon and rectum.

the abdominal cavity. On the sides of the uterus the perimetrium is continuous with the broad ligament which connects the uterus with the uterine tubes. The myometrium is a thick middle layer composed of layers of smooth muscle. During delivery the hormone oxytocin stimulates coordinated contractions of the myometrial smooth muscle to help expel the baby from the uterus. The inner layer, lining the uterine cavity is termed the endometrium. This has a permanent basal layer next to the myometrium which is not lost during menstruation. An inner functional layer thickens during the first half of the menstrual cycle and becomes rich in blood vessels. At the end of a menstrual cycle, if pregnancy does not occur, this layer is shed and discharges through the vagina as menstrual flow. After menstruation it is the basal layer which gives rise to a new functional layer during the next menstrual cycle.

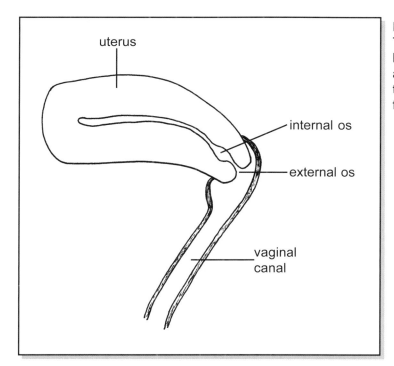

Diagram 15.2
There is an angle between the vagina and the uterus with the uterus projecting forwards.

uterus

internal os

external os

vaginal canal

Uterine tubes

These tubes (also called Fallopian) are about 10 cm long and extend from the uterus. They pass from the pelvis into the abdominal cavity by passing through the peritoneal membrane. The widened ends of the uterine tubes are very close to the ovaries so that they can collect the released ovum. The open end of the uterine tubes house part of the ovaries, almost like holding a tennis ball in an open hand. After ovulation the cilia lining the fimbriated openings to the uterine tubes waft the ovum into the tubes. (Fimbriated describes a border with branched, finger like projections.) From here the ovum is slowly propelled towards the uterus by peristaltic contractions generated by the smooth muscular walls. Ovum movement is also aided by wafting actions of the ciliated epithelium lining the uterine tubes. This epithelium secretes mucus to nourish and lubricate the movement of ova and also acts as a medium for sperm to swim in. If an ovum is fertilized this usually takes place high in the uterine tube. The zygote, which is formed by the fusion of a sperm and ovum, is then propelled towards the uterus for implantation.

Ovaries are the female gonads

Gonads is a collective term which describes the testes and ovaries, the organs which produce the reproductive cells. Ovaries are situated on either side of the uterus to which they are anchored by the ovarian ligament. The ovaries have two principle functions; they produce the female sex hormones oestrogen and

Diagram 15.3
The uterus consists of the cervix, body and fundus. In reality the infundibulum and fimbriae project backwards.

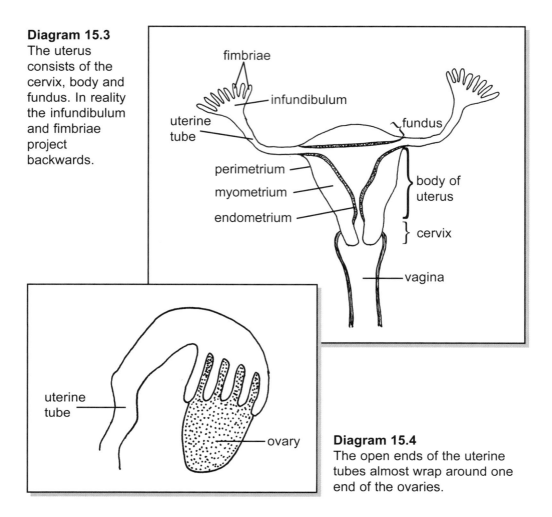

Diagram 15.4
The open ends of the uterine tubes almost wrap around one end of the ovaries.

progesterone and they produce and release the ova. The inner part of an ovary is termed the medulla. This consists of connective tissues, blood vessels, lymphatics and nerves. The outer layer is the cortex where the ova develop and from where they are released. When a baby girl is born her ovaries already contain all of the immature potential ova she will ever produce. These potential ova are surrounded by a single layer of follicular cells and together they form a primordial follicle. (Follicle means little bag.)

The female ovarian cycle

This monthly sexual cycle is also termed the menstrual cycle or endometrial cycle. The purpose of the ovarian cycle is to prepare the lining of the uterus to receive a fertilized ovum. If an ovum is fertilized it implants itself into the prepared vascular endometrium. As the endometrium is vascular it is able to provide oxygen and nutrients for the developing embryo until the placenta develops.

An average ovarian cycle is 28 days long, although there may be considerable variation in this time. Day one is defined as the first day of menstruation because it is obvious when this occurs. The first half of the menstrual cycle is termed the follicular phase. This phase ends with ovulation which typically occurs on day 14, although this time may also vary. The second half of the cycle is termed the luteal phase and continues from ovulation to the onset of the next menstrual period. It is the second half of the menstrual cycle which is most consistently around 14 days. So if a cycle was 30 days, ovulation probably occurred around day 16.

The events of the ovarian cycle are controlled by hormonal signals from the anterior pituitary gland. Coordination of the cycle is essential as the endometrium must be in a developed condition, ready to receive a fertilized ovum at the appropriate time of the month. A fertilized ovum can only develop and grow into a fetus if it is nourished and oxygenated in the vascular endometrium. Anterior pituitary cells produce gonadotrophic hormones, particularly follicular stimulating hormone (FSH) and luteinizing hormone (LH). Without the stimulation of FSH and LH the ovaries remain inactive, as is the case during childhood. Each month after puberty until menopause the anterior pituitary gland secretes follicular stimulating hormone which stimulates the development of a few primordial follicles. The primordial follicles are immature ova which have been present since the birth of a woman. While 8 to 12 follicles begin to develop every month only one will progress to become the mature follicle which will eventually give rise to ovulation. This is important as it means that in the vast majority of pregnancies only one fetus will develop.

Under the influence of FSH the follicular cells (also called granulosa cells) divide, eventually forming a much larger mature follicle. Maturation of the follicle is further stimulated by oestrogen, produced by the follicle itself. The oestrogen produced by the developing follicle also stimulates the development of the endometrium during the first half of the menstrual cycle. A mature follicle contains many layers of follicular cells and an internal collection of follicular fluid also develops. This mature follicle is also referred to as a Graafian follicle. The mature Graafian follicle moves to lie just under the outer layer of the ovary. Under the influence of another anterior pituitary hormone called luteinizing hormone (LH), the mature Graafian follicle ruptures. This releases the ovum from the follicle, through the surface of the ovary in the process termed ovulation. Ovulation normally occurs from alternate ovaries each month, i.e. each ovary will release an ovum every two months. Ova are released into the peritoneal cavity but are quickly propelled by the action of cilia into the opening of the uterine tubes.

In the next few hours after ovulation there is a marked change in the nature of the follicular cells which remain in the ovary. They enlarge in size by two or three times and fill with lipids which give them a yellowish appearance. This change in the nature of the follicular cells into luteal (or lutein cells) is stimulated by luteinizing hormone. This is where the LH derives its name as luteinizing means yellowing. In the 7 to 8 days after ovulation this mass of cells grows to be about 1.5 cm in diameter and is termed the corpus luteum. These cells secrete oestrogen and large amounts of progesterone. Most oestrogen is produced by the Graafian follicle and most progesterone by the corpus luteum. These high levels of progesterone, and to a lesser extent oestrogen, maintain the developed vascular state of the endometrium during the second half of the ovarian cycle. If no pregnancy occurs, the corpus luteum degenerates after 12 days greatly reducing the volumes of oestrogen and progesterone the ovaries secrete. As the level of these hormones in the blood drop, the lining of the endometrium is no longer maintained. This allows the endometrium to degenerate and slough away resulting in menstruation.

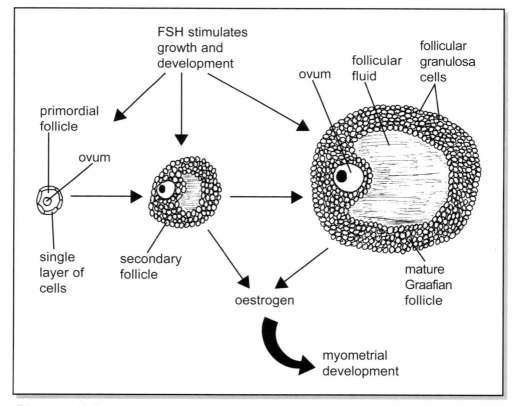

Diagram 15.5
A primordial follicle which has been present in the ovary since birth is stimulated by follicular stimulating hormone (FSH). This stimulates division of the follicular granulosa cells, therefore increasing the size of the follicle. FSH also stimulates growth of the ovum. The follicle in turn secretes oestrogen which goes on to stimulate the development of the endometrium.

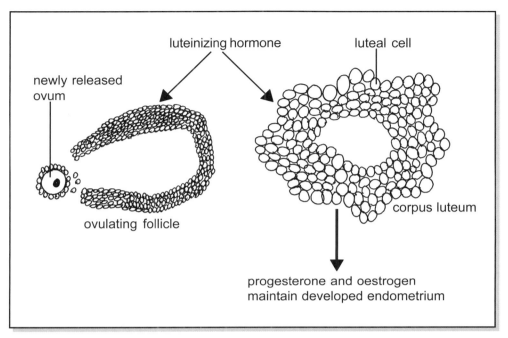

Diagram 15.6
At ovulation luteinizing hormone (LH) stimulates the release of the ovum from the Graafian follicle and also converts the follicular cells into luteal cells which comprise the corpus luteum. After 12 days, if there is no conception, the corpus luteum degenerates into a small cluster of fibrous tissue called the corpus albicans. If a pregnancy does occur, human chorionic gonadotrophin stimulates the corpus luteum to grow to about 2.5 cm in diameter and to live on for about 3 months.

Menstruation

Menstruation is the loss of the necrotic inner lining of the endometrium with some blood and serous fluid loss. During the follicular, first half, of the cycle there is increased development of the endometrium with growth of new blood vessels. At the time of ovulation the endometrium is 3 to 5 mm thick. After ovulation this developed state is maintained partly by oestrogen but mostly by progesterone produced by the corpus luteum. When the levels of oestrogen and progesterone fall due to the degeneration of the corpus luteum there is a vasospasm of the new blood vessels in the developed functional layer of the endometrium. Combined with the loss of hormonal stimulation this vasospasm leads to necrosis (death) of most of this functional layer. Ejection of blood, serous fluid and the necrosed layer of endometrium is aided by prostaglandins which promote contraction of the uterine myometrium. It is this contraction of the myometrium which may give rise to period pains. Blood loss ceases 4 to 7 days after the onset of a period because the endometrium has re-epithelialized.

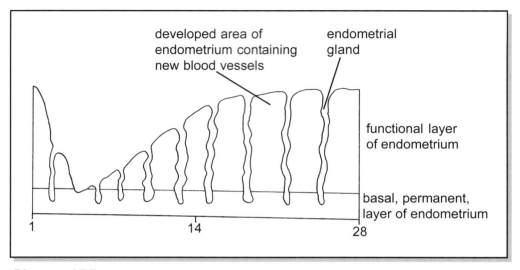

Diagram 15.7
This diagram illustrates the stages of breakdown and development of the endometrium during one ovarian cycle. In the first few days of the cycle thickness is lost due to menstruation. Endometrial development is stimulated by oestrogen from the developing Graafian follicle and maintained by progesterone and oestrogen released from the cells of the corpus luteum.

Conception

Conception refers to the union of a sperm and ovum to begin a new life. Sperm are released high in the vagina and swim through the cervical canal, uterus and uterine tube to reach the ovum. If fertilization is going to occur it normally takes place within 24 hours of ovulation. However, the fertile period is longer than this as sperm may remain viable in the female genital tract for 5 days. This means fertilization can occur as a result of sexual intercourse which occurred a few days before ovulation. A fertilized ovum passes down the uterine tube and enters the uterus 3 to 4 days after ovulation. Once in the uterus it is nourished by a glycogen rich endometrial secretion termed 'uterine milk'. Implantation of the fertilized ovum into the endometrium takes place 7 to 9 days after ovulation.

For the first 3 to 4 months of pregnancy the corpus luteum continues to secrete oestrogen and progesterone to maintain the developed state of the endometrium. If levels of these hormones were not maintained, menstruation would occur and the pregnancy would be lost. After the third month of pregnancy the placenta produces the oestrogen and progesterone required. During the early stage of a pregnancy the corpus luteum is maintained by a hormone called human chorionic gonadotrophin. This is produced by the chorion and may be detected in a pregnant woman's blood and urine as little as 8 days after fertilization. The chorion is one of the membranes which form the embryonic sac and later develops into part of the placenta. The placenta is a complex structure which allows for the transfer of nutrients and oxygen from the maternal to fetal blood. Likewise, waste products of metabolism pass through the placenta from fetus to mother.

Puberty

Between the ages of 9 to 12 years the anterior pituitary gland produces progressively more FSH and LH. As these hormones influence the activity of the ovaries (the female gonads) they are referred to as gonadotrophic hormones. These hormonal influences lead to the onset of regular monthly ovarian cycles, usually beginning between 11 to 15 years of age. This time of change is termed puberty and the first menstrual cycle as menarche.

During puberty the secretion of oestrogens increases 20 fold. There are three main oestrogen type hormones found in the blood; oestradiol, oestrone and oestriol. Oestrogens stimulate the growth and further development of the external and internal sexual organs. Oestrogens also change the vaginal epithelium from cuboidal to a stratified squamous type which is more resistant to trauma and infection.

Oestrogens stimulate the development of breast tissue and increase fat deposition in the breasts. Progesterone is also involved in the development of breast lobules and alveoli.

Oestrogens stimulate bone growth causing a rapid increase in height for several years. However, oestrogens also cause the epiphyses (end parts) of bones to unite with the shafts, across the bony growth plates. After this has occurred the bones can not increase in length meaning that the young woman will stop growing. As testosterone does not have such a strong bone uniting effect boys continue to grow later than girls. Oestrogens also cause fat to be deposited in the subcutaneous tissues, especially over the breasts, buttocks and thighs. It is the presence of subcutaneous adipose tissue which gives women a more rounded appearance compared to men. Pubic and axillary hair grows mostly as a result of androgens (male type hormones) produced by the adrenal cortex.

Menopause

Typically, between the ages of 40 to 50 years the ovarian cycle becomes irregular and ovulation often fails to occur. Eventually the cycles will stop all together and menstruation will no longer occur. With increasing age all of the primordial follicles, which were present from birth, are used to produce Graafian follicles or have degenerated. This means that despite the presence of large amounts of FSH and LH there are no primordial follicles left to be developed. As it is the Graafian follicle and corpus luteum which produce oestrogen the levels of this female hormone produced by the ovaries is reduced to almost nothing. This reduction in oestrogen levels causes many changes associated with the menopause.

As it is oestrogen which stimulates bone growth and development, bone density will start to reduce. In severe cases loss of bone mass may lead to increasing bone fragility with an increased risk of fracture, a condition termed osteoporosis. Women also have an increased risk of developing arterial diseases after the menopause, such as coronary arterial disease. This is because before the menopause oestrogens help to lower cholesterol levels, but after the menopause the lower oestrogen levels allow cholesterol levels to rise. Other transitional menopausal features include hot flushes, irritability, fatigue and anxiety.

Breasts

Breasts are composed of skin, connective tissues, adipose tissue and mammary glands which are the milk producing structures. Immediately under the skin is a superficial fascia of connective tissue which provides additional support. The mammary glands are composed of clusters of alveoli which are arranged in systems of secretory lobules. These lobules are connected to a system of mammary ducts, lined with columnar epithelium, which transports milk towards the nipple. The ductal system from the lobules converges into 15 to 20 lactiferous sinuses and ducts. Each lactiferous duct opens independently onto the nipple. The combination of a system of lobules and mammary ducts, together with their associated connective and adipose tissues, forms a lobe of the breast. A breast is therefore composed of a radial arrangement of lobes.

Within a breast are a series of suspensory ligaments which surround the lobes and extend to the skin surface. Suspensory ligaments are arranged in a radial pattern, like the spokes of a wheel. They are particularly prominent in the upper areas of the breasts and provide support for the weight of breast tissue. In addition to providing support they form divisions between the lobes of the breast. Carcinoma of the breast causes tension on these ligaments leading to pitting in the skin. Suspensory ligaments also become looser with increasing age or as a result of repeated strain as might be caused by jogging. This is why the breasts should be supported during high impact exercise or sport.

In addition to the superficial fascia and suspensory ligaments, breasts are supported by the underlying pectoral muscles; if these are well developed the breasts will be supported higher on the chest wall. These pectoral muscles lie over the upper part of the chest and are covered by a sheath of tough fibrous tissue called the deep fascia. Between the base of the breast and the deep fascia of the pectoral muscle is a layer of loose connective tissue called the submammary space, which allows a degree of breast movement over the deep pectoral fascia.

Surrounding the nipple is a pigmented area called the areola which contains numerous sebaceous glands. There are also sebaceous glands in the nipple. The sebum these glands produce helps to lubricate the nipple during suckling. Before a woman has been pregnant the areola is usually pink (less so in darker skinned individuals) but after the first pregnancy it changes to brown and remains so for life. Breasts are not round as is often supposed, but there is a tail of tissue which extends towards the axilla. Variation in breast size in non-lactating women is largely determined by the amount of adipose tissue they contain.

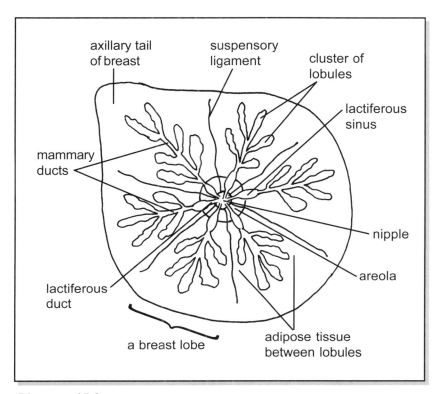

Diagram 15.8
A breast is composed of a radial arrangement of lobes. These lobes
are composed of clusters of mammary lobules and ducts with
associated adipose and connective tissues. Mammary ducts drain
milk from the clusters of lobules into a widened area of milk duct
called a lactiferous sinus. These allow for a reservoir of milk during
lactation. A lactiferous duct transport milk from a lactiferous sinus
onto the surface of the nipple. Suspensory ligaments divide the
lobes and provide support. Most breasts are composed of 15 to 20
lobes but only 6 are illustrated in this diagram.

Hormonal control of breast development and lactation

Breast development and enlargement is stimulated at puberty under the influence
of oestrogen released during the monthly sexual cycle. High levels of oestrogen are
secreted by the placenta during pregnancy. These high oestrogen levels cause the
lobular and ductal system of the breasts to grow and branch in preparation for
milk production, leading to an increase in breast size. In the later stages of pregnancy
progesterone leads to further development and maturation of the breast lobules.
During late pregnancy and lactation most of the mass of the breast is composed of
this highly developed system of secretory lobules. When not pregnant or breast
feeding the mammary lobules and ducts account for about 50% of breast mass,
the remainder being mostly adipose tissue.

During pregnancy the anterior pituitary gland produces increasing amounts of prolactin which stimulates the syntheses and secretion of milk. During breast feeding nerve signals from the nipple travel to the hypothalamus stimulating ongoing prolactin secretion. This is why the breasts will continue to produce milk

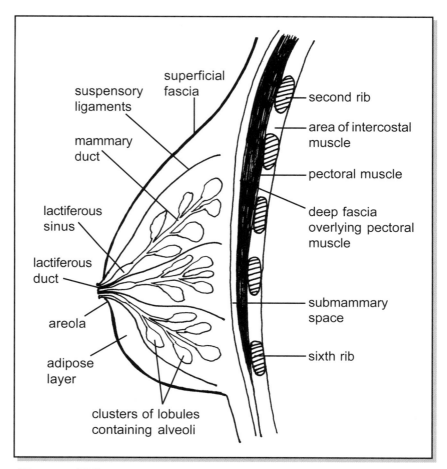

Diagram 15.9
The attached portion of the breast normally extends from the level of the second or third rib, down to the sixth rib. The chest wall is composed of the ribs and intercostal muscles. Overlying this is the pectoral muscle (specifically the pectoralis major). The deep fascia overlies the pectoral muscle. Above this is the submammary space which allows the breast a degree of movement relative to the chest wall. This allows the breast to move a little depending on the overall position of the body. Suspensory ligaments divide the lobes and provide support. External support is supplied by the superficial fascia. Milk is formed in the alveoli in the lobules which drain milk into the mammary ducts. After passing through a lactiferous sinus milk is expressed through a lactiferous duct onto the nipple.

as long as a child continues to suckle although the volumes of milk produced will reduce after about eight months.

Milk is secreted continuously into the alveoli of the breasts. However, to convey this milk from the site of production, through the ductal system, to the nipple requires the action of another hormone called oxytocin. Suckling causes oxytocin to be secreted from the posterior pituitary gland. In the breasts oxytocin causes the contraction of myoepithelial cells which surround the alveoli and mammary ducts. These contractile cells have fibres which surround the alveoli to aid overall contraction causing milk to be ejected into the ductal system at a pressure of 10-20 mmHg. As a result of this pressure in the ductal system the baby can suck out the milk with minimal effort. This process is called milk ejection or let-down. Regulation of let-down by oxytocin means the baby will receive large volumes of milk within 30 to 60 seconds of starting to suckle. It also means the breasts do not dribble milk in between feeds. Mixed in with the milk the breasts secrete many types of antibodies as well as neutrophils and macrophages. These all protect the baby against potentially lethal infections.

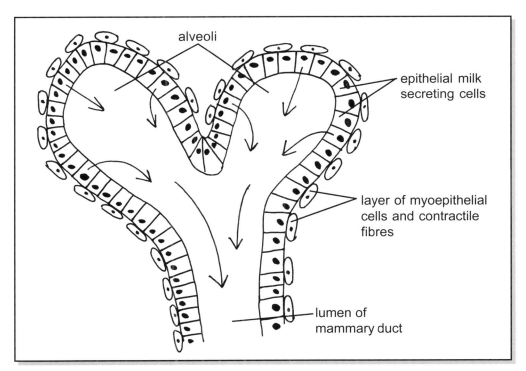

Diagram 15.10
A breast lobule. During lactation milk is produced in the secretory epithelium lining the alveoli and milk ducts. Once formed this milk 'buds' from the surface of the individual cells into the lumen. This process is continuous for the duration of breast feeding. Suckling causes hormonal contraction of the surrounding myoepithelial cells to facilitate milk secretion. Arrows show direction of milk movement.

CHAPTER 16

Eyes

Overall structure of the eye

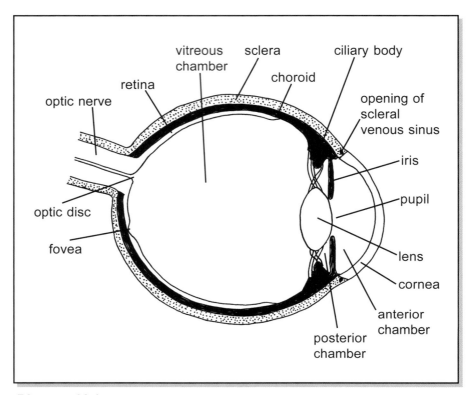

Diagram 16.1
Structures of the eye. The tissues are arranged in 3 layers. An outer fibrous layer consists of the sclera which is continuous with the transparent cornea. The middle vascular layer is composed of 3 continuous structures which are the choroid, ciliary body and iris. An inner light sensitive layer of pigmented and neuronal tissue is called the retina. The eyes are protected within the orbital cavity of the skull. Between the eyeball and the bone of the orbit is a layer of fat which is also protective.

Sclera and cornea form the outer layer

The sclera is a tough, fibrous outer layer which maintains the shape of the eyeball. At the front the sclera can be seen as the 'white of the eye'. In order to allow light into the eye the sclera is transparent at the front. This transparent section is called the cornea. Light rays passing through the cornea are refracted (bent). This starts the process of light ray convergence, however, the degree of refraction cannot be varied. With eye injuries or infection it is important to avoid scarring of the cornea as this will interfere with the normal passage of light through this transparent structure.

Six extrinsic eye muscles connect the sclera to the bone of the orbit. Contraction of these muscles allows the eyes to look in a particular direction and both eyes to fix on the same spot. Most of these extrinsic eye muscles are controlled by the oculomotor nerve which is cranial nerve III.

Conjunctiva is a sensitive outer membrane

Lining the front of the sclera, cornea and inside of the eyelids is a fine transparent, sensitive membrane called the conjunctiva. This is a mucous membrane which secretes mucus to lubricate the front of the eye. The conjunctiva covers the sclera and cornea at the front of the eye and reflects back to cover the inside of the eyelids. Conjunctivitis describes inflammation of this membrane which may be caused by bacterial infection or an allergic reaction. Lack of vitamin A can lead to a wrinkled dry looking conjunctiva with little grey bubbles called Bitot's spots. This disorder is called xerophthalmia and can lead to blindness if foods containing vitamin A are not eaten.

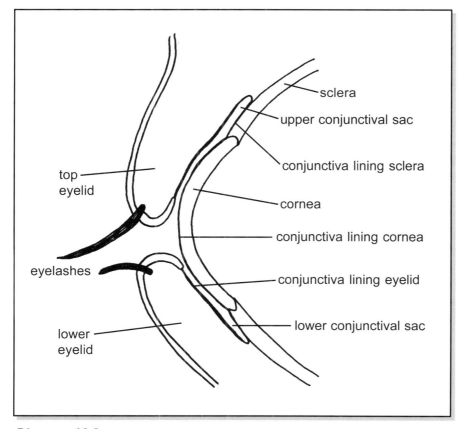

Diagram 16.2
The conjunctiva reflects from the front of the eye to line the inside of the eyelids. The lower conjunctival sac is useful for dropping eye drops into.

Lacrimal glands produce tears

Tears are produced by the lacrimal glands and lubricate the conjunctiva. Tear fluid also contains an enzyme called lysozyme which is protective against infection. The lacrimal gland is located in the upper outer (superior lateral) area of the orbit. Several ducts convey tears onto the surface of the conjunctiva. They then flow across the surface of the conjunctiva, washing away any small particles which may have entered the eye. Blinking of the eyelids helps to sweep tears over the surface of the eye. Leaving the eye, tears flow into two ducts on the nasal corner of the eye. From here they flow into the nasal cavity via the nasolacrimal duct. This explains why we get a runny nose if more tears are produced than normal. Irritation of the conjunctiva increases tear production via a parasympathetic reflex. This helps to wash away the cause of the irritation.

The choroid is dark coloured and vascular

This vascular layer contains many small blood vessels to supply the eye with oxygen and nutrients and to remove metabolic waste products. As the choroid is dark brown, it absorbs any reflected light. If light reflected from the retina was not absorbed it could reflect back onto the retina for a second time producing double images.

The ciliary body contains the ciliary muscles

The ciliary body is triangular in cross section and forms a complete ring around the eyeball. Ciliary muscle fibres are contained within the ciliary body. As the ciliary muscle is mostly composed of circular fibres, contraction has the effect of decreasing the diameter of the ring formed by the ciliary body. Ciliary muscles are attached to the suspensory ligaments which in turn attach to the capsule containing the lens. This means that contraction of the ciliary muscles will reduce tension on the lens allowing it to become fatter and more convex. Conversely, relaxation of the ciliary muscles will increase the size of the ring formed by the ciliary body and so will stretch the lens making it thinner and less convex. Contraction and relaxation of the ciliary muscle therefore changes the shape of the lens and so the degree to which it refracts light. This alteration in the refractive index allows for accurate focusing of light rays passing through. Contraction of the ciliary muscles is stimulated by branches of the oculomotor nerve.

The iris gives the eyes their colour

This is the visible coloured part of the eye which lies behind the cornea and in front of the lens. Eye colour is determined by the colour of the iris and is under genetic control. In the centre of the iris is the dark opening of the pupil which is the only portal through which light may enter the eyeball. The reason the pupil appears dark is that there is no light emanating from within the eyeball.

Light which does enter the eye is absorbed once it has stimulated the retina, so is not reflected back out of the pupil.

Within the iris are circular and radial muscle fibres which facilitate alterations in pupil size. This will therefore regulate how much light is able to enter the eye. Contraction of the circular muscle fibres constrict the pupil while contraction of the radial muscles dilates it. When there are high levels of ambient light the iris will constrict to reduce the size of the pupil and therefore the amount of light entering the eye. Conversely, in low light levels the iris will dilate, so increasing the diameter of the pupil which in turn increases the amount of light entering the eyeball. This regulation allows retinal function across a wide range of ambient light levels so we can see in very bright or dim conditions. Sympathetic stimulation of the iris will result in dilation of the pupil while parasympathetic stimulation will lead to constriction. Atropine based eye drops may sometimes be given to dilate the pupils prior to a clinical examination. This works because atropine blocks parasympathetic nerve stimulation.

Nerve supply to the iris

Contraction of the iris, and therefore size of the pupil, is controlled by branches of the oculomotor nerve (cranial nerve III). This nerve arises from the midbrain of the brain stem and passes along the base of the skull into the eye. As all cranial nerves are in pairs, there are a pair of oculomotor nerves. The nerve arising from the right side of the midbrain supplies the right eye and the one arising from the left side the left eye. If there is an increase in the pressure on one side of the cranial cavity this will press on the relevant oculomotor nerve reducing its ability to function. If the oculomotor nerve is not working the pupil on the same side will not constrict normally when a light is shone into the eye. The pupil will become sluggish and dilated. If this clinical feature is noted it is a sign of serious head injury and should receive immediate neurosurgical attention.

The lens focuses light rays

The lens is just behind the iris and pupil and is suspended by the suspensory ligaments which connect to the ciliary body. It is the lens which changes shape to focus on near and far objects. When the ciliary muscles contract they push down on the lens causing it to become thicker. Relaxation of the ciliary muscles stretches the lens, making it thinner. In order to focus on near objects, incoming light rays must be refracted through a greater angle by a thicker lens. To focus on distant objects the light rays need to be refracted less so the ciliary muscles will relax, allowing the lens to become thinner.

The reason the lens is able to focus light rays accurately on the retina is because it bends the light as it passes through. Refraction describes the bending of light rays as they pass from a medium of one density to another. The more convex the lens is the more it will refract the light rays passing through. As a result of the

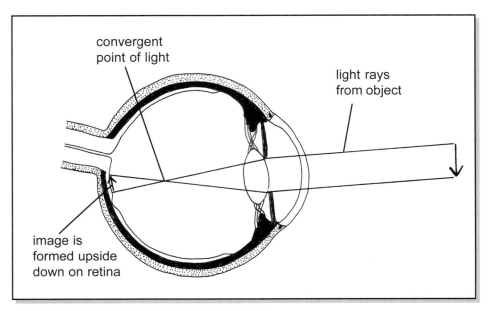

Diagram 16.3
Light rays are refracted by the lens to such a degree that they converge
before the retina. Light rays pass through each other without any interference
and therefore images are formed upside down on the retina. If the lens
develops cloudiness or opacity this is termed a cataract.

lens refracting light rays they all converge at a point in front of the retina. They
pass through this point before forming an image on the retina. As light travels
in straight lines this means that the focused image formed on the retina is upside
down. Fortunately the occipital lobes of the brain reverse these images allowing
us to perceive the world the right way up.

Accommodation allows focusing

Accommodation describes the ability of the lens to change shape in order for
the eyes to focus on near or far objects. When an object is more than about 6
metres away the combination of the refraction of the cornea and lens are able to
focus light rays on the retina without any contraction of the ciliary muscles.

In order to focus on objects less than 6 metres away an increased degree of
accommodation is required. Firstly, to focus on a near object the pupils constrict.
This means more light passes through the central area of the lens which is more
convex and therefore refracts light rays through a greater angle. Secondly, the ciliary
muscles contract making the lens shorter and fatter with a more curved surface.
This will increase the refractive index of the lens, again bending the light rays
through a greater angle. From this it can be seen that active ciliary muscular
contraction is needed to focus on close objects while they may simply relax while
focusing at a distance.

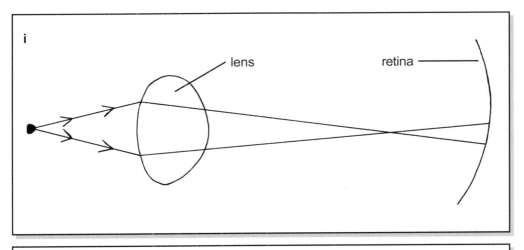

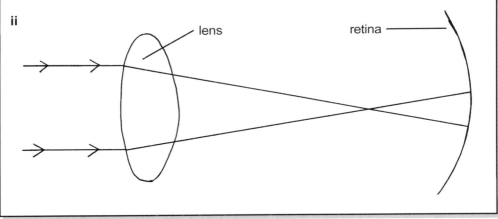

Diagram 16.4

(i)   Light rays from near objects are very divergent (i.e. are moving apart at large angles) so need to be refracted (bent) through a large angle in order to focus on the retina. In the process of accommodation the ciliary muscles contract causing the lens to become shorter and fatter. This makes the surface of the lens more convex and so will increase the angle through which light rays will be refracted. This allows light from close objects to be accurately focused on the retina. With increasing age the lens hardens and is therefore less able to accommodate. This makes it harder to focus on close objects resulting in the age related problem of presbyopia. This is why people need reading glasses after a particular age, usually at some stage in their forties.

(ii)   Light rays from distant objects are more parallel than those from close objects. This means less refraction is required. When the lens is thin it will refract light rays through a smaller angle than when it is fat. So in order to focus on distant objects the ciliary muscles relax stretching the lens causing it to become thinner. The cornea also causes some refraction of light but this is by a constant angle. It is the lens which facilitates the variable focusing of accommodation.

Thirdly, the eyeballs move in the process of convergence. This changes the angle at which light rays enter the eyes in order to generate images on the corresponding areas of the retina in each eye. If convergence did not occur the two retinas would each form an image in a different position leading to double vision (diplopia). This is why someone almost appears 'cross eyed' when trying to focus on the tip of their nose.

Visual acuity (VA)

This describes the ability to distinguish two separate points of light. Visual acuity is at its best when the light rays fall on the cones of the fovea. The fovea is the central area of the retina and is densely populated with colour sensitive

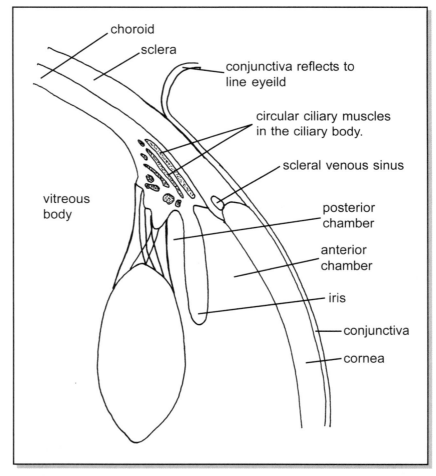

Diagram 16.5
The anterior and posterior chambers are both in front of the lens, behind the cornea, both filled with aqueous humour. Behind the lens is the vitreous body.

cone cells with high levels of acuity. VA's are usually tested with a Snellen's type chart which starts with big letters and works down to progressively smaller ones. A standard chart should be viewed from a distance of 6 metres and each eye should be tested separately.

Anterior and posterior chambers are filled with aqueous humour

The anterior chamber is behind the cornea and in front of the iris while the posterior chamber is behind the iris. These two chambers are continuous through the pupillary opening. Both of these chambers are filled with a fluid called aqueous humour. This fluid is secreted into the anterior chamber from the epithelium of the ciliary body. From here it flows through the pupil into the anterior chamber and is absorbed into the scleral venous sinus (formally called the canal of Schlemm). If there is an increase in the volumes of aqueous humour production, or a reduction in drainage, the volume of fluid will increase. This will increase the intraocular pressure which is the pressure inside the eyeball. This increase in intraocular pressure is called glaucoma which may eventually lead to blindness as a result of compression of the retina and its blood supply.

Vitreous body

Behind the lens and in front of the retina lies the vitreous chamber. This is filled with the vitreous body which is a transparent gelatinous substance. This maintains the shape of the eye and transmits light from the lens to the retina.

Retina is the light sensitive layer

The retina is the inner layer of the wall of the eye. A pigmented layer is firmly attached to the choroid and lying on top of this is a neural layer composed of delicate neuronal tissues. When specialised cells in the retina are exposed to light they generate new nerve impulses which pass along the nerve fibres of the optic nerve. When the occipital lobes of the brain receive these nerve impulses they are perceived as vision.

The optic disc is where the optic nerve leaves the retina; as this area has no light sensitive cells it is described as the blind spot. It is lighter in colour than the surrounding retina and branches of the central retinal artery spread out from this point to supply blood to the retina. If there is an increase in pressure within the cranial cavity as a result of trauma or disease, the optic discs swell with oedema. Swelling of the optic discs can be seen using an ophthalmoscope and is termed papilloedema.

Detached retina describes an abnormal situation where the neural layer separates from the pigmented layer. As the neural layer of the retina receives much of its nutrient and oxygen supply from the underlying layers, prolonged detachment can lead to retinal necrosis (death of tissue) with subsequent blindness.

Diagram 16.6
Test for the presence of your blind spot. Close one eye and hold the page close to your other eye and stare at the circle. Gradually move further away from the page, but keep staring at the circle. You will find there is a position at which the cross disappears. This is the point at which light rays from the cross are hitting your blind spot so cannot be perceived.

Rods and cones convert light rays into nervous impulses

The actual light sensitive nerve cell receptors are described as rods and cones. This is because rod cells are long and thin, like a rod, while cone cells are shorter and fatter. Each retina contains about 3 million cone cells which generate colour vision in good light levels. Cones have low levels of sensitivity but high levels of acuity. Although cones look the same there are three different types, each containing a different photopigment. These photopigments are lipoproteins which detect the presence of red, green or blue light. The photopigment erythrolabe detects red light, chlorolabe green light and cyanolabe blue light. Our perception of colour is generated by the blend of signals created by these three types of cones. The different colours we perceive actually represent light waves of different frequencies in the electromagnetic spectrum.

The macula lutea (or yellow spot) is a relatively thin area of posterior retina containing dense arrays of light sensitive cells. In the middle of this area is a small depression called the fovea centralis which contains only cones. When we look directly at an object the light rays fall on the fovea. This means we have high resolution colour vision when looking directly at an object in good light levels. Colour blindness describes a reduced ability to perceive the full range of colours. The most common form of colour blindness is a sex linked genetic disorder called red-green colour blindness. Males are affected more than females and sufferers cannot distinguish reds and greens.

Rods are insensitive to colour but work well in low light levels (such as moonlight). There are about 100 million rod cells per retina and they perceive shades of grey. Rods therefore have high sensitivity but low acuity. This is why we only see in black and white in low light levels. The area of the retina at the back of the eye contains a high concentration of cones while in the more peripheral areas of the retina there are relatively more rods. This is why we can sometimes see very dim objects if we do not look directly at them but a little to the side. This will mean the light rays fall onto the periphery of the retina which contains a higher proportion of rods.

Dark adaptation takes time

Rods work by light acting on a photosensitive pigment called rhodopsin (also called visual purple). Bright light will degrade the rhodopsin meaning the rod cells will not function. This is not a problem in bright light as the cones will generate detailed colour vision. However, if we move into a dark area the cones will no longer function in the reduced light levels. As the rhodopsin in the cones has been inactivated by the bright light we will not have rod or cone function for a period of time. As a result we will not be able to see anything. If we remain in a dark area for some minutes, gradually we will be able to see objects in the reduced light levels. This happens because rhodopsin is being regenerated within the rods allowing them to function. This process is referred to as dark adaptation or night vision. In order to preserve night vision it is important not to look at bright objects such as car headlights or flares. The normal synthesis of rhodopsin is dependent on the presence of vitamin A, explaining why a deficiency of this vitamin will cause 'night blindness'. This problem is rapidly reversed when vitamin A is given. Increasing vitamin A intake beyond an adequate level will not, however, improve night vision.

Binocular vision

Binocular (also called stereoscopic) vision allows us to gain three dimensional information about the objects we see. This depth perception allows us to estimate how far away they are, where they are in space and their speed. Binocular vision is possible because the two eyes are a slight distance apart and therefore perceive an object from a slightly different angle. From this slight difference the occipital lobes of the brain are able to calculate and allow us to perceive three dimensional information. For example it is very hard to estimate the speed of an approaching vehicle with one eye closed. To experience the benefits of binocular vision in a safer experiment, simply try any ball game with one eye covered.

Optic nerves carry impulses from the eyes to the brain

There are two optic nerves (cranial nerve II), one leaving each eye. The optic nerves carry visual information in the form of electrical nerve impulses generated by the rods and cones. Over the area where the optic nerve leaves the eye there are no light sensetive rods and cones resulting in a 'blind spot'. The two optic nerves meet together under the base of the brain at a point called the optic chiasma. They then separate into two nerves again and synapse in the thalamus before carrying the visual information into the occipital lobes of the brain where vision is generated.

CHAPTER 17

Ears

Essential science

Sound is produced by mechanical vibrations in a medium, usually air. As an object vibrates it sets up vibrations in the air molecules it comes into contact with. These vibrating molecules come into contact with adjacent molecules and so the sound is propagated through the air as waves of compression. The rate at which a sound source vibrates is described in terms of vibrations per second or hertz (Hz). For example if an object (such as the vocal cords or a guitar string) is vibrating 261.63 times per second, that is with a frequency of 261.63 hertz, a middle C will be generated. If the frequency doubles to 523.25 Hz the pitch will have moved up one musical octave to a higher C. Speech is a complex combination of frequencies, mostly in the 400-2000 Hz range. People can hear sound from a frequency range of about 20Hz up to as high as around 20 000 Hz in children. However, with increasing age the ability to hear high frequency sound is reduced, older people may not be able to hear sounds above 5000 Hz.

The speed of sound varies depending on the density of the medium it is passing through; the denser the medium the faster sound will travel through it. For example sound travels at 1500 m/s in sea water as it is a relatively dense medium. As air is less dense transmission of sound waves is slower. At sea level, at 21°C, sound normally travels at 344 m/s (1238 km/h, 770 mph).

Ultrasound describes sound which has a higher frequency than can be heard by people, above a frequency of 20,000 Hz. Ultrasound may be channelled into the body where it reflects from internal structures. These echoes or reflections can then be used to generate anatomical images. Ultrasound investigations do not use potentially dangerous X-rays, and as far as is known have no adverse effects at all. These factors make ultrasound a useful and safe diagnostic tool. Conversely, sound which is too low a frequence for humans to hear is termed infrasound. This will have a frequency of below 20 Hz.

Outer ear

This includes what most people would call the ear, correctly referred to as the auricle (also called the pinna). The auricle is a relatively thin structure and consists of cartilage covered with skin. Between the cartilaginous parts there are some muscles which may change the shape of the auricle, thus altering its sound collecting and channelling properties. There are also some external muscles which may change the position of the auricle, again altering the sound collecting properties.

All of these muscles are controlled by the facial nerve (cranial nerve VII). At the bottom of the auricle is a fleshy lobule, commonly called the ear lobe.

Once sound waves have been collected and channelled by the auricle, they are directed into the second part of the outer ear, the external acoustic (auditory) meatus. This canal runs through the temporal bone of the skull for about 2.5 cm

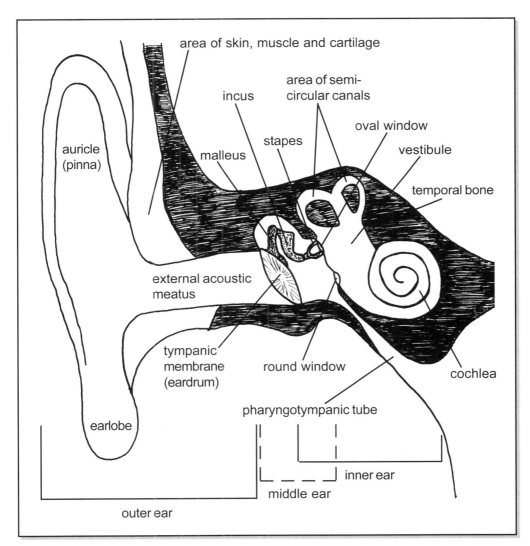

Diagram 17.1
The ear is the organ of hearing and balance; it is divided into three main parts, the outer, middle and inner ear. The outer ear extends from the auricle to the tympanic membrane. The middle ear begins with the tympanic membrane and extends to the oval and round windows and arguably includes the pharyngotympanic tube. The inner ear lies on the medial side of these windows and contains the cochlea and semicircular canals.

from the auricle to the tympanic membrane (or eardrum). The skin lining this meatus contains some hairs and modified sweat glands which produce cerumen (earwax). The function of the external acoustic meatus is to convey sound waves to the tympanic membrane; it is slightly curved to protect the eardrum from penetrating objects.

The tympanic membrane separates the external acoustic meatus from the middle ear. It is composed of connective tissue, lined with a thin layer of skin on the outside and mucous membrane over the inner surface. A ring of fibrocartilage surrounds the tympanic membrane connecting it firmly to the temporal bone of the skull. The external acoustic meatus and tympanic membrane can readily be examined using an otoscope; this provides illumination and magnification for detailed examination.

Excessive ear wax

Normally the cerumen is self clearing from the external acoustic meatus, but it can sometimes accumulate in the narrow canal. This may cause temporary deafness as a result of impacted cerumen preventing sound from reaching the tympanic membrane. Often the impacted wax can be softened by warmed olive oil to improve natural removal. In more severe cases irrigation with warmed water may be needed to clean out the meatus.

Middle ear

The components of the middle ear are housed in a mucous membrane lined cavity within the temporal bone of the skull. As the middle ear is connected to the nasopharynx by the pharyngotympanic (Eustachian) tube it is filled with air at atmospheric pressure. If there is a reduction in atmospheric pressure (for example when going uphill) there will be a higher pressure in the middle ear than in the external acoustic meatus causing the tympanic membrane to be pushed out. Swallowing can open the normally closed pharyngotympanic tube, allowing air out into the nasopharynx. This will reduce the pressure in the middle ear and so equalize the pressure on both sides of the tympanic membrane. When going under water the increased pressure will push the tympanic membrane inwards causing pain. If the pressure is not equalized by 'clearing the ears' it is possible for the external pressure to burst the tympanic membrane (eardrum).

The middle ear begins at the tympanic membrane. Sound waves traveling down the external acoustic meatus cause vibration of the tympanic membrane. Directly attached to the tympanic membrane is the malleus which is the first of three small bones called auditory ossicles. The malleus in turn forms an articulation with the second ossicle called the incus. This bone in turn articulates with the third auditory ossicle which is the stapes bone. Vibrations of the tympanic membrane are therefore mechanically transmitted through the middle ear, via these three middle ear bones. Finally the stapes is physically connected to the oval window. This mechanical arrangement means that vibrations of the tympanic membrane cause equivalent vibration of the oval window.

Muscles attached to the malleus and stapes can contract to reduce the amount of vibrations which pass through the middle ear. This occurs in response to loud noises and prevents too much sound being transmitted through to the inner ear. This modulation can be seen as a form of 'volume control' for the inner ear.

Otitis media is caused by middle ear infection

This describes inflammation of the middle ear caused by infection. Viruses or bacteria may migrate into the middle ear via the pharyngotympanic tube. Once in the middle ear they cause an accumulation of inflammatory fluid which will cause pressure on the tympanic membrane. Despite being painful this disorder is usually self-limiting. Sometimes the infection causes a perforation of the tympanic membrane allowing the excessive fluid to drain relieving the pressure and pain. Perforations of the tympanic membrane normally heal up in a few weeks but as they do so it is important not to allow any water into the middle ear.

Inner ear

Inner ear structures are located within the bony labyrinth of the temporal bone. The main parts of this bony labyrinth are the vestibule, semicircular canals and the cochlea. This interconnected bony cavity is lined with periosteum and contains a clear fluid called the perilymph. Housed within the bony labyrinth is the membranous labyrinth. This continuous structure consists of the cochlear duct, three semicircular canals and two sacs located in the vestibule called the utricle and the saccule. These membranous spaces are filled with endolymph.

The cochlea houses the organ of hearing

This coiled structure basically consists of three tubes, the scala vestibuli, cochlear duct and scala tympani. Vibrations of the oval window are caused by vibrations of the stapes. As the oval window vibrates this causes vibrations in the perilymph of the scala vestibuli of the cochlea.

When the oval window vibrates slowly, representing very low pitched sound, slow vibrations are set up in the perilymph. These travel from the oval window into the start of the scala vestibule at the base of the cochlea. From here the vibrations are propagated through the perilymph to the apex of the cochlea in the scala vestibuli and then back to the round window via the scala tympani. Such vibrations, which pass all around the cochlea in the perilymph of the scala vestibuli and scala tympani, represent sounds which are of too low a pitch for us to hear. Such sounds usually have a frequency of 20 Hz or less and are referred to as infrasounds.

However, faster vibrations, representing sounds in the audible range, occur too quickly to allow perilymph to be displaced all around the cochlea. These faster vibrations displace the vestibular membrane and so vibrate the endolymph in the cochlear duct. From the endolymph of the cochlear duct the vibrations pass through the spiral organ (of Corti). As the sound passes through the spiral organ, the sound sensitive cells it contains also vibrate. It is this vibration which generates a new auditory nerve impulse. After passing through the spiral organ a vibration passes on through the basilar membrane and into the perilymph of the scala tympani. These vibrations in turn displace fluid in the perilymph of the scala tympani. One way to think of this is that sound of a particular frequency takes a 'short cut' from the scala vestibuli to the scala tympani, passing through the spiral organ as it does so. Vibrations in the scala tympani cause movement in the round window. Displacement of the round window effectively allows the vibrations to leave the cochlea. If this did not happen the vibrations would be deflected backwards causing echoes.

The actual organ of hearing is the spiral organ (of Corti). This contains sound sensitive cells which respond to particular frequencies of sound. When these sound sensitive cells vibrate at a particular frequency (representing a particular pitch) they generate a new nerve impulse. The sound sensitive cells are called hair cells. They do not have actual hairs but very sensitive (hair like) microvilli which project from the apex of each cell.

Cells which are sensitive to higher frequency sounds are near the base of the cochlea while those which respond to lower pitch are near the apex. In practice most sounds contain a range of frequencies so a number of regions of the spiral organ will be stimulated at the same time. This means a range of nerve impulses will be simultaneously generated and passed to the brain. Once new nerve impulses have been generated they are conveyed to the auditory cortex of the brain via cranial nerve VIII, the vestibulocochlear nerve. In the brain these nerve impulses are interpreted as sound.

Localization of sound

As well as hearing sound we can usually detect the direction of a sound source. This is because sound coming from the left will reach the left ear very slightly before it reaches the right. Despite this minimal difference in arrival times, the brain is able to compute directional information allowing us to perceive the direction a sound has come from.

Deafness

Deafness is usually partial but may be complete in some people. Conductive deafness is caused by impaired conduction of sound to the cochlea. It may therefore be caused by disorders of the outer or middle ear. For example, sticky, tenacious secretions may accumulate in the middle ear, often as a result of the nasopharyngeal tube not clearing secretions adequately. This is correctly termed secretory otitis media with effusion (or glue ear) and prevents normal movements of the auditory ossicles.

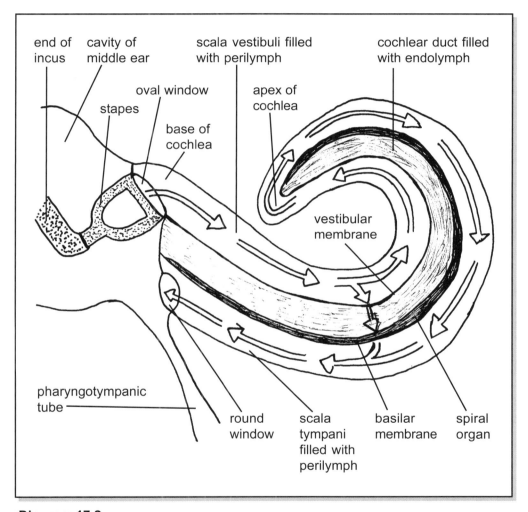

Diagram 17.2
A simplified diagram of an 'unwound' cochlea. (In reality the cochlea twists on itself two and a half times). Arrows indicate the direction sound vibrations take through the cochlea. Vibrating sound waves pass from the perilymph of the scala vestibuli, through the vestibular membrane, into the endolymph of the cochlear duct. From here they pass through the hair cells of the spiral organ which are located on the basilar membrane. Vibrations in the hair cells generate new sensory nerve impulses. Once the hair cells have been stimulated the sound vibrations pass through the basilar membrane into the perilymph of the scala tympani. These vibrations will leave the inner ear via the round window.

Damage to the cochlea, nerve pathways or auditory areas of the brain may lead to sensoryneural deafness. This form of hearing loss may be caused by exposure to excessive noise, trauma, side effects of drugs, meningitis, tumours or may be present at birth. It is also a common observation that hearing declines in older people; this is caused by loss of hair cells in the spiral organ of Corti of the cochlea. The ability to hear high frequency sounds is lost first. Exposure to excessive loud noise will accelerate the loss of hearing. This is why ear protection should be worn in noisy environments. Consistently listening to loud music is another factor.

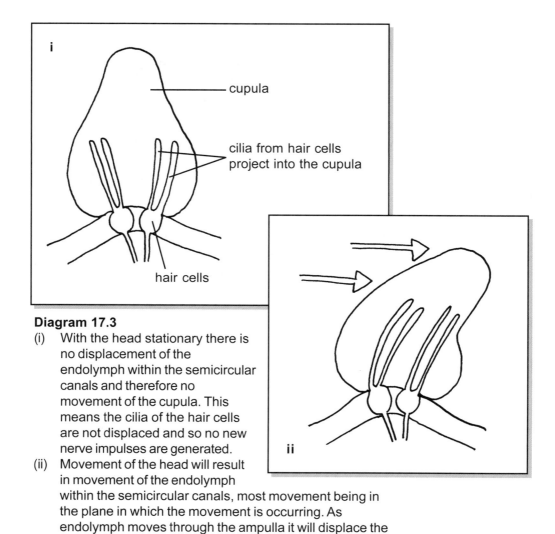

Diagram 17.3

(i) With the head stationary there is no displacement of the endolymph within the semicircular canals and therefore no movement of the cupula. This means the cilia of the hair cells are not displaced and so no new nerve impulses are generated.

(ii) Movement of the head will result in movement of the endolymph within the semicircular canals, most movement being in the plane in which the movement is occurring. As endolymph moves through the ampulla it will displace the cupula and so the cilia it contains. This will cause the hair cells to generate new nerve impulses which will be detected in the brain as acceleration and movement. (Arrows indicate movement of endolymph.)

Semicircular canals are essential for balance

There are three semicircular canals, each forms two thirds of a circle. They are connected at both ends to the utricle and contain endolymph. Each canal is at right angles to the other two. This means there is a semicircular canal in each of the three planes (i.e. dimensions). At the end of each canal is a dilated area called the ampulla. In each ampulla is a group of hair cells with sensitive cilia projecting from the cell surfaces. These cilia project into a gelatinous mass called the cupula.

When the head moves in a particular direction, the cupula is moved by the mass of endolymph in the semicircular canal. As the cupula moves this will stimulate the ciliated hair cells which will respond by generating new nerve impulses. These nerve impulses travel along nerve fibres which pass through the vestibular and vestibulocochlear nerves to the brain where they are interpreted as the sensation of movement. As there is a semicircular canal in all three planes, all changes of direction may be detected. During acceleration and deceleration the cupula will be moved by the endolymph allowing us to experience the changes. However when we are at rest or moving at a constant speed there will be no movement of the cupula and therefore no sensation of acceleration, deceleration or movement.

Saccule and utricle

Both the saccule and utricle are filled with endolymph. They have an area in their walls called a macula (this term simply means spot). These two maculae (spots) are perpendicular (i.e. at right angles) to each other. Like the cupula they also contain hair cells with sensory cilia which allows them to detect side to side and forward to back movements of the head. They provide sensory information on the position of the head essential for maintenance of balance and body posture.

The saccule and utricle are both located in the vestibule of the bony labyrinth. Each ampulla and cupula are also close to the vestibule. This is why these structures are collectively described as the vestibular apparatus. The nerve which leaves these vestibular structures is called the vestibular nerve. This vestibular nerve merges with the cochlear nerve to form the vestibulocochlear (VIII) cranial nerve.

Vertigo is an unpleasant feeling

Vertigo describes a sensation of whirling, either of the person or the world around, where the person feels dizzy and disorientated. This may occur as a result of disorders of the inner ear, often the semicircular canals. Motion sickness is a form of vertigo caused by repeated stimulation of the vestibular system. It is more likely to develop when there is inconsistency between movement and vision; this is why it may be better to look out of a front window while in a moving vehicle. Sea sickness is also a form of motion sickness.

CHAPTER 18

Inflammation and Immunity

The inflammatory response

Inflammation is not a disease in itself but it is the local reaction of the body to some insult or injury. The inflammatory response is both normal and necessary. As inflammation is the first stage in the healing process, it is a necessary initial reaction which promotes further tissue regeneration after injury. Inflammation literally means 'to set afire' and the suffix 'itis' is used to describe an inflammatory response. Conditions with an inflammatory component are seen daily in any form of clinical practice. For example, bronchitis describes inflammation of the bronchial passages. Tonsillitis is inflammation of the tonsils. Appendicitis is inflammation of the appendix. Peritonitis, the peritoneal membranes. Conjunctivitis, the conjunctiva lining the front of the eye. Meningitis, the meningeal layers of the dura, arachnoid and pia mater. Gastritis, the stomach. Cholecystitis, the gallbladder. Cystitis, the bladder. Pyelonephritis, the kidneys. Colitis, the colon.

Causes of inflammation

Any insult to a tissue, i.e. anything which damages a tissue, will lead to a local inflammatory response. Although inflammation may be caused by a wide variety of tissue insults, the nature of the response is always the same. Mechanical trauma, such as cuts, abrasions, crush, friction or pressure injuries may all cause inflammation. Direct tissue contact with any corrosive agents such as acids or alkalis are another range of possible causes. For example, leakage of bile or intestinal contents into the peritoneal cavity can cause severe peritonitis. Thermal injuries, caused by exposure to excessive heat or cold, will lead to inflammation. Radiation, such as ultraviolet, may cause inflammation as is the case with sunburn. An inflammatory response may be caused by immunological reactions; this may well be the cause of swollen, painful joints in rheumatoid arthritis. A similar immunological reaction explains sensitivity to some environmental agents; pollen grains are an example of this, as anyone who suffers from hay fever is only too aware. Infection describes the growth of microorganisms in the body tissues and is a common cause of inflammation. The presence of foreign, infective organisms or the toxins they secrete, stimulates a vigorous immunological inflammatory response.

Inflammatory mediators

Inflammatory mediators are chemicals released locally into the tissues which bring about the inflammatory response. One group of inflammatory mediators is derived from tissue cells which have been damaged as a result of tissue insult. When tissue cells are injured or killed, phospholipids from damaged cell membranes are released into the local tissues. This free phospholipid is then acted on by an enzyme which occurs naturally in the tissues called phospholipase A. This phospholipase A converts the phospholipids into another fatty based substance called arachidonic acid. This arachidonic acid is then acted on by another enzyme present in the tissues called cyclo-oxygenase (COX). Cyclo-oxygenase converts the arachidonic acid into a powerful group of inflammatory mediators called prostaglandins. Free prostaglandins will then generate an inflammatory response.

Sometimes in clinical practice it is necessary to inhibit the natural inflammatory response. Corticosteroids, such as prednisolone, are a very powerful group of inflammatory inhibiting medications. These work by inhibiting the action of phospholipase A. If the phospholipase A is inhibited the phospholipids will not be converted into arachidonic acid. Non-steroidal anti-inflammatory drugs (NSAIDs), such as aspirin or ibuprofen, work by inhibiting the action of cyclo-oxygenase, preventing arachidonic acid being converted into prostaglandins.

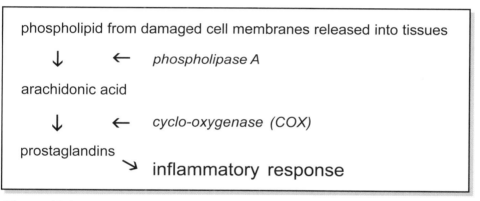

Figure 18.1
Cell membranes are largely composed of phospholipids. These structural molecules contain a combination of phosphates and lipids. When a cell is damaged these molecules are released into the local tissue spaces. Whenever phospholipids are released they will be converted into prostaglandins by the action of the tissue based enzymes phospholipase A and cyclo-oxygenase. Therefore any tissue insult which damages cell membranes will result in the release of inflammatory mediators and therefore an inflammatory response.

Tissue insult will also cause release of inflammatory mediators from mast cells. These specialised cells are found in many of the connective tissues and are plentiful in the dermis of the skin and in the mucosal surfaces of the airways and gastrointestinal tract. Mast cells are very similar to circulating basophils, but remain localised in their tissues.

Like basophils they contain large granules in their cytoplasm; these granules are actually vesicles containing inflammatory mediators. When a tissue is insulted the sensitive mast cells degranulate, shedding the inflammatory mediators into the local tissue spaces. These inflammatory mediators include bradykinin and histamine. This explains why antihistamine drugs have an anti-inflammatory effect; they are particularly helpful in allergic inflammation.

Clinical features of inflammation

The five clinical features of inflammation are redness, heat, swelling, pain and loss of function. All clinical staff must memorise these features. These clinical features can all be explained in terms of the physiological changes which occur in the inflammatory process.

Redness and heat

Inflammatory mediators act as powerful vasodilators, dilating the microscopic blood vessels including the capillaries. Vasodilation of local blood vessels increases blood supply to the area, this is called a hyperaemia. Increased volumes of blood give the inflamed area a reddened appearance. Inflamed areas feel warmer than the surrounding body surface. This heat is explained by the increased volumes of warm blood, from the body core, circulating through the inflamed area.

Swelling

Because the capillaries dilate, the physical size of the gaps in their walls increases which increases their permeability. Inflammatory mediators also cause the endothelial cells to contract, further increasing the size of the gaps in the capillary walls. As the gaps between the cells of the capillary walls get bigger, the permeability of the capillary increases, making it easier for blood components to migrate into the tissue spaces. Increased capillary permeability increases the volume of tissue fluid formed and also allows larger molecules such as plasma proteins to escape into the tissues. White cells such as neutrophils and monocytes may squeeze out, through the dilated capillary walls, into the tissue spaces. The resultant fluid is termed inflammatory exudate. It is the presence of increased volumes of fluid in the tissues which causes the swelling.

Pain and loss of function

In addition to dilating local blood vessels, inflammatory mediators act on the pain receptors. Inflamed areas are very sensitive to touch or movement because the inflammatory mediators increase the sensitivity of local nociceptors. They do this by reducing the depolarisation threshold, making it more likely a stimulus will produce a new nerve impulse. Even the pulse in a tissue may be a sufficient stimulus to cause pain. You may remember your thumb throbbing the last time you hit it with a hammer. This increased pain response is termed a hyperalgesia. Pain will also inhibit the use of part of the body resulting in a loss of normal function. For example, we will not go jogging on an inflamed sprained ankle.

Systemic effects of inflammation

Extensive inflammation, as might be caused by a serious injury or infection, will result in some systemic, i.e. whole body effects. These systemic effects are mediated by the release of inflammatory mediators and cytokines into the blood.

Cytokines are signal molecules, released by one cell to communicate with other cells. Many cytokines are released from white blood cells which are involved in the local inflammatory reaction. Circulating inflammatory mediators and cytokines influence the brain to give rise to reduced appetite, drowsiness, malaise (generally feeling unwell) and fever. There can also be achy muscles and joints. The liver is also stimulated to produce a range of proteins which are secreted into the blood. These are called acute phase proteins and have a range of immunological functions. One of these acute phase proteins is C-reactive protein. This protein is commonly tested for in clinical practice as an inflammatory marker. If it is raised it is a sign that there is an inflammatory response going on somewhere in the body. Fibrinogen (the clotting protein) is also synthesised and released in increased amounts.

The purpose of inflammation

Wound healing is a metabolically active process, using large amounts of energy. This is because damaged areas need to be cleared of dead and damaged tissues and any infection which might have been introduced. After this, tissues need to be repaired and new tissues constructed. Both of these healing processes are anabolic (involves building up new large molecules), and energy is always required for building work. A hyperaemia will fuel this requirement by increasing the blood supply, and therefore glucose and oxygen delivery to the area.

Increase in the volumes of tissue fluid increases the supply of amino acids, vitamins and minerals to the damaged area. Amino acids are essential to build up new proteins, vitamins help to catalyse some of the essential anabolic reactions. Several minerals, such as zinc, are also necessary for normal healing. Increased volumes of tissue fluid will also dilute any bacterial toxins which might be in the area. When toxins are diluted their potential to cause further tissue damage is reduced.

Increased capillary permeability will allow fibrinogen (a blood clotting protein) to enter the tissues. In the tissue spaces, fibrinogen is converted into strands of insoluble fibrin. This forms a provisional structural framework for the new tissue and allows the passage of cells required for further healing. Fibrin also forms a physical mesh which helps to isolate areas of infection. This promotes consolidation (isolating infection together in one place), and inhibits spread of any infection. Strands of fibrin will also block local lymphatic vessels, preventing the spread of infection around the body.

Immunoglobulins are antibodies which are immune proteins. Passage of these from the blood into the tissue spaces, through the dilated capillary walls, can quickly start to combat any infection which might have been introduced into an injury.

White blood cells are able to escape into the tissues where they phagocytose dead tissue cells and bacteria. Removal of dead tissue is essential to allow young cells to migrate over living tissues. Living cells will not travel over areas of dead tissue. Also, if dead tissue is left in a wound it acts as a ready-formed habitat and food source for potential infection. Leucocytes also release chemical mediators which promote the healing process. Interestingly, maggots introduced onto a wound also preferentially eat dead (necrotic) tissue. In this sense their debridement role is similar to phagocytes (debride means to remove foreign or dead material from a wound). This is the basis of the revival of the ancient treatment of larval therapy.

Immobilisation of an injured area promotes healing. When an area is injured and painful, local muscles are stimulated to contract and protect the injury. For example, if you sprain an ankle the lower leg muscles will tighten to splint the injured area. If there is a peritonitis the abdominal muscles will tighten to protect the painful inflamed area below. These reactions are referred to as muscle guarding.

From these examples it can be seen why inflammation is essential for normal healing. This is illustrated by the poor wound healing observed in patients taking corticosteroid drugs which inhibit the inflammatory response.

Immunity and the problem of infectious disease

There has recently been an increased awareness of the problem posed by infectious diseases with the emergence of antibiotic resistant bacteria. Bacteria such as methicillin-resistant Staphylococcus aureus (MRSA) and Clostridium difficile have become well known. However, we live in a world full of microorganisms and some of these have the potential to cause disease.

Throughout human history infectious disease has been a constant threat. The Bible describes the plague of Ashod. This occurred in what is the modern day Gaza Strip around 1100 BC, probably killing many thousands of people. Black Death arose in 14th century England and killed an estimated 100,000 people. Bubonic plague in 1665 killed at least 68,000 people in London alone. Cholera epidemics in England during the 1850s also killed thousands of people. Between 1568 and 1620 the indigenous population of Mexico fell from 30 million to 1.6 million, largely due to infectious disease introduced by European invaders, to which the local people had no immunity. Influenza killed between 20 to 40 million people in 1919; it is likely that such a pandemic will strike us again. Smallpox killed 300 million people in the 20th century before it was eradicated. In many poorer areas of the world, 70-80% of deaths are caused by infections. Children under five are often extensively affected; diarrhoea and vomiting is still the most common cause of death in the world's children. Simple bacterial chest infections also kill many children every year.

Over 3000 children die from malaria in Africa every day. At the time of writing 33 million people are infected with the human immunodeficiency virus (HIV) and over 2 million die each year from acquired immunodeficiency syndrome (AIDS).

Any microorganism with the potential to cause disease is a pathogenic microorganism, In clinical practice this is often abbreviated to 'pathogen' or

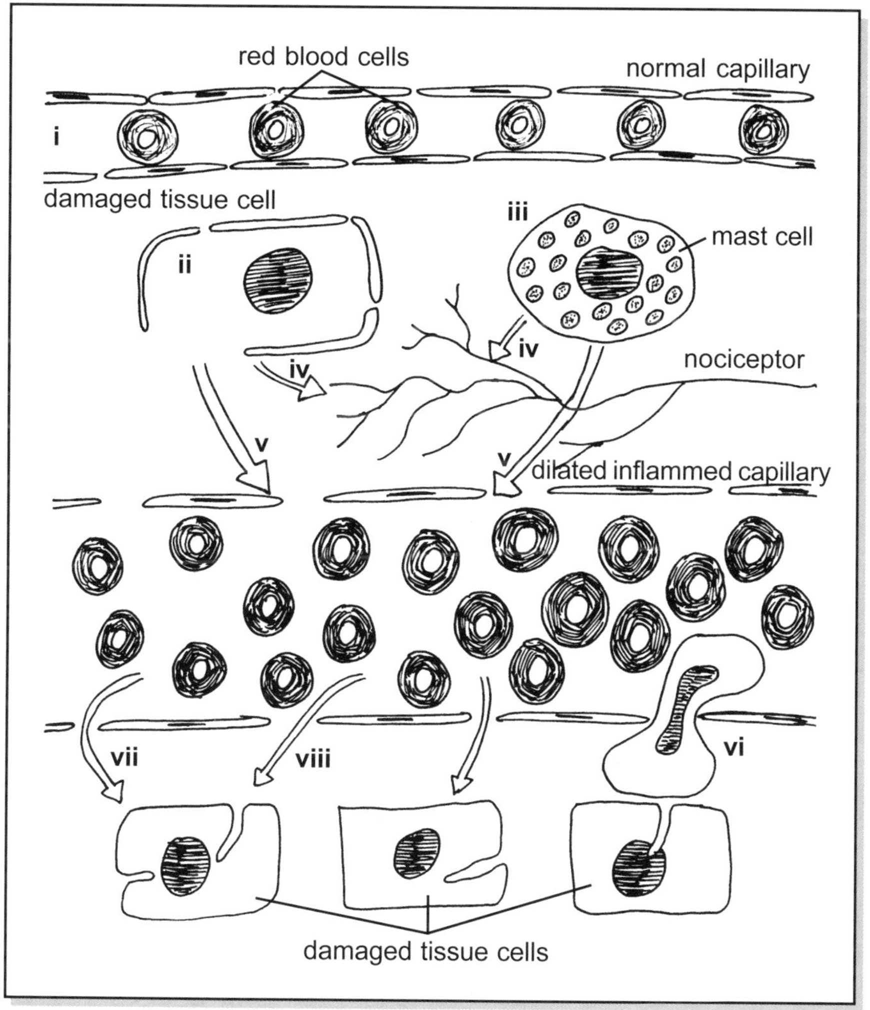

Diagram 18.1

The process of inflammation.

(i) A normal capillary has a narrow lumen and relatively tight junctions between the endothelial cells which comprise the wall. Red cells pass through the small capillaries one at a time.

(ii) Damaged tissue cells release phospholipids which are converted into prostaglandins, these act as inflammatory mediators. This conversion depends on the presence of phospholipase A and cyclo-oxygenase.

(iii) Mast cells release histamine, another inflammatory mediator.

(iv) Inflammatory mediators sensitise local nociceptors producing hyperalgesia, this will also lead to 'guarding' of the injured or infected area.

(v) Inflammatory mediators cause dilation of local blood vessels leading to hyperaemia. This will increase the oxygenation of the area.

(vi) White blood cells are able to migrate through the dilated capillary wall. Once in the tissue spaces they will phagocytose dead tissue cells and bacteria. They also release cytokines.

(vii) Increased supplies of tissue fluid, transporting amino acids, vitamins and minerals move out of the blood into the tissue spaces. These building blocks are necessary for regeneration of the damaged tissue.

(viii) Fibrinogen is able to escape from the dilated capillary to form physical barriers which will aid in the consolidation of infection. Immune proteins also migrate out into the tissue spaces.

'bug', referred to in common speech as a germ. Microorganism is usually abbreviated to microbe. Even bacteria which do not normally cause disease, such as those in the colon, certainly cause problems if they get into the blood, peritoneum or bladder. The common forms of organisms which may cause disease are bacteria, viruses, fungi, protozoa and parasitic worms. Infection simply means the presence of a microbe in a body tissue or structure.

Fortunately humans are equipped with a wide range of mechanisms to protect us against this always present threat. Immunity may be described as the ability of the body to resist infections. Normally the immune mechanisms are so effective that the body tissues are sterile, completely free of any microorganisms at all.

Two types of immunity

The body is protected against microorganisms in basically two ways. The first is by innate immunity which is also referred to as non-specific. These non-specific mechanisms act against a wide range of potential infectious agents in a non-discriminating way. Secondly, immunity may be acquired, also called specific or adaptive immunity. In this form of immunity the body learns how to combat a particular species of microorganism.

Leucocytes

White cells are essential for innate and adaptive immunity. Although they are often called white blood cells some are found in the tissues as well. For example, macrophages are large white cells found in many body tissues and are a specialised form of monocyte. All of the leucocytes derive from stem cells found in the bone marrow. It is useful to consider the leucocytes as cells involved in innate and adaptive immunity separately, although in reality the boundaries are blurred and there are interactions between the two groups.

Innate immunity

The structures and mechanisms of innate immunity already exist in the body before there is any contact with a particular potential infection. In innate immunity there is no change in the structure or mechanism involved as a result of exposure to a potential infection.

Skin

Skin is a barrier to nearly all potential pathogens as long as it remains intact. However when the skin is broken, the way is clear for organisms from the exterior to enter. This simple principle explains why wounds may become infected. If there is a widespread area of disruption to the integrity of the skin, such as a burn, infection becomes much more likely. Keratin in the outer layers of the epidermis improves the hardness and quality of the physical barrier. Oily sebum prevents skin from drying out. Dry, cracked skin is much more likely to become infected than oily skin. Sweat also contains acids which kill bacteria.

Mucous membranes

Mucous membranes, lined with mucus, are able to prevent the transmission of most potential pathogens as long as the surface remains intact. Such mucous membrane is found in the mouth, lining the gastrointestinal tract and airways, inside the eyelids and lining male and female genital tracts. Some organisms such as those which cause sexually transmitted disease (STD) are able to penetrate intact mucous membranes. Human immunodeficiency virus (HIV) can pass through intact membranes, but not readily. Perhaps one of the reasons HIV spread so quickly through many African countries was because there was already a lot of pre-existing STD in the population. This would have disrupted the integrity of the genital mucous membranes. This in effect left an open door for the HI virus to get in and infect the individual.

Tears and saliva

Mucus, tears and saliva all contain lysozyme. This is an enzyme which does not act against human tissues but will digest bacterial cell walls. Usually, the presence of lysozyme helps to keep these areas free from infection, despite always being exposed to the outside world.

Respiratory system defences

The respiratory system is protected by hairs and mucus in the nose. Much of the mucous membrane lining the respiratory tract is also covered with cilia. Bacteria stick to mucus which is then wafted into the trachea by the beating action of cilia. The combination of the mucus and the cilia which move it along the airways is called the mucociliary clearance system. Once it has been cleared to the trachea, coughing and sneezing expectorate the mucus, containing the trapped bacteria, through the vocal cords and into the oropharynx. General mobility, and respiratory pattern changes, aid this expectoration of sputum.

Patients on bed rest are at increased risk of sputum stasis and subsequent infection which may lead on to bronchopneumonia. This is one of the main reasons we do not keep patients on bed rest for any longer than is absolutely necessary.

Acid in the stomach

Hydrochloric acid in the stomach kills most organisms which are swallowed in food. Some elderly people produce less stomach acid than they used to, increasing their risk of infectious gastritis. The alkaline nature of the small intestine is also active against some organisms.

Competition from harmless organisms

Areas of the body such as the colon, mouth and vagina contain large numbers of bacteria. This situation is normal, the bacteria compose the normal 'flora'. The presence of flora means that there is competition from harmless bacteria if any harmful organisms attempt to colonise the area. This means any pathogenic organisms entering are unlikely to become established. Organisms which live with us in this symbiotic way are called commensal; by living together we benefit each other. The value of this competition to us can be seen when antibiotics kill off the normal flora in the gut and vagina causing diarrhoea and thrush respectively. Antibiotic use also makes it more likely that the colon will become infected with an organism such as Clostridium difficile potentially causing severe colitis. Antibiotics may also be a factor in the cause of irritable bowel syndrome where fungal infections may be part of the problem.

Flushing effects

Flushing effects occur wherever there is a flow of fluid from one place to another. Any bacteria present are moved along with the flow. Tears wash over the surface of the eye and saliva through the mouth before it is swallowed. Bile is produced in the liver and flows down the bile ducts and into the gall bladder, before flowing on to the duodenum. Urine is produced in the kidneys; the one way flow down the urinary tract washes out any bacteria which may be present. This is why it is important to drink plenty of water if there is a urinary infection; larger volumes of water will help to flush bacteria out of the body. The importance of flushing effects is clearly seen if there is an obstruction leading to stasis. For example, a bile stone may block the flow of bile leading to infection of the gall bladder, a condition called cholecystitis. Obstruction to the flow of urine, or passing small volumes of urine, increases the likelihood of urinary tract infections (UTIs). Diarrhoea is another flushing mechanism, explaining why it is usually a bad idea to give anti-diarrhoeal medications in infectious diarrhoea. If the motility of the colon is reduced the bacteria causing the infection will be retained in the colon where they will continue to reproduce, resulting in a more severe and prolonged infection. Vomiting is another natural defence mechanism, ejecting infection from the stomach and upper part of the small intestine.

Complement

Some body fluids and blood contain a series of about 20 proteins collectively referred to as complement. These form a cascade which may be triggered by the presence of bacterial cells. Like any cascade, one product triggers the formation of the next in the cascade. Intermediate chemicals in the complement cascade have a variety of immune and inflammatory functions. These include acting as opsonins and inflammatory mediators, attracting white blood cells to specific areas and facilitating local vasodilation.

The final component of the cascade is a protein which forms the shape of a tube. This tubular protein has an exciting sounding name, membrane attack protein; it works by puncturing a hole through the outer wall and cell membrane of bacterial cells. Water from the body fluids is then free to pass through the tube and into the bacterial cell. As the bacterium fills with water it will swell, then once a certain volume of water has entered, the cell will burst, just like an overfilled balloon. This will clearly kill the bacterial cell.

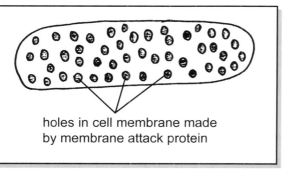

holes in cell membrane made by membrane attack protein

Diagram 18.2
The effect of membrane attack protein on an E. coli bacterial cell. Numerous holes are punched into the bacterium cell membrane leading to cell death.

Interferon

Unlike bacteria viral particles are not capable of independent reproduction; they can only reproduce by hijacking a host cell. Once a new host cell is infected, the virus hijacks the cells normal protein synthesising machinery and forces it to manufacture more viral particles. When an infected cell has produced a large number of new viruses it will burst releasing many new viral particles into a tissue to infect more body cells. One way cells protect themselves against viral infections is by using interferon.

When certain cells are invaded by viral particles they release a group of chemicals called interferons. Interferons from an infected cell will diffuse to the body cells in the surrounding area. They communicate with adjacent cells by binding onto specific interferon receptor sites on the external cell membranes. When the interferon receptor is stimulated two things will happen. Firstly the cell will be stimulated to produce specific antiviral enzymes which inhibit the ability of the virus to express its own genetic material, so they cannot make copies of themselves. Secondly the ability of the cell to synthesise any new proteins is inhibited (interferons interfere with the cells ability to produce proteins). If these body cells are no longer able to synthesise proteins they will not be able to produce new viruses. Interferon therefore essentially creates a barrier (a sort of 'fire break') around infected cells. Some forms of interferon also act against some cancer cells.

Opsonins

Opsonins are a form of chemical labelling system used by the immune system to clearly identify foreign material for destruction. There are a variety of chemicals which may act as opsonins including some components of the complement cascade, some antibodies and other proteins in the bloodstream. Opsonins bind onto the surface of particular components of a pathogen, which they are

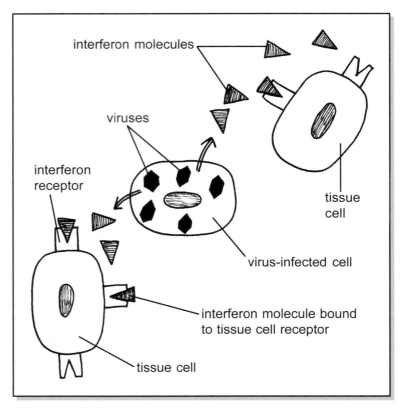

interferon molecules

viruses

interferon receptor

tissue cell

virus-infected cell

interferon molecule bound to tissue cell receptor

tissue cell

Diagram 18.3
A virus-infected cell releases interferon which combines with a specific receptor on surrounding cells. Activation of the receptor by interferon inhibits the production of viral particles, should the cell become infected. (In reality the interferon molecules and receptors are several hundred times smaller than illustrated; this is true of all of the signal molecules and receptors illustrated in this chapter.)

able to recognise as being foreign. This is possible because the chemical makeup of microorganisms is different from the cells of the body. In addition to the ability to bind to foreign material, opsonins can also bind onto receptors on the surface of phagocytes. In other words they form a bridge between antigen and phagocyte. So opsonins adhere the pathogen onto the phagocyte, making its destruction inevitable. Phagocytosis can work without opsonins but opsonisation increases the efficiency of the process.

Cells involved in innate immunity

There are three types of white cells involved in innate immunity; the granulocytes, monocytes and the natural killer (NK) cells. Granulocytes occur in three forms. Neutrophils are the most common white cell type in the blood, the other two

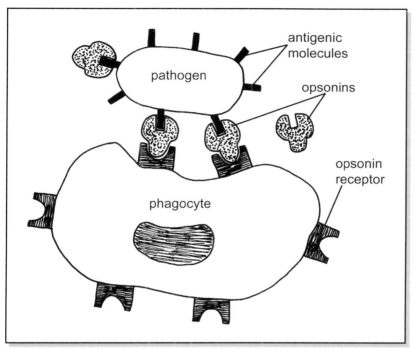

Diagram 18.4
The process of opsonisation helps in the identification and adherence
of an antigenic foreign organism to a phagocyte. Phagocytosis and
death of the pathogen will rapidly follow.

are eosinophils and basophils. Mast cells found in tissues are a form of basophil. Eosinophils also spend most of their time in the tissues. Granulocytes are named because of the granular appearance of the cytoplasm. The granules contain various substances, some of which are capable of digesting bacteria in the process of phagocytosis. While eosinophils and basophils are capable of phagocytosis it is the neutrophils which are most active in this eating process. If we develop an infection the numbers of neutrophils in the blood increases to combat the infecting bacteria. An increase in the number of white blood cells in the blood is termed a leucocytosis.

Monocytes may also be found in the blood and tissues. So called 'wandering' monocytes circulate in the blood. These circulating cells are attracted to areas of infection or injury where they are able to migrate out of the inflamed capillaries. Once in the tissues they grow in size and are then referred to as macrophages (big eaters). Other macrophages are described as being fixed. These live permanently in a particular tissue or organ. This means that if an infection gets into an organ, there is a ready made phagocytic defence force in place. Fixed macrophages have been identified in a range of tissues including brain, lungs, liver, lymph nodes, spleen, kidneys, synovial joints and bone marrow.

Cytotoxicity

Natural killer (NK) cells and eosinophils are able to directly kill other cells. Eosinophils come alongside foreign material and essentially bomb it. Digestive enzymes and other toxins are released from the eosinophil onto the foreign target. These will damage the cell membrane of the pathogen and this will usually be enough to kill the cell. This mechanism is also effective against a wide range of multicellular parasites which may invade the body, explaining why the number of eosinophils is raised in parasitic infections.

NK cells are large granular lymphocytes. They are able to act against body cells with a wide range of viral infections. NK cells are able to recognise when a body cell has become infected with a virus. When a cell has been taken over by a virus, some viral glycoproteins appear on the surface of the cell membrane and it is these viral fragments the NK cells are able to recognise. Once the NK cell has identified an infected body cell it comes along side and releases a chemical called perforin. As the name suggests this perforates the outer cell membrane of the infected cell, causing it to swell and burst. The NK cell therefore attacks the viral infection by killing infected cells. In is now widely accepted that NK cells also protect us against some forms of cancer by identifying and killing malignant cells. It is currently unclear how important this activity is in maintenance of health, but some malignant disease may be caused by a lack of NK activity.

Diagram 18.5
Natural killer cells
attack;
(i)   a cancer cell.
(ii) a virally infected
      cell.

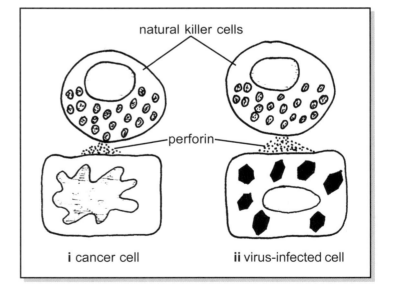

Adaptive immunity

Acquired or adaptive immunity only develops after there has been contact with a particular antigen. An individual is said to be immune to a particular pathogen when it may be introduced into the body, without causing illness. In contrast to innate immunity, the immune system is changed as a result of exposure to a particular antigen.

Acquired immunity is specific to a particular antigen. For example, previous exposure to the measles virus will have allowed the immune system to adapt,

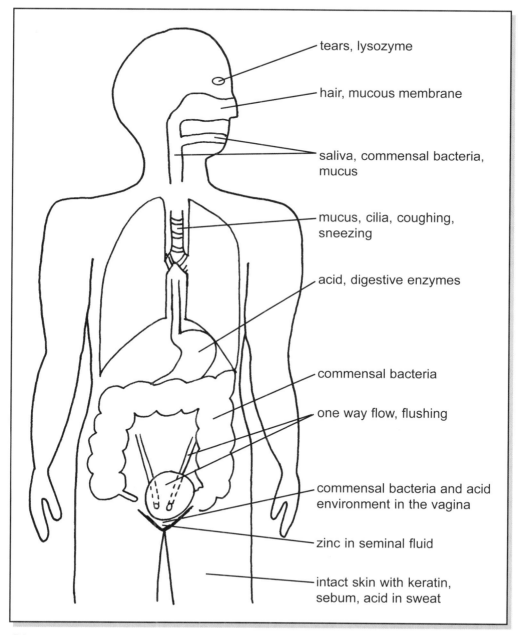

Diagram 18.6
Review of the main physical and chemical mechanisms of innate immunity.

generating immunity to any future measles infection. However, because the response is specific, the individual may still suffer from mumps, influenza, or indeed any other antigenic organism it has not previously been exposed to.

Antigens (antibody generators)

An antigen is anything the immune system recognises as being foreign. When detected, antigens generate an immune response in the body. It is antigens which stimulate the production of antibodies, which are the immune proteins. Usually an antigen is a foreign protein that the body recognises as non-self. The outer coatings of bacteria and viruses contain such foreign proteins. Non-protein large molecules (with a molecular mass of over 1000) will also be antigenic if introduced into the body. So a wide variety of living and non living things can act as antigens; such things are said to possess antigenicity. The specific component of an antigen the immune system recognises as foreign is termed an epitope.

Diagram 18.7
An antigen possesses specific molecules the immune system is able to recognise as foreign, these are called epitopes.

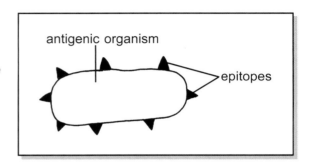

Cells involved in adaptive immunity

The important classification of white cells involved in adaptive immunity is the small lymphocytes. Small lymphocytes have a large nucleus with only a small area of cytoplasm. In addition to being found in the blood, there are many small lymphocytes in the structures of the lymphatic system, such as the spleen, tonsils and lymph nodes.

Small lymphocytes are able to recognise antigenic material, this is essential if they are to mount an immune response. It is estimated that small lymphocytes are capable of producing 100 million different shapes of surface receptors in order to recognise 100 million different forms of antigen. This diversity seems to allow the immune system to recognise all of the possible antigens on the surface of the planet.

Despite this amazing diversity, any individual small lymphocyte can only recognise one single form of antigen. There may be just a few individual small lymphocytes for each of the 100 million possible antigens we may come across during a lifetime. The small group of lymphocytes capable of recognising an individual antigen all have the same form of surface receptor, generated by the same genetic instructions. For this reason, the members of this small lymphocyte group are described as clones, comprising a clonal group. The particular part of an antigen which the small lymphocyte receptor is able to recognise is the epitope. There are basically two types of these small lymphocytes, B and T.

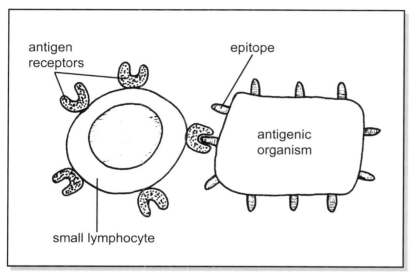

Diagram 18.8
A small lymphocyte is able to detect the presence of a particular antigen by recognising the shape of a particular epitope. The shape of the epitope is recognised because the small lymphocyte has a reciprocally shaped receptor in its surface. In other words, the lymphocyte is able to detect the presence of the antigen because the epitope of the antigen fits into the immunoglobulin on the surface of the cell. This fit is very specific; the antibody will only accommodate an epitope of a particular shape.

B lymphocytes

B lymphocytes are so called because they mature in the bone marrow. Each small clonal group of B cells has one particular antigen recognising receptor on its surface. In the case of the B cells these receptors are surface bound immunoglobulins (immunoglobulins and antibodies are different names for the same thing). In fact, each individual B cell has about 100,000 copies of the same immunoglobulin molecule on its surface. After contact with a specific antigen, the particular clonal group of B cells divides to produce a population. In other words, it is the presence of a particular antigen which stimulates mitosis in the clonal group which is complementary to it.

Some of the original clonal group divide to become memory B cells and others differentiate into vast numbers of plasma cells. These plasma cells are able to produce, and export from the cell, large numbers of antibodies. Each of the antibodies produced will be the same as the immunoglobulin located on the cell membrane of the original B cell. This means they will be active against the antigen that was initially recognised. Antibodies are then free to circulate in the blood and tissue fluids to perform their immune functions.

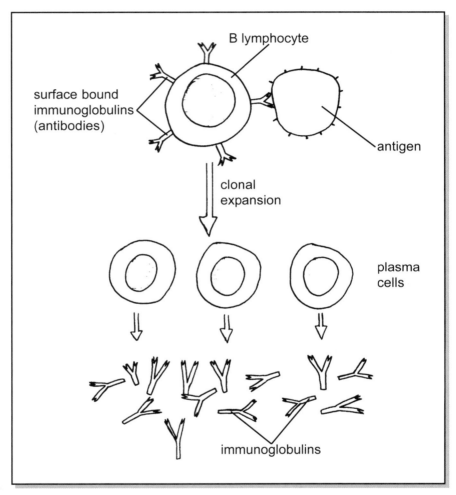

Diagram 18.9
Surface bound immunoglobulins on a B lymphocyte detect the presence of a particular antigen. Contact with the antigen activates the B cell to divide, producing a large population of plasma cells. These produce multiple copies of the original immunoglobulin molecules.

T lymphocytes

The second grouping of small lymphocytes are the T cells. T lymphocytes are so called because they mature in the thymus gland. Like the B cells, all of the T cells are only able to recognise, and react, to a single antigen. After antigenic exposure their numbers will be increased by clonal expansion so they can rapidly eliminate the specific infection. There are three types of T lymphocytes; cytotoxic, helpers and suppressors.

Cytotoxic T lymphocytes

Cytotoxic T cells directly attack the body's own cells when they become infected with viruses. Once a cytotoxic T lymphocyte recognises a specific antigen it will undergo clonal expansion to generate a population of specific cells which will rapidly eliminate all of the virus infected cells. A clonal group of cytotoxic T cells will only kill a body cell if it presents the specific viral epitope the T cell is able to recognise. T cytotoxic cells are also active against some malignant cells. The mode of action of the small cytotoxic T lymphocytes is much the same as their larger counterparts, the NK cells. Killing one's own cells may appear somewhat radical; however, the antibodies produced by the adaptive immune response cannot pass into individual tissue cells. If a virus-infected cell is left alone, it will produce many more viral particles which will go on to infect other cells, and the cell will be killed by the virus anyway.

T helper lymphocytes

These cells produce a range of signal molecules which stimulate activity in other cells involved in immunity. These signal molecules are made up of small proteins called peptides. As the role of these signal molecules is for one cell to communicate with other cells they are another example of cytokines. These cytokines stimulate B plasma cells to produce antibodies. Neutrophils and monocytes are stimulated to be more phagocytic. Other signal molecules stimulate mast cells to produce an inflammatory response and cytotoxic cells to kill infected body cells.

Human immunodeficiency virus attacks T helper cells and will kill large numbers of them. When there are not enough T helper cells to stimulate the activity of other immunologically active cells there is a general reduction in the efficiency and physiological activity of the immune system. When this decline starts to reduce immune function, the condition is referred to as AIDS related complex. As immunodeficiency increases and becomes severe, full blown AIDS results. Sufferers will die from some infection, such as pneumonia, which they are unable to combat.

T suppressor lymphocytes

T suppressor small lymphocytes limit cytotoxic T cell activity and they also inhibit antibody production. The function of the T suppressors is therefore to limit the extent of the immune response. This function means a specific immune response can be terminated once the antigenic threat has been eliminated. As a result the numbers of lymphocytes and plasma cells will return to normal after an infection.

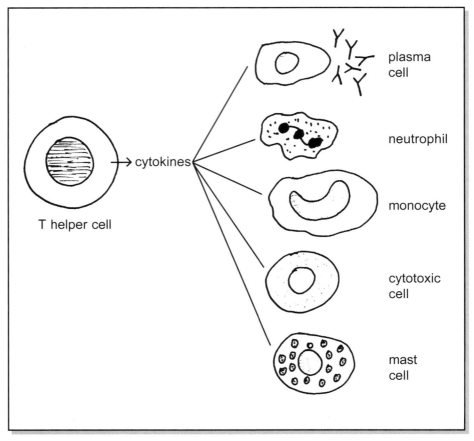

Diagram 18.10
Helper T cells stimulate and coordinate the activity of other immune active cells by the release of cytokines.

Primary and secondary adaptive immune response

A primary response describes the reaction of the immune system to an infection it is encountering for the first time. Such a primary response takes 7-10 days to fully develop. During this time the pathogen may have the opportunity to multiply, causing the person to suffer from the infection. As the adaptive response strengthens, the newly developed, specific immunity, will overcome the particular pathogen and the person will recover. However, if the pathogen was able to reproduce rapidly during this period of immunological mobilisation, the person may die or suffer significant tissue damage as a result of the infection.

If a person who has already mounted a primary response to an antigenic organism is then subsequently re-infected, the secondary adaptive response is much more rapid, starting within a few days. The secondary response is also much more vigorous. So when a person is infected with an organism for the second time the illness is much milder and shorter lived. Indeed the secondary immune response may prevent the person being aware of any clinical features at all. From this it can be seen that the immune system is able to remember how to mount a response to the antigen concerned, a phenomenon referred to as immunological memory. This phenomenon can be explained by the process of clonal expansion.

Clonal expansion

At birth we only have a few individual lymphocytes capable of recognising an individual antigen. When a particular antigen enters the body, the few lymphocytes with the complementary receptors will come into contact with the foreign epitopes and bind onto them. In this sense, it is the antigen which 'selects' the specific reciprocal antibody on the surface of the lymphocyte. This binding of the epitope of the antigen to the antibody of the lymphocyte then triggers the lymphocytes, with their appropriate receptors for the antigen, to start dividing. This results in the lymphocytes producing further copies, or clones, of themselves. Repeated mitosis in the particular clonal group means that large numbers of the clone will be produced; it is this process which is referred to as clonal expansion. The time taken for the process of clonal expansion to occur explains the delay in mounting the primary adaptive response.

As the primary response is mounted the lymphocytes modify the precise nature of the antibodies they produce to be even more specific to the particular antigenic epitope. In other words the lymphocytes learn more about the exact nature of the epitope as time goes on. This means that after a few days the antibodies which are produced are even more effective against the antigen than they were at the beginning of the primary response.

Once the infection has been eliminated, the numbers of the particular clonal group involved start to decline, as there is no longer a need for a large clonal population. However, some of the lymphocytes produced in the clonal expansion process are long lived cells. These long lived lymphocytes are referred to as memory cells, and of course they retain the same specific receptor as the rest of the clonal group.

In addition to living for a long time, memory cells are able to reproduce by further divisions; this can impart specific immunity which may be life long. After an initial infection, the memory cells of a particular clonal group number a few thousand, as opposed to the few members present before the process of clonal expansion. In addition the antibodies they express are even more specific to the particular antigen which caused the infection. So if the person is subsequently exposed to the same antigen, there are already a few thousand, highly specific memory cells, from the original clonal group ready for action. These can rapidly divide to produce sufficient clonal lymphocytes to combat any re-exposure to the infection. If there is a second exposure to the antigen this will further strengthen specific immunity by further increasing the numbers of memory cells.

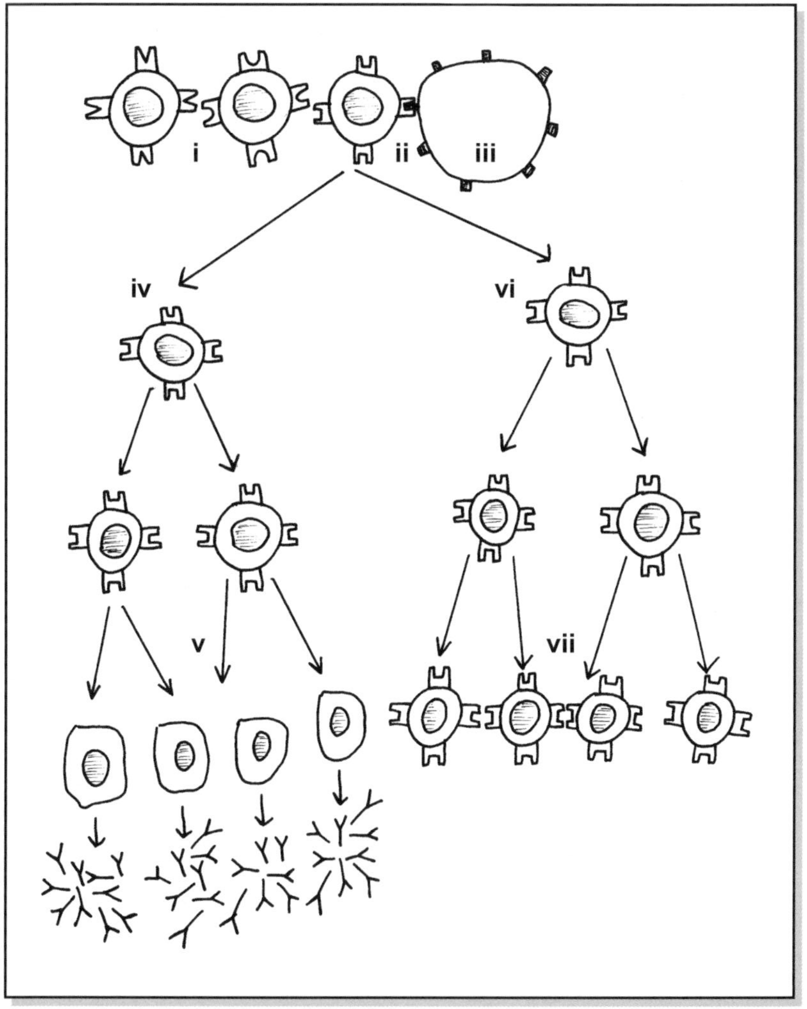

Diagram 18.11

The process of clonal expansion. This diagram illustrates expansion of B cells but the process is essentially the same for the production of an expanded clonal group of T cells.

(i)   Small lymphocytes which do not carry the specific complementary receptor do not bind with the epitope so are not activated.

(ii) Binding takes place between the lymphocyte with the complementary receptor for the epitope on the antigen.

(iii) The antigen is bound to a small lymphocyte with a complementary receptor.

(iv) One cell line of activated small lymphocytes divides into a larger clonal group.

(v)   This clonal group differentiates into plasma cells which produce antibody molecules, each one specific to the original epitope.

(vi) This cell line divides to produce a population of memory cells, all clones of the originally activated cell.

(vii) Several thousand memory lymphocytes are produced.

The end result of this process is that there are larger numbers of memory cells for antigens which have been repeatedly encountered. For antigens which have been encountered only once, there will be smaller but probably adequate numbers. For one of the many millions of antigens which have not been encountered, there will only be a few lymphocytes from the original inborn clonal group.

Antibodies

Antibodies (i.e. immunoglobulins) are complex immune glycoproteins. They are mostly protein but also contain some sugar molecules. Each individual plasma cell can produce several thousand antibodies per hour. There are 5 different classes of antibodies which are produced to carry out specific immune functions; however, they all have the same basic Y structure.

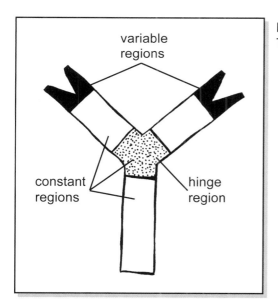

Diagram 18.12
The basic structure of an antibody.

Variable regions are different in each individual form of antibody produced by a clonal group of lymphocytes. It is this variable region which is the antigen binding site, produced to precisely complement the shape of the antigen's epitopes. The remainder of the molecule is a constant region which is the same in all other antibodies of the same class. The presence of the 'hinge' region allows an antibody molecule to move its arms. This allows the molecule flexibility in binding to epitopes in different positions.

The combination of articulating arms and two epitope binding sites means than a number of antibodies may stick a lot of antigens together. This collects a clump of antigens together in the process of agglutination. As a result an agglutinated cluster of consolidated antigens can be easily phagocytosed. It has been said the 'antibodies prepare the food for the phagocytes table'. In addition

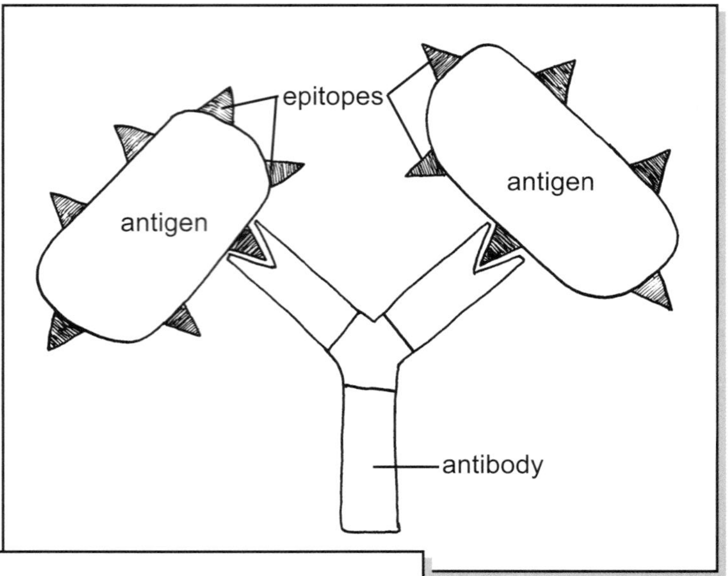

Diagram 18.13
An antibody bound to reciprocal, complementary epitopes; because antibodies have two arms they are able to bind two antigens together.

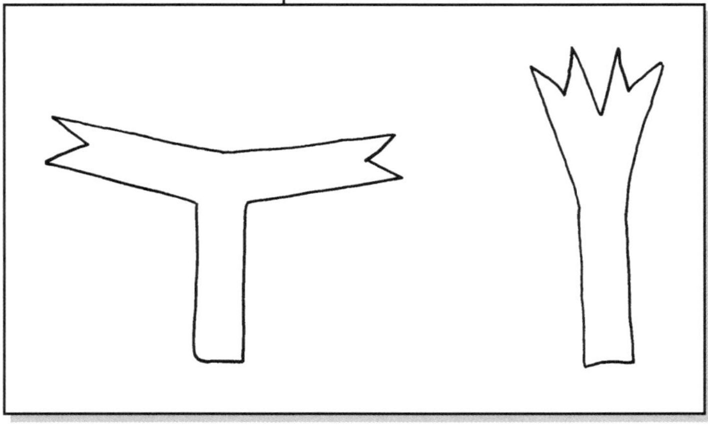

epitopes

antigen

antigen

antibody

Diagram 18.14
An antibody molecule with arms open and closed. The arms are able to alter their position because of the hinge regions.

to clumping together bacteria or viruses, antibodies can also bind together toxic antigenic molecules in solution, such as tetanus toxin. This will lead to precipitation of the toxin and subsequent phagocytosis. This activity is referred to as toxin neutralisation.

As we have already mentioned, some antibodies function as opsonins to enhance the process of phagocytosis. Other antibodies cause mast cell degranulation which initiates the inflammatory response. Inflammation then mobilises immune resources to a damaged or infected area, and reduces spread of infection through a tissue. Antibodies may also act as a trigger for complement cascade activation. Some antibodies can even directly attack antigenic cell membranes causing the cell to rupture. From this it can be seen that antibodies have a number of immune functions and have been correctly described as the 'foot soldiers' of the immune system.

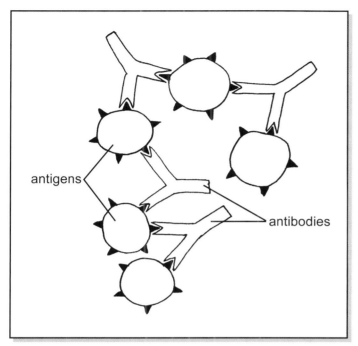

Diagram 18.15
Several antigens have been aggregated by a group of
specific antibodies.

In the study of viral serology many tests do not look for an antigen but instead look for the antibody in the blood. If an antibody is found this indicates that a particular antigen is, or has been, present. In the case of HIV for example, infection is diagnosed by detection of antibodies to HI virus, rather than detecting the presence of the virus itself. An individual may be antibody positive or negative. All nurses should have their hepatitis B titre levels checked every few years to make sure they are still immune after their immunisations (titre describes the levels of antibodies in the blood).

Forms of adaptive immunity

Traditionally acquired, adaptive immunity has been described under three subheadings; active, passive and active on passive.

Active acquired immunity

In this case the individual has acquired immunity to a specific infectious agent, usually a bacterium or virus. The body produces specific antibodies and memory lymphocytes to the antigen which then confer immunity from future infections. This is why an individual should not usually contract the same disease twice.

However, with conditions such as influenza or the common cold there are a large number of possible viruses. This means an individual may be re-infected with a different virus and suffer similar symptoms again.

Passive acquired immunity

This is immunity the individual has acquired without making his or her own antibodies. Injections of human immunoglobulins will give passive immunity, e.g. gamma globulin. In natural physiology, passive immunity is acquired by a baby from the mother. This happens by the trans-placental transfer of antibodies and by the ingestion of antibodies from colostrum and milk in the first few days of life. Passive immunity is short lived (a few months) as the antibodies are progressively lost from the blood and not replaced.

Active on passive immunity

In this circumstance the body enjoys passive immunity to a particular infectious agent, and at the same time is exposed to that same active infection. This means two things; firstly the condition is not suffered from, due to passive immunity, and secondly the individual can make their own active antibodies against the antigen. This is very important in the first weeks and months of life. Children are exposed to many antigens, but due to passive immunity received from their mother, they do not become ill. However, because they are exposed to the antigens they develop long lasting, active acquired immunity.

Clinical applications of immunity

Vaccination

A vaccination stimulates the immune system without the need for the individual to first suffer the condition. This is achieved in one of four ways. Firstly, by giving a live but weakened pathogenic microorganism which the body recognises as foreign and so produces memory cells and antibodies to combat. Examples of live, but attenuated vaccines include measles, mumps and rubella, BCG vaccine for tuberculosis and yellow fever. Because the organism is attenuated it does not cause the disease state, unless the recipient is immuno-compromised in some way. Secondly, a dose of the infectious agent may be given which is dead (e.g. cholera or hepatitis A vaccines). As these dead organisms still contain epitopes they act as antigens, stimulating clonal expansion and antibody production. Clearly, because the infectious agents are dead they cannot reproduce. Thirdly, a vaccination may consist of a toxoid (e.g. tetanus toxoid vaccine). These contain inactivated bacterial toxins which the body recognises as antigenic and clonal expansion is again stimulated. Fourthly the preparation may contain immunising components of a broken up pathogenic microorganism (e.g. meningococcal or pneumococcal vaccines).

Allergies

A healthy immune system can recognise each antigen specifically. This ability of the immune system is called antigen specificity. This further allows the immune system to ignore other molecules which do not pose a threat such as those from latex, shellfish or nuts. This ability not to recognise substances as antigenic is called immunological tolerance. Allergies are caused by the generation of an unnecessary, inappropriate immunological response. A substance which should be neutral and immunologically tolerated is recognised as antigenic and antibodies are produced. These antibodies cause mast cell degranulation when combined with the antigen. As the degranulation leads to the release of inflammatory mediators, such as histamine, an inflammatory reaction is caused. Because antigens to which a person is sensitive will cause this inflammatory allergic reaction they are referred to as allergens. These allergic problems include food and drug allergies, asthma and eczema (dermatitis).

Auto-immunity

In this pathological condition the immune system attacks the bodies own tissues. Normally body tissues should be recognised as part of the 'self' and no immunological response initiated. This normal tolerance of the body's own tissues is referred to as self tolerance. In auto-immunity there is a breakdown of the self/non-self recognition system. The immune system can efficiently destroy a particular tissue type it mistakenly considers to be foreign. It is now known that diabetes mellitus type 1 occurs after the immune system has destroyed the beta cells in the pancreatic islets. Other autoimmune conditions include rheumatoid arthritis, Hashimoto's disease of the thyroid, pernicious anaemia, coeliac disease, multiple sclerosis, SLE (systemic lupus erythematosus) and myasthenia gravis.

Healthy dirt

It has been suggested that exposure to respiratory infections in early life may reduce the probability of asthma later on. Others have suggested that exposure to bacteria in soil may help the immune system to mature and develop. Such exposure probably helps to increase the ability of the immune system to differentiate between potentially harmful antigens and foreign material which should be tolerated. These ideas indicate that allergies and autoimmunity develop, at least in part, because children in Western countries are kept too clean. It also now seems likely that exposure to some gastrointestinal worms reduces the likelihood of diabetes mellitus and other autoimmune and allergic diseases. Early stimulation of the immune system may even reduce the possibility of some cancers in later life.

If this thinking is supported by further research, it would mean that people in the West suffer from lack of exposure to microorganisms while people in developing countries suffer from over exposure which is somewhat ironic.

CHAPTER 19

Genetics

Principle of inheritance

Observation makes it clear that offspring resemble their parents. Firstly, humans have baby humans not giraffes or monkeys. Secondly, children resemble their parents more than they do other members of the same species. The reason for this is that we all inherit our genetic material from our parents, half from mother and half from father. All the information required to construct the human body is carried as a coded sequence of chemical instructions in molecules of deoxyribonucleic acid (DNA). DNA is essentially the recipe to make the proteins of the body. A sequence of a DNA molecule, which carries enough information to produce a specific protein, is referred to as a gene.

The DNA which codes for the genes is part of the chromosomes, which are located in the cell nucleus. When it is time for a gene to be expressed the information is transferred from DNA into another molecule called ribonucleic acid or RNA. RNA then travels out of the nucleus to the ribosomes in the cytoplasm; here amino acids are synthesised into the proteins coded for by the DNA information. Unfortunately as well as carrying useful genetic information genes may also carry disease conditions. Although most purely genetic diseases are rare, over 4000 separate disorders have been identified.

Chromosomes

Chromosomes are composed of genes in the form of DNA; they also contain proteins which give the chromosomes structure. All living cells contain chromosomes in their nucleus, the only exception being mature red blood cells. These contained chromosomes when they were developing in the bone marrow, but they were lost at about the time the cells entered the circulating blood.

People have 46 chromosomes, each of which is one of a pair. Twenty-two of these pairs are termed autosomes; these are the non-sex chromosomes. The final pair of chromosomes are called gametosomes; these are the sex chromosomes. Sex chromosomes are so called because they are different between the sexes. In a male, the sex chromosomes are referred to as the X and the Y. Females also have 2 sex chromosomes, both of which are called X chromosomes. This means everyone has 44 autosomes and 2 gametosomes, 23 pairs in all. An individual receives one member of each pair of chromosomes from their mother and the other from their father. The two chromosomes in a pair are usually the same so are termed homologous chromosomes or homologues.

There are various diseases which may be caused by an abnormality in the number of chromosomes present in an individual's cells. Perhaps the best known example is Down's syndrome where there is usually an extra chromosome, giving a total of 47. Because the extra chromosomal material is from the 21st chromosome the condition is now often referred to as trisomy 21 syndrome.

Individual chromosomes can be identified by using staining and light microscopy. Each chromosome can be identified by its characteristic size and pattern of alternating light and dark bands.

Genes and DNA

Genes contain a unit of genetic information which is usually described as the information required to produce one protein. Together, they carry the genetic code for a wide range of proteins. The proteins coded for by DNA form the body. For example, proteins may be structural, forming part of an organelle, a component of muscle or any of the organs. Proteins may also be produced in cells and then secreted to perform an external function. For example, plasma proteins and clotting factors are secreted by liver cells into the blood. Protein based hormones are secreted by endocrine cells into the blood. Cells also produce and secrete extracellular tissue components such as collagen or elastin.

As genes are carried on the chromosomes, there is usually a copy of each gene on both of the chromosomes which comprise a homologous pair. The result of this is that any one gene may be present in two different forms, one on each homologous pair. For example, the gene for eye colour may code for blue or brown eyes. These different forms of a gene are referred to as alleles. This is one of the facts that makes genetics interesting, an individual may carry one gene for blue eyes and one for brown. This means they have the genetic potential to have children with brown or blue eyes.

Genes are composed of DNA which is the famous double helix molecule arranged in a spiral. It is like a circular staircase. A double helix formation means that the two outer strands can unwind. This allows new subunits to be added to the two open halves of the original double helix, resulting in the formation of two new complete double helix molecules. DNA is therefore a unique molecule; it is able to replicate or reproduce, making copies of itself. It is the self-replicating properties of DNA which transmits genetic information from parents to children. During meiosis one chromosome from each pair is incorporated into a gamete (a sperm or ovum).

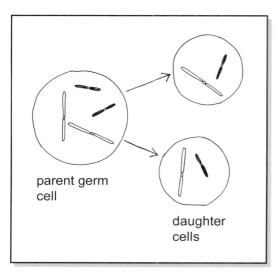

parent germ cell

daughter cells

Diagram 19.1
In the process of meiosis one chromosome from each homologous pair enters each gamete. This halves the number of chromosomes from 23 pairs to 23 (only 2 pairs of chromosomes are illustrated). At fertilisation, these 23 individual chromosomes combine to form 23 pairs in the newly formed fertilised egg cell which is then referred to as a zygote. All of the information needed to form a new body is contained in DNA, in the 46 chromosomes of the zygote.

Dominant and recessive genes

As mentioned, two forms of a single gene may exist in an individual as different alleles. In the case of some genes, both alleles present have an effect on the individual. An example of this is blood group AB. Blood groups are genetically determined. A person with group AB has an allele which codes for group A on one homologous chromosome while the other one codes for group B. In this case both genes are expressed.

In the case of many other genes, one allele is expressed and the other is not. The allele which is expressed is apparent in the individual. This form of the gene, which is expressed if present, is described as dominant. If another form of the gene is present on a chromosome, but is not expressed in the person, it is described as recessive. So if a dominant gene is present this will express itself in preference to a recessive gene. This means a recessive gene can only be expressed in the absence of a dominant gene.

In other words, a dominant gene will always be expressed in the individual if it is present on either of the homologous chromosomes. A recessive gene will only be expressed in the absence of a dominant gene.

When both genes for a specific characteristic are recessive it will be expressed in the person. Genes for blood groups A and B are dominant while the group O gene is recessive. Therefore if a person has one allele for group A and one for group O they will have blood group A. The recessive O gene is masked by the dominant A. When both genes on the two homologous chromosomes code for group O the person will be group O.

Another example is eye colour. Brown eye colour is dominant to blue eye colour. This means a person with brown eyes may have two genes for brown eyes or one for brown and one for blue. A person with blue eyes must therefore have two genes for blue eyes, on each of the homologous chromosomes.

Homozygous or heterozygous

When both alleles on each of a pair of chromosomes are the same, the individual is said to be homozygous for that trait. However, if the two equivalent genes on the homologous chromosomes are different then the person is described as heterozygous. ('Homo' means the same and 'hetero' means different.)

Genotype and phenotype

All of the information carried in the genes of an individual is described as the genotype. Phenotype describes the way these genes are expressed in a particular person. Therefore in the example below, diagram (i) illustrates a person who is genotypically homozygous for blood group A and phenotypically group A. Diagram (ii) illustrates an individual who is genotypically heterozygous for blood groups A and O and who is therefore phenotypically blood group A. This phenotype is explained by the recessive group O gene not being expressed in the presence of the dominant group A gene. The phenotype is therefore an expression of the combination of dominant and recessive genes in a genotype.

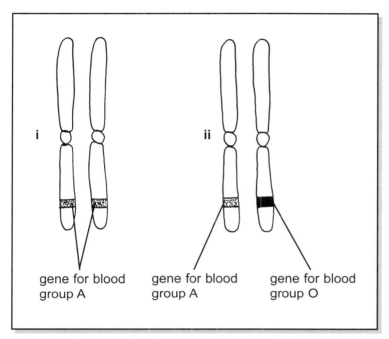

Diagram 19.2
(i)   This pair of homologous chromosomes is homozygous
      for the trait of blood group.
(ii) This pair of homologous chromosomes is heterozygous
      for the trait of blood group.

Monohybrid inheritance

This form of inheritance examines the transmission of a single characteristic from
parents to children. Research in this area was first carried out on pea plants by the
recognised founding father of modern genetics. He was an Abbot from
Czechoslovakia called Gregor Mendel, 1822-84. (Indeed, monohybrid inheritance
is still often referred to as Mendelian.) Gene studies in monohybrid inheritance
are usually carried on the autosomes. We will illustrate this principle using two
diseases; firstly one carried by a dominant gene, then a recessive condition.

Autosomal dominant inheritance

Huntington's chorea, (HC) is a condition which causes chronic, progressive chorea
(abnormal movements) and dementia. Although the abnormal gene is present
from the time of fertilisation, it is not usually expressed until the person is in their
thirties. Death typically occurs within about 15 years of the first symptoms. HC is
caused by a dominant gene which will be expressed if present. If a parent carries
one copy of the HC gene there will be a 50% chance that it will be incorporated in
any one gamete they produce. Therefore an individual with an affected parent will
have a 50% chance of inheriting the condition.

A parent with HC will almost certainly have one gene for HC and one normal gene. As long as the other parent does not have HC they will have two recessive normal genes.

Other examples of conditions demonstrating autosomal dominant inheritance include achondroplasia (a form of dwarfism), adenomatous polyposis (possibly leading to colon cancer), hypercholesterolaemia (high cholesterol) and polycystic kidney disease (leading to renal failure). In addition the BRCA-1 and BRAC-2 (BR-breast CA-cancer) genes are transmitted as autosomal dominant traits and greatly increase the possibility of the individual developing breast and ovarian cancer.

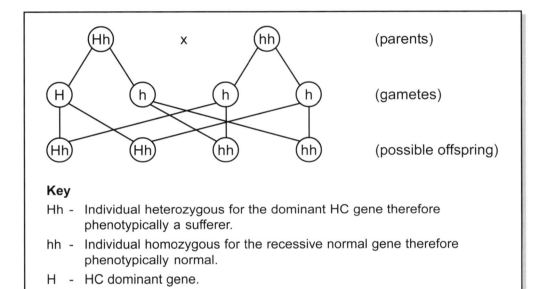

Key

Hh - Individual heterozygous for the dominant HC gene therefore phenotypically a sufferer.

hh - Individual homozygous for the recessive normal gene therefore phenotypically normal.

H - HC dominant gene.

h - normal recessive gamete.

Figure 19.1
Possible offspring from a marriage between one normal parent and a parent with Huntington's chorea as an example of monohybrid dominant inheritance. This form of diagram below may be used to estimate the probability that any potential offspring will inherit a particular gene. The top row represents the genotypes of the parents. During meiosis the homologous chromosomes separate so the second row represents the potential gametes which might be produced. The third row represents the possible children. It is conventional to use upper case letters for dominant and the lower case to represent recessive genes.

Autosomal recessive inheritance

Cystic fibrosis (CF) will be used to illustrate this principle. CF results in abnormally viscous secretions and affects about 1 in 2000 live births in the UK. If one recessive gene for CF is present the disease state will not be expressed because a normal dominant gene is also present. A person with a normal and a CF gene will be disease free (i.e. the heterozygous person is phenotypically normal). However, such a person may carry the defective gene on to future generations.

Cystic fibrosis will only be expressed if CF genes occupy both alleles. This is most likely to occur as the result of a marriage between two heterozygous individuals. (About 1 in 20 people in the general population carry the CF gene.) In this instance there will be a one in four chance that any individual, born to these parents, will suffer from CF. There is a further 50% chance that any offspring will carry the disease but be phenotypically normal. Finally, there is a one in four chance that a child will be phenotypically and genotypically normal. Another way of expressing the one in four chance is to say that there should be three phenotypically normal children born for every child who is phenotypically a sufferer. This is the well known 3:1 ratio of monohybrid inheritance.

Other examples of conditions demonstrating autosomal recessive inheritance are albinism, phenylalanine hydroxylase deficiency (leading to phenylketonuria or PKU), sickle cell disease and thalassaemia (causing abnormal haemoglobin).

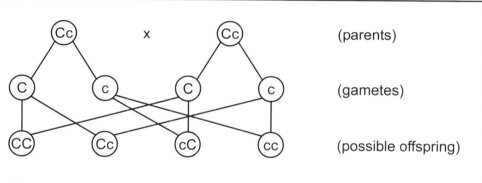

Key

Cc - Individual heterozygous for recessive cystic fibrosis gene, therefore phenotypically normal.

CC - Individual heterozygous for normal dominant gene, therefore phenotypically normal.

cc - Individual homozygous for the recessive cystic fibrosis gene, therefore phenotypically a sufferer. The probability of this in any one pregnancy is 1 in 4.

C - normal dominant gene.

c - recessive gene for CF.

Figure 19.2
The inheritance of cystic fibrosis as an example of monohybrid recessive inheritance. In this case both parents are clinically normal but may have a child who suffers from the disease because they are both heterozygous.

Determination of sex

A female has 44 autosomes and 2 X chromosomes. Males also have the same 44 autosomes with 1 X and 1 Y chromosome. During meiosis the two sex chromosomes separate. This means a female may only produce gametes which contain 22 autosomes and one X chromosome. Men however, may produce sperm which contain 22 autosomes plus an X chromosome, or 22 autosomes plus a Y chromosome.

From this it can be seen that the sex of a fertilised zygote is determined by the fertilising sperm. If the sperm carries an X chromosome the zygote will be female, if it carries a Y chromosome it will be male. As half of the sperm carry an X and half a Y chromosome there are approximately the same number of boys as girls born. In practice baby boy births slightly out number baby girl births but the reason for this in not clear.

Diagram 19.3
(i)   Formation of ova
(ii) Formation of sperm

Note, each germ cell has 46 chromosomes and each gamete 23.

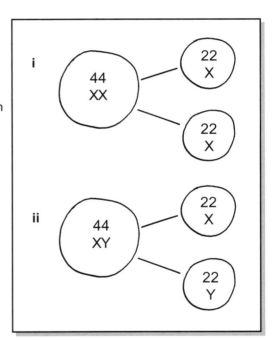

X linked inheritance

Genes carried on the X chromosome may be expressed differently depending on the sex of the individual. This arises because females have two X chromosomes and males only have one. Because of this difference between gene expression in males and females this area is often referred to as sex linkage.

Haemophilia and blue-green colour blindness are the classical examples of traits carries by genes on the X chromosome. However, over 100 other gene defects have been documented on the X chromosome. As with other conditions and

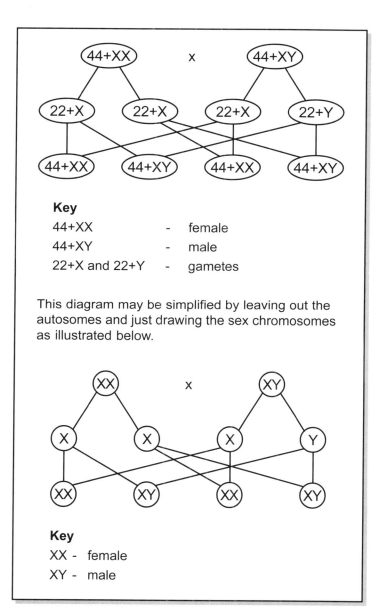

Figure 19.3
Determination of the sex of an individual baby.

characteristics transmitted genetically, sex linked traits may be dominant or recessive.

The reason boys suffer from an X linked trait when girls are usually only carriers is related to the physical size of the X and the Y chromosomes. The X chromosome is bigger than the Y chromosome. However, there are regions of the Y chromosome which have equivalent parts compared to the X chromosome. These regions of the

Y chromosome are homologous and carry the same genes as the equivalent part of the X chromosome. Any genes on the rest of the X chromosome, where there is no analogous part on the Y, have therefore only one chance of being represented in males. If one of these genes is defective on the male X chromosome there is no backup equivalent gene on the Y, so the product of the normal gene cannot be expressed in that male individual.

Diagram 19.4
Diagrammatic representation of the X and Y chromosome to show the X carries more genes than the Y.

(i)   A normal female has 2 genes which may code for the production of factor VIII. This means that if one of the genes is defective there is still a 'spare' copy on the other chromosome.

(ii)   In a male there is only one gene for factor VIII production. The equivalent site on the Y chromosome does not exist. This means that if the gene on the X chromosome is defective there is no backup gene on the Y chromosome to take over production.

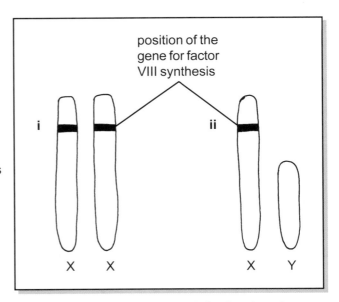

Genetic blood clotting deficiencies occur in about 1 in 4000 live births in the UK. Haemophilia is the best known example and is inherited as a sex-linked recessive characteristic. In order for normal blood clotting to occur 12 factors are required which form the clotting cascade. A person suffering from haemophilia lacks clotting factor VIII. This means the clotting cascade is unable to pass on down to factors VII to I and so the individual suffers from prolonged haemorrhage after injury. In fact physiological blood clotting occurs all the time, for example, normal joint impacts may cause small bleeds into the synovial fluid. If the blood in unable to clot, this may lead to significant haemorrhage into joints, causing pain. Bleeding into a joint is termed haemoarthrosis.

As the defective gene for haemophilia is recessive, an individual can only be a sufferer in the absence of the normal dominant gene. Female carriers of the condition are heterozygous and so are asymptomatic. All the factor VIII needed for normal clotting can be produced from the normal gene on the other X chromosome. In other words, in a female carrier one gene is normal and one is haemophiliac. If a female carrier passes the defective gene on to her female children the child will be phenotypically normal as they will have a normal gene on the X chromosome, which they inherited from their father. If a male child inherits the X chromosome with the normal gene he too will be normal. However if a male child inherits the X chromosome with the defective gene he will suffer from haemophilia.

The result of this is that there is only a one in four probability a heterozygous mother will have a child who suffers from haemophilia. There will be a further one in four chance she will have an asymptomatic carrier daughter. In other words, half of the sons will be affected and half the daughters will be carriers. The symptomatic child will always be male and the asymptomatic carrier will always be female. A female would only suffer from haemophilia if they inherit a haemophiliac gene from each parent. This would mean a man who suffers from haemophilia would have to reproduce with a female carrier, an unlikely scenario.

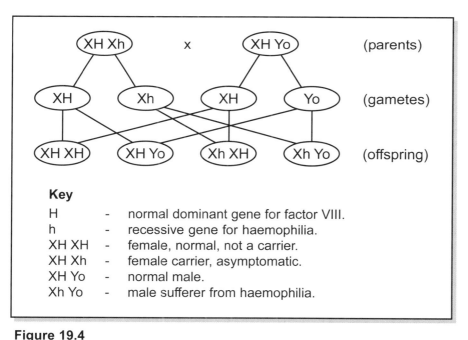

Key

H	-	normal dominant gene for factor VIII.
h	-	recessive gene for haemophilia.
XH XH	-	female, normal, not a carrier.
XH Xh	-	female carrier, asymptomatic.
XH Yo	-	normal male.
Xh Yo	-	male sufferer from haemophilia.

Figure 19.4
Inheritance of haemophilia. Note Yo (Y zero) indicates the absence of the equivalent locus on the Y chromosome (locus means the position a gene occupies on a chromosome).

Twins

There are two forms of twins. Firstly two ova may be released by a potential mother in a single menstrual cycle. If both of these are subsequently fertilised, by two separate sperm cells, two separate zygotes will be formed. These will then develop to term. Such twins may be of the same or different sex. Genetically they are no more closely related than any other siblings. Because these twins formed from two separate zygotes they are referred to as dizygotic (DZ, non-identical or fraternal) twins. The incidence of dizygotic twins is about 12 per 1000 births, although this is higher in African populations.

Other twins develop from a single zygote. Normally, after the first mitotic divisions in the zygote, the daughter cells generated stick together. However, if the early daughter cells physically separate, they will each carry on to develop into a separate embryo. These embryos will then develop into two separate babies. As these children developed from a single zygote they will always be of the same sex; in fact they are genetically identical. Such twins are referred to as monozygotic (MZ or identical twins) and will be clones of each other. The incidence of identical twins is much the same all over the world at about 4 per 1000 births. Very occasionally identical triplets are born.

There is no genetic factor in the likelihood of having MZ twins. However DZ twins do tend to run in the female line. A mother who is herself a DZ twin is 2.5 times more likely to have DZ twins herself than the general population.

Nature or nurture

It is often difficult to determine if a characteristic is genetic, or determined by the environment an individual is exposed to. This is referred to as the nature versus nurture debate. Nature refers to the inborn genetic makeup of the individual, determined from the point of conception. Nurture is the combination of environmental conditions an individual has been exposed to, before and after birth. All thinkers in this area agree that both genetic and environmental factors affect an individual, but often disagree on the relative importance of nature or nurture on a particular characteristic.

Human height is a relatively uncontroversial example of the interaction between genetics and environment. A person may be born with the genetic potential to grow to a certain height. However, if the individual suffers repeated childhood illnesses or is malnourished, they will not attain their genetic potential. Young men in the UK today are much taller than they were 100 years ago. This is not because there has been a change in human genetics, but in human environments. However, no matter how good the environment, a person genetically programmed to be short will never become tall.

Interactions between genetic and environmental factors are also important in the cause of disease. A few diseases have an aetiology (aetiology just means cause) which is entirely genetic, but most are caused by an interaction of factors. Coronary heart disease seems to be partly genetic despite the influence of risk factors which may be modified by life style. Interaction of genetics and environment is also important in conditions such as many malignant diseases, type 2 diabetes mellitus, obesity and probably schizophrenia. People still argue about the relative influences of nature or nurture on intelligence and personality. Homosexuality is another common topic in this form of debate.

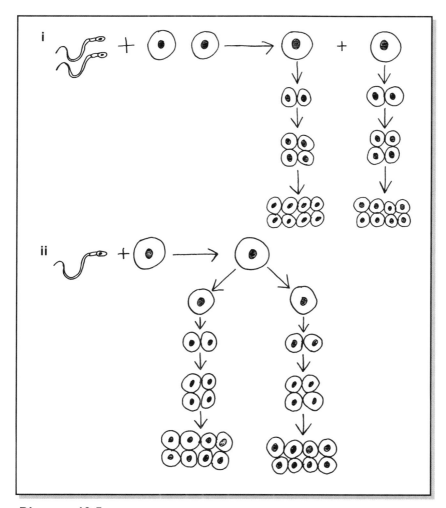

Diagram 19.5

(i)   Dizygotic twins are formed when two sperm fertilise two ova in the same menstrual cycle.

(ii) Monozygotic twins are formed when one sperm fertilises one ovum, then after mitosis the two daughter cells physically separate and develop into two individuals.

Genetic or congenital

Some people get confused between the terms genetic and congenital. A genetic disorder is inherited via the genes. Congenital simply means present at birth. Congenital disorders may be genetic, or occur as a result of developmental abnormalities. Any factor which may cause abnormal fetal development is referred to as teratogenic; thalidomide being a tragic example of this. However, more common substances may also be detrimental as illustrated by fetal alcohol syndrome.

Mutations

A mutation describes any change to the genetic material of a gene or chromosome. Mutations are often caused by harmful factors in the environment such as chemicals or radiation. Usually, a mutation will cause an alteration in the DNA sequence of bases and so result in the synthesis of an abnormal protein product which will contribute to a disease process. At the present time geneticists are aware of 1500 different disease causing mutations which affect the human germ line and which can be inherited and cause disease.

While purely genetic diseases are relatively rare the contribution of genetic factors to almost every disease state is being increasingly recognised. These conditions usually depend on the interaction of many genes and are therefore described as polygenic. The causation of a particular disease is often complicated by the interactions of environmental factors in addition to several genetic factors; this is why many conditions have a multifactorial aetiology.

New developments in genetics

Genetics is a rapidly expanding area of knowledge and, in the longer term, has the potential to affect health care practice significantly.

Mitochondrial DNA

In addition to the DNA found in the chromosomes in the nucleus of the cell it is now known that there is some DNA in the mitochondria which are located in the cytoplasm. The mitochondrial DNA (mtDNA) is found in one circular chromosome and contains 16,500 base pairs probably coding for 37 genes. This is a minute amount of DNA compared to the amount found in the nuclear chromosomes. The genes in the mtDNA partly code for some components of ribosomes, RNA molecules and proteins which are part of mitochondrial structure or function. For example, proteins coded for by mtDNA include the ones which are involved in respiration to produce ATP, i.e. in the process of oxidative phosphorylation. Despite this, the majority of the genetic information to synthesise the1500 or so proteins required to construct mitochondria are carried in the nuclear DNA.

During fertilisation, the sperm contributes 23 chromosomes to the zygote. However, the mitochondria in the zygote all come from the mother. This means an individual's mitochondrial DNA is all inherited from the mother, not the father. So I have my mother's mtDNA which she inherited from her mother, which she inherited from my great grandmother. As a man, my mtDNA will die with me. Because mtDNA is only inherited through the maternal line, it is possible for geneticists to deduce relationships between different people groups alive today, tracing this back to make deductions about our ancestors. This data shows that all races of people are very closely related. The data also strongly suggests that all humans descend from one woman, usually referred to as mitochondrial Eve. This data of course provides powerful scientific evidence against any form of racism; we are all cousins.

Detection of carriers

A carrier has a particular gene which may be transmitted to future generations. In the past it was only possible to infer which genes a person possessed from the phenotype of an individual or their offspring. It is now possible to detect the presence of a number of genes which are not expressed. This is particularly important when studying abnormal genes in people without any clinical features. If the presence of abnormal genes can be identified, the likelihood that a particular baby will be affected can be quantified. Carrier status may be identified in some conditions by clinical examination, physiological studies, microscopy or radiography. Other conditions may be detected by analysis of gene products by biochemists. Finally DNA analysis allows for the direct detection of many individual genes. It is now possible to test for carrier status in most of the common genetic diseases.

Gene therapy

This would involve replacing a defective gene with a normal one. An individual who has a genetic condition would have the defective gene replaced by a healthy one. In theory this would mean the individual was physiologically normal from the time the gene they received was expressed. This technique is referred to as somatic gene therapy as the gene transfer would only affect the body of the individual recipient. Although there would be a change in the genetics of the individual, this would not be passed on to future generations. Somatic gene transfer may be possible in the medium term. Research is currently being carried out into treating cystic fibrosis in this way.

There is a second approach to gene therapy called germ line therapy. This would involve correcting a genetic disorder so the alteration would be passed on to any children. This is controversial as it would be altering the genetic basis of humanity. Due to the complexity of the interaction between genetics and the individual, it is possible this technique could generate totally unforeseen serious problems.

Stem cells

More than 200 different forms of cell combine to make up the human body. Specialist tissues are composed of specialised populations of cells. Generalised cells differentiate into specialised cells via the process of differentiation. A generalised cell which has the potential to differentiate is termed a stem cell. Most differentiation takes place in the first 12 weeks after conception. Stem cells are classified according to the potential to differentiate they possess. Unipotent stem cells are capable of developing into a single specialised cell type. Pluripotent stem cells may develop into a few different but related cell types. Finally multipotent (sometimes called totipotent) stem cells are capable of differentiating into any cell type found in the body.

It is the presence of some forms of stem cells which allows certain tissues to regenerate throughout life. When a stem cell divides it produces two daughter cells; one is another stem cell and the second will develop into the cell type required. Epidermis, gastrointestinal mucous membrane and liver are examples of tissues which continue to have powers of regeneration. Other cell types, such as neurones and muscle cells, have limited or no ability to regenerate after injury or disease.

In the future it may be possible to inject a damaged organ with stem cells which would then differentiate in situ, to regenerate a damaged organ or tissue. The problem is of course, where to obtain the stem cells required. Up until recently it was believed that the only source of multipotent stem cells available were from early embryos (with all of the attendant ethical ambiguities). However, ideally in the medium future it may be possible to harvest stem cells from an adult individual and persuade them to differentiate into the type of cells required. Recently some researchers have claimed to have found multipotent stem cells in adult bone marrow. If true, it could become possible to cure paralysis caused by spinal cord lesions, heart muscle damaged by an MI, dementia, renal failure, diabetes, liver failure and many more diseases. Another possible source of stem cells is from a person's own placenta and umbilical cord which could be frozen just after birth. These structures contain blood stem cells which could be cloned or manipulated, before being re-introduced into the individual in later life.

Cloning

Clones are two or more individual organisms with the same genetic makeup. Monozygotic twins are natural examples of clones. Cloning, as a new development in genetics, broke into popular consciousness with Dolly the sheep. An ovum was harvested from an adult female sheep and the nucleus removed using micro-manipulative techniques. Another nucleus from an adult sheep cell was then implanted into the vacant ovum cell. This new 'combination' cell was stimulated to divide. This can be done by passing a low voltage electrical current through the cell or by treating it chemically. Mitosis then started to produce a new embryo which was then implanted into a sheep uterus where Dolly went to term and was born. Dolly was therefore a second organism with the same genetic makeup as the adult nucleus she was cloned from.

At the time it was suggested that the same technique could be used to clone a human. However, subsequent cloning experiments have produced baby animals with severe deformities. Even if it were desirable, for whatever reason, to clone a human being this would be far too dangerous to contemplate using current techniques.

The human genome project

In 2003, an international collaboration published the genetic make-up of the entire human genome. A genome is the totality of DNA an organism possesses. All of the cells in the body, except mature red blood cells, contain a complete copy of the genome. Genes are composed of DNA arranged as sequences of chemical bases that encode instructions for the synthesis of proteins. These bases are called adenine, thymine, cytosine and guanine. It is the order in which these bases are arranged that determines the nature of the gene, and therefore the product coded for. The bases are analogous to letters which spell out the instructions required to generate a person.

The human genome project revealed that our DNA is composed of 3.2 billion (3.2×10^9) bases arranged in pairs. Despite this massive amount of DNA it has been estimated that only 2-3% of the DNA actually encodes for active genes. It was a surprise to discover that there are only 20,000 to 25,000 active genes. Remaining DNA is non-coding. This may regulate where, when, and in what quantity proteins are synthesised. It may also increase the structural integrity of the chromosomes.

It was found that 99.9% of the genome is identical between individuals, indicating how closely all people groups are related. Despite comprising only 0.1% of our total DNA, this still leaves many millions of base pairs which vary between individuals. These genetic variations are referred to as polymorphisms and account for the differences seen between races and between individuals within races.

While the mass of data relating to the human genome identifies all human DNA, it does not tell us what the genes do, or how they function and interact. In other words the book is written but has yet to be interpreted into practical helpful applications. Physiologically, the genome generates what is now described as the proteome. This encompasses all of the proteins contained in the body's cells. Genes code for proteins, proteins comprise the cells, which in turn make up the tissues, organs and body. Currently around 20,000 genes have been identified which encode known proteins. Many of these proteins have a known structure and function.

Because of this ordering, from molecules to the whole body, some have suggested that a comprehensive understanding of the genome and proteome will provide a total understanding of the molecular basis of health and disease. However, others argue that the body is so complex, it may work as what mathematicians describe as a 'chaotic' system. This does not mean the body is in any way chaotic, but that emergent behaviours and properties are generated by the interactions of billions of molecules, the behaviour of which is not directly predictable.

Eugenics

Eugenics describes a belief that the human race can be improved by selective breeding programmes. This may be done using a positive or negative approach. In a positive eugenics programme, people with desirable characteristics would be selected for reproduction. Negative eugenics would seek to improve the quality of the race by preventing individuals with undesirable characteristics from reproducing. The scientific basis for a belief in eugenics is very weak. In addition there are several problems with eugenics, for example who decides what characteristics are 'desirable' or 'undesirable'. Hitler seemed to like fair hair and blue eyes, but I like any kind of hair and have no preference for eye colour. The policy in western countries seems to be to allow anyone to reproduce who wants to. However, pre-natal screening for conditions such as cystic fibrosis and Down's syndrome often results in abortion. This is, in essence, a negative eugenics programme - which no one is willing to admit exists.

Summary of genetic terms

alleles two forms of the same gene.

autosome a non-sex chromosome, i.e. one of the 44.

clone two organisms with the same genotype.

dipliod a cell containing 46 chromosomes in 23 pairs, the number in a somatic cell.

dominant gene a gene which will be expressed irrespective of the presence of a recessive gene.

DNA deoxyribonucleic acid, the double helix molecule which carries the genetic code.

factor VIII an essential blood clotting factor deficient in haemophilia.

gamete a sperm or egg cell, always haploid.

gametosome a sex chromosome, i.e. X or Y.

gene the coded genetic instructions for production of a protein.

genotype the genes present in the cells of an individual.

germ line cell a cell which gives rise to gametes for the production of the next generation.

haploid a cell containing 23 chromosomes, half the number of a somatic cell.

heterozygous when the two alleles represent different genes on a pair of homologous chromosomes

homologous chromosomes members of a pair.

homologous the same, as in the two members of a pair of homologous chromosomes.

homozygous when the two alleles on each homologous chromosome are represented by identical genes.

locus the position on a chromosome where a particular gene is located.

meiosis reduction cell division, used in the formation of gametes, chromosomal number halved.

mitosis body cell, (somatic) division, chromosomal number maintained.

ovum a female gamete, contains 23 chromosomes.

phenotype the expression of the genotype as seen in the presentation of an individual.

recessive gene a gene which will only be expressed in the homozygous state, (in the absence of a dominant gene).

somatic cell a normal body cell containing 46 chromosomes.

sperm a male gamete, contains 23 chromosomes.

stem cell a generalised cell which is able to differentiate into different cell types.

zygote the fertilised egg (ovum), a diploid cell which mitotically divides to generate the body.

CHAPTER 20

Nutrition and Metabolism

Nutrients

The essential components of the diet are water, carbohydrates, fats, proteins, minerals, vitamins and fibre. These are the seven nutrient groups that are needed for the maintenance of health. A nutrient is a chemical found in food which is needed for body growth, maintenance or repair. A healthy diet must contain a balanced and adequate proportion of these seven dietary nutrient groups. (It can be argued that fibre is not a nutrient as it is not absorbed into the body but remains in the gut.)

Malnutrition

Malnutrition refers to a state of abnormal nutrition. This will develop when there is a deficiency or excess of one or more dietary components. Deficiencies are most likely to occur at times when more nutrients are required such as during pregnancy, lactation, growth or recovery from illness or trauma. Obesity is also a form of malnutrition as too much of some nutrients are consumed. One of the great ironies of our world is that many people suffer from the effects of overeating while others are not able to access enough food to fulfil their physiological requirements.

Carbohydrates

Carbohydrate molecules contain carbon, hydrogen and oxygen and in most healthy diets should be the principle energy source. Carbohydrates include sugars, starch and glycogen and can be classified as monosaccharides, disaccharides and polysaccharides.

Monosaccharide literally means one sugar. They are simple, hexagonal single unit sugars with the empirical formula $C_6 H_{12} O_6$. They include glucose, fructose and galactose. Glucose is mostly derived from digested starch molecules. Fructose is found in fruit and is also a component of cane sugar. Galactose is a component of the milk sugar lactose. All carbohydrates are broken down into monosaccharides during the process of digestion. Like all water soluble nutrients, glucose, fructose and galactose are absorbed into the hepatic portal circulation. From here they are directly transported to the liver, via the hepatic portal vein, where fructose and galactose are rapidly converted into glucose. This means the only sugar found in the systemic circulation is glucose.

Disaccharides are made up of two chemically combined single sugar units. Sucrose is a disaccharide derived from sugar cane or beets. Other examples are lactose found in milk and maltose which is a product of starch digestion. Disaccharides are digested in the gut to give two monosaccharide units; for example, sucrose is broken down into one glucose and one fructose molecule. Lactose yields one molecule of glucose and one of galactose. Maltose is broken down into two component glucose molecules.

Starch is a polysaccharide (poly means many) composed of long chains of chemically combined monosaccharide molecular units. Foods derived from plant sources such as potatoes, grains, bread and cereals are all high in starch polysaccharides. Glycogen is also a polysaccharide but is found in animal tissues and is often referred to as 'animal starch'.

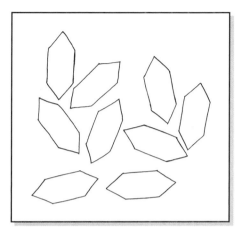

Diagram 20.1
Monosaccharides are simple, hexagonal, single units. All carbohydrates are broken down to monosaccharides prior to absorption. They are small molecules and are readily soluble in water.

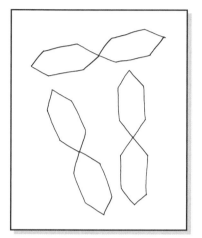

Diagram 20.2
Disaccharides are composed of two monosaccharide units and are highly soluble in water. Sucrose, lactose and maltose are all disaccharides.

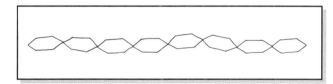

Diagram 20.3
Polysaccharides are composed of long chains of chemically combined sugar units.

Glucose physiology

Glucose in the body may be used in mitochondria for the generation of energy via the synthesis of the energy storage molecule adenosine triphosphate (ATP). Catabolism of glucose by oxygen in the process of respiration produces this form of readily available energy. As glucose may be quickly and efficiently oxidised in the mitochondria it is the body's preferred fuel molecule. People involved in vigorous work or exercise should eat plenty of carbohydrates to supply their energy requirements. Some tissues, particularly CNS neurones, are dependent on a constant supply of glucose to maintain their function. This is why blood glucose levels are homeostacially regulated within a fasting range of 4.5-5.6 mmol/L (millimoles per litre of blood).

If more glucose enters the blood than is required for immediate metabolic processes some of it is synthesised into a polysaccharide called glycogen. This conversion occurs under the influence of insulin. A single glycogen molecule is made up of hundreds of glucose monosaccharide units. Glycogen therefore constitutes a glucose based energy reserve which is stored in the skeletal muscles and liver.

However, the amount of glycogen the muscles and liver are able to store is limited. Typically the liver will store about 90g of glycogen with a further 300g in the skeletal muscles. Once the storage capacity of the liver and muscles is reached, excess glucose is converted by liver cells into glycerol and fatty acids which are then combined to form triglycerides. Once formed these lipid molecules are transported to the adipocytes which are the fat storage cells. Most of the fat stored in the body is in the form of triglycerides. As the volumes of fat stored in adipocytes increases the cells swell. Women usually store reserves of fat subcutaneously resulting in an overall rounded appearance. Men primarily store fat in and around the abdomen. From this it can be seen that eating too many carbohydrates will contribute to obesity.

In addition to these metabolic uses of glucose some is required for the production of certain amino acids which may then be used in protein synthesis.

Fibre

Fibre is also referred to as roughage or non-starch polysaccharide. A lot of dietary fibre is in the form of cellulose derived from plant cell walls. Other substances which act as fibre include lignin, found in the woody parts of plants and pectins and mucilages from fruit. As humans do not produce any digestive enzymes capable of breaking down these substances they pass through the length of the gut chemically unchanged. (Interestingly many animals, such as cows and rabbits, have symbiotic bacteria in their guts which may break down cellulose into absorbable nutrients.)

Fibre is usually classified as water soluble or water insoluble. Water soluble fibre is found in fruits, vegetables, nuts, lentils, peas, oats and barley. Insoluble fibre is composed of cellulose, hemicellulose or lignin and is present in whole grain products such as wholemeal breads, cereals and pasta. Other sources include beans, brown rice, seeds, lentils and maize. With diets which contain large amounts of fibre it is also important to drink adequate amounts of fluids.

Functions of fibre

A healthy diet should contain both the soluble and insoluble forms of fibre. Both forms of fibre decrease the transit time of faecal material through the colon which results in the rapid elimination of any toxins. Insoluble fibre will also absorb and retain water which has the effect of increasing the bulk of faeces.

Increased bulk allows peristaltic movements of the large intestine to efficiently move the stool along and out of the colon. This will prevent constipation and straining to pass stools, reducing the probability of developing piles (haemorrhoids). Fluid retaining and bulk forming effects also reduce the likelihood of colon cancer and diverticular disease.

Soluble fibre delays the absorption of sugars from the GI tract explaining why it is better to eat whole fruits rather than juices. This reduces peak blood sugar levels and therefore insulin secretion. Delays in absorbing sugars decreases the glycaemic index of food which may help to prevent diabetes mellitus type 2. Soluble fibre also slows gastric emptying, delaying the onset of hunger. Some waste cholesterol is excreted in the bile and if water soluble fibre is present this will be absorbed and retained by the fibre. As this cholesterol is retained in the fibre it cannot be reabsorbed into the blood but is passed out in the faeces. This explains why water soluble fibre reduces serum cholesterol levels and hence the development of cardiovascular and cerebrovascular disease.

Glycaemic index (GI)

This index ranks foods based on the effect they have on blood sugar (glucose) levels. Glycaemic index runs from 0 to 100 based on using pure glucose as a reference value of 100. The effects eating other foods have on blood sugar levels are then compared with this. If the carbohydrate component of a food is released rapidly, leading to a dramatic rise in blood sugar levels, the GI will be high. Conversely, if the blood sugar levels rise slowly after eating the GI will be low. Generally, it is better to eat foods with a low GI as this will mean that the carbohydrate component will be absorbed from the intestine slowly, but over a prolonged period. This will prevent insulin levels from rising dramatically and will provide readily available energy for a duration of time. As blood sugar levels are maintained, the appetite will not be stimulated and the person will not feel hungry.

When high GI foods are consumed the blood sugar levels will rise rapidly. This will stimulate the beta cells to release insulin, which will then dramatically lower blood sugar levels again. Once blood sugar levels have been lowered, the insulin present in the blood will carry on working for a period of time. As insulin continues to lower blood glucose levels there will be a so called rebound hypoglycaemia. This means blood glucose levels may be lower than before the high GI food was consumed and the person will feel hungry again. People who want to lose weight are therefore advised to eat more low GI foods.

Proteins

Proteins contain the elements carbon, hydrogen, oxygen, nitrogen and, in smaller amounts, sulphur. They are essential for growth, repair and maintenance of body tissues. Adults require 0.8g of protein per day per kg of body weight. This

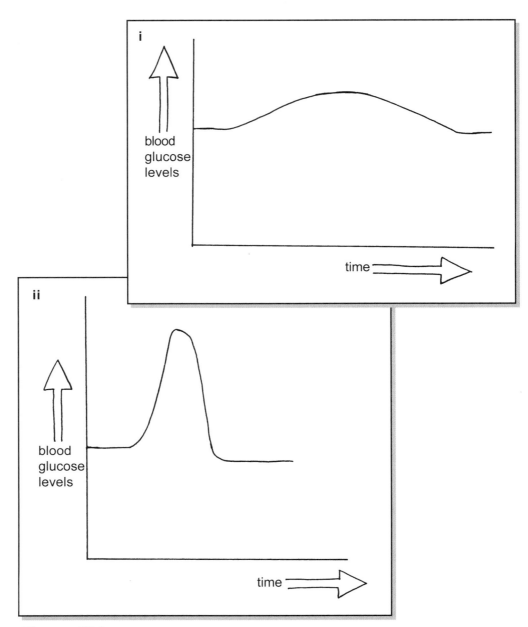

Diagram 20.4
(i)   Low GI foods cause a gradual but more sustained rise in blood sugar levels. This continues to provide energy and reduce hunger for a period of time.
(ii) High GI foods rapidly raise blood sugar levels. As high blood sugar levels stimulate insulin release, levels are rapidly brought back down again. Insulin may lower blood glucose levels below the original values resulting in a rebound hypoglycaemia.

figure may increase to as much as 1.8g per kg per day during periods of metabolic stress such as serious illness or when recovering from trauma, burns or surgery. More protein is also required during pregnancy, lactation and during childhood for growth. Young growing children require proportionally more protein in their diet than adults; for the first 6 months of life children probably need 2g/kg/day. During adolescence protein requirement is about 1g/kg/day, but this seems to increase during 'growth spurts'.

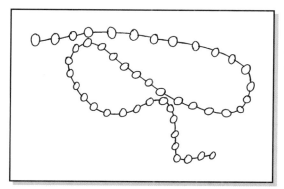

Diagram 20.5
Proteins are composed of long chains of amino acid units chemically combined using peptide bonds.

Amino acids are the subunits of proteins

All proteins are composed of 20 amino acid units which are the fundamental building blocks of proteins. In a protein many amino acids are chemically combined together by peptide bonds. A typical protein molecule is a highly ordered arrangement of around 400 amino acids but some larger proteins may contain many thousands.

Using a process called transamination, the liver is able to synthesise ten of the amino acids from other amino acids. This leaves ten which the liver is unable to synthesise. As the liver cannot synthesise these they are essential components in the diet. These ten must be eaten already formed and so are described as the essential amino acids. As the remaining ten may be synthesised if not present in the diet they are described as the non-essential amino acids.

Proteins are found in a large range of foods derived from animal sources such as meat, eggs and dairy products. These foods will contain all of the essential amino acids and are described as complete proteins. Numerous foods derived from plants also contain proteins. Rich sources include peas, beans, lentils, and soya. Potatoes, rice and cereals also contain protein. However, most plants do not contain all of the required amino acids so are described as incomplete proteins. These protein sources must be eaten in combinations to provide all of the essential amino acids in adequate amounts. Providing a good variety of foods are consumed a vegetarian diet can supply all of the required amino acids. For example, rice combined with lentils can supply all of the essential amino acids.

Protein physiology

Dietary proteins are broken down by proteolytic digestive enzymes into amino acids. Once absorbed these may be oxidised to produce energy or reassembled to form human proteins. Proteins are the fundamental structural components of all body cells, tissues and organs. For example, collagen is an essential structural protein found in most body organs, skin and bone. Actin and myosin are contractile proteins found in muscles. Proteins are essential for the structure and function of neurones. Haemoglobin is a complex protein which transports almost all of the oxygen carried by the blood as well as some carbon dioxide. Digestive enzymes are proteins which are secreted by exocrine glands into the digestive tract where they break up complex food molecules into simpler components prior to absorption. Numerous protein based enzymes are also present within all body cells where they facilitate, regulate and increase the rate of almost all biochemical reactions.

Clotting factors are essential for the normal coagulation of blood after an injury; several of these such as fibrinogen and prothrombin are proteins. Wound healing requires an adequate supply of amino acids to reconstruct cells and tissues. Several endocrine hormones, such as insulin and human growth hormone, are proteins. Albumin is synthesised by the liver and is an essential plasma protein; it generates plasma osmotic pressure which causes tissue fluid to be reabsorbed at the venous end of capillaries.

Proteins play a key role in immune defence against infection. They are essential for the healthy formation and maintenance of the structural barriers of the skin and mucous membranes of the lungs, gastrointestinal and genital tracts. Mucous membranes also secrete mucus. Mucus is a glycoprotein and therefore a supply of amino acids is essential for its normal production. As mucus plays an important role in protecting mucous membranes from infection, protein deficiency predisposes to infection in these areas.

Antibodies (immunoglobulins) are specific proteins produced by lymphocytes to provide acquired, specific immunity. If there is not an adequate supply of amino acids the lymphocytes will not be able to mount a full antibody response to infection. As the body is not able to combat infections effectively, even small infections may develop into more serious, potentially life threatening diseases.

In many poor areas of the world children are at particular risk of protein deficiency. This leads to infections, causing the child to feel ill and anorexic. As a result they will eat even less and be on a downward spiral. This is why it is important to ensure an adequate diet is restored in addition to treating any infections. Part of the immune suppression suffered by patients with HIV / AIDS may be caused by poor nutrition compounding the effects of the disease process.

Unlike fats and carbohydrates, proteins are not stored in the body. When more proteins are consumed than are immediately required, the liver converts the excess amino acids into glucose or triglycerides in the process of deamination. This converts amino acids into chemical forms which can be used by mitochondria or stored as fat. Deamination generates waste nitrogen which forms ammonia (NH_3). As ammonia is very toxic the liver converts it into urea for subsequent excretion by the kidneys.

Lipids (fats)

Fats and lipids are synonymous terms; chemically they contain carbon, hydrogen and oxygen, with proportionately less oxygen than carbohydrates. Fats are composed of subunits called fatty acids. Fatty animal meats contain high proportions of fat and there is some fat even in lean meats. Fats are also found in high concentrations in dairy products and oily fish. Vegetables generally contain much lower amounts of fat but nuts and oils are rich sources. Many processed foods, especially meat products, contain a lot of fat as do many cakes, pastries and biscuits.

Fat saturation

Dietary fat is often described as being saturated, monounsaturated or polyunsaturated. Saturation describes the number of hydrogen atoms attached to the carbon atoms in the fat molecules. In saturated fat all of the carbon atoms use their chemical connections (valencies) to combine with hydrogen atoms; it is saturated with hydrogen. Monounsaturated fats contain proportionately less hydrogen atoms and polyunsaturated fats contain even less.

Animal fats, such as pork, beef and lamb, usually contain fatty acids which are saturated. These saturated fats form solids, like lard or butter, at room temperature. However, not all animal fats are saturated; goose fat, for example, is high in monounsaturated fatty acids. Generally vegetable fats are unsaturated and are liquids at room temperature. For example, sunflower oil is high in polyunsaturated fatty acids (PUFAs) and olive oil contains monounsaturated fats. Fish and nuts are other sources of monounsaturated fat. Unfortunately food manufacturers often choose to saturate the vegetable fats they use forming trans fat. This affects the body in much the same way as saturated fat and is associated with causing arterial disease. Reheating vegetable fats also causes them to become saturated.

Many people eat more saturated fat than they need; this will raise LDL cholesterol and contribute to arterial disease. However, monounsaturated fat and some polyunsaturated fats will raise HDL cholesterol and so have a protective effect on the arteries. Omega 3 polyunsaturated fatty acids are found in fish oils and nuts and have a beneficial effect by lowering serum triglyceride levels. In most Western countries people need to eat less fat overall and reduce the proportion of saturated fat consumed.

Lipid physiology

Lipids may be oxidised to produce energy. While fats release energy more slowly than carbohydrates, metabolism may be maintained over a long period of time by using reserves of fat. The majority of the body's energy reserves are held as fat in the adipocytes. Lipids store large amounts of energy. For example, a typical 70Kg adult will be about 20% fat. This is 14kg of fat which stores 131,600 kcal of energy. It is logical for the body to lay down fat reserves when food is readily available as in a natural situation this will confer a survival advantage during periods of food shortages. If adequate energy reserves are not stored in the body death by starvation would ensue.

Fats are essential for some anatomical structures. All cell membranes contain a lot of lipids in the form of phospholipids. Prostaglandins are lipid based molecules which coordinate several physiological processes and play a major role in generating an inflammatory response. As myelin sheaths are composed mostly of lipids, fats are a major component of the brain and spinal cord. The kidneys are protected by layers of fat which means that trauma to the loins is less likely to result in renal injury. Subcutaneous fat protects underlying tissues and provides a layer of thermal insulation, preventing excessive loss of heat from the body. Significant deposits of fat are found in the omenta, behind the eyes, between muscles and around the genitals. Lipids are needed for the synthesis of lipoproteins and a clotting factor called thromboplastin. Fat soluble vitamins are also absorbed dissolved in fats.

There are two essential fatty acids the body is unable to synthesise; these are linoleic and linolenic acid. These are essential for the synthesis of many other fatty acids which are needed in numerous physiological processes. These two fatty acids are needed in relatively small amounts and are found in vegetable fats, nuts, leafy vegetables and fish oils.

Lipid transport around the body

Most fats are not soluble in water; they are described as being hydrophobic. This means that if fat molecules are to be transported in the water based blood plasma they must first be made water soluble. This is achieved by combining lipid molecules with proteins, synthesised by the liver and intestines, to form combinations called lipoproteins.

Different forms of lipoproteins are classified according to their density; lower density lipoproteins contain proportionally more fat while higher density lipoproteins contain more protein. The lightest form of lipoproteins are called chylomicrons. With a slightly higher density are very low density lipoproteins (VLDLs), then low density lipoproteins (LDLs) while the most dense form are high density lipoproteins (HDLs).

Chylomicrons transport absorbed lipids from the gut

Chylomicrons form in the epithelial cells of the small intestine to transport dietary fat. They pass through the lacteals of the villi into the lymphatic system before entering the venous blood for transport around the body. If there are a lot of chylomicrons in the blood after a fatty meal, the blood plasma has a milky appearance. Such a blood sample is described as lipaemic. Fat transported

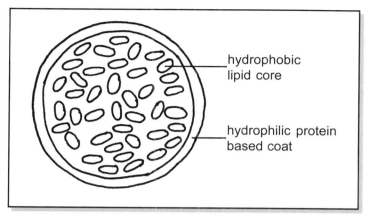

hydrophobic
lipid core

hydrophilic protein
based coat

Diagram 20.6
A lipoprotein is constructed to transport fatty hydrophobic
molecules around the body. The outer core is based on
protein molecules which are hydrophilic and so able to
dissolve in water. Inside is a core composed of numerous
lipid molecules. This means hydrophobic lipid molecules
are not in direct contact with water in the plasma.

by chylomicrons may be taken up by metabolically active cells to be used in
energy production or by adipocytes for storage.

VLDLs

Very low density lipoproteins are formed in the hepatocytes of the liver. They
transport lipid molecules, most of which have been formed in the liver, to adipocytes
and metabolically active cells such as those in skeletal muscle. VLDLs are converted
to LDLs when they transfer some of their triglycerides to fat storage cells.

LDLs

Low density lipoproteins transport most of the cholesterol which is carried in the
blood. Cholesterol is a compound called a steroid alcohol and is needed for functions
such as the formation of bile salts, maintenance and repair of cell membranes and
the synthesis of steroid hormones. LDLs can enter specific cells where they are
broken down so the cholesterol may be used in cellular biochemistry.

The liver is able to produce the cholesterol required by the body and eating large
amounts of saturated fats will increase the amounts of LDL cholesterol the liver is
compelled to synthesise, resulting in increased plasma levels. Excess cholesterol is a
problem as it may be deposited in arterial walls forming plaques of atheroma. Raised
LDL levels will transport too much cholesterol and fat into the blood where it may
lead to atheroma formation. Cholesterol transported by LDLs is called LDL-
cholesterol. As this has the potential to cause atheroma it is often referred to as
'bad' cholesterol.

HDLs

High density lipoproteins remove excess cholesterol from the blood and body cells. This is then transported to the liver where it can be broken down and partly excreted in the bile. As HDLs transport cholesterol which is removed from the blood by the liver, high levels of HDL are associated with preventing the formation of atheroma. For this reason HDL-cholesterol is often referred to as 'good' cholesterol.

Minerals

These inorganic elements all occur naturally on our planet and are essential nutrients. An organic compound contains carbon whereas an inorganic compound or element does not contain carbon. Some minerals such as sodium and potassium are present in the body in the form of ions dissolved in water. As ions have an electrical charge they are described as electrolytes. Other minerals such as iron, iodine and fluoride combine with other elements to form compounds.

Sodium and chloride

Sodium chloride is normal salt. In solution it forms positive sodium and negative chloride ions. Na^+ and Cl^- both act as electrolytes and are the most common ions found in extracellular fluids. A physiological distribution of electrolytes is essential for neuronal transmission and muscle contraction. Sodium also acts as an osmotic regulator in body fluids. Sodium is found in a wide variety of foods from animal and vegetable sources.

Salt is added to so many processed foods, as a preservative and flavour enhancer, that many people eat too much of it. As this may contribute to raised blood pressure it is recommended that no more that 6g should be eaten per day. Salt deficiency is uncommon but may occur when there is excessive sweating over a period of time. Deficiency leads to muscle cramps, low blood pressure and tiredness.

Potassium

This is an essential electrolyte; in the form of K^+ it is needed for normal electrical activity in all nerve and muscle cells. Potassium is the most common positive ion found in intracellular fluid with relatively low levels in the plasma. If the levels of potassium in the blood are too high or low, or change rapidly, cardiac arrest may ensue. This is why we never give bolus intravenous injections of potassium. Potassium is present in most foods but fruit, tea, coffee and crisps are rich sources. Plenty of potassium in the diet is healthy as it helps to lower blood pressure.

Calcium

Calcium is an essential component of bones and teeth. It also functions as an electrolyte in the form of Ca^{2+} ions in solution. Physiologically calcium plays a role in muscle and nerve activity, normal blood clotting, migration of chromosomes during cell division and the movement of motile cells such as phagocytes.

Absorption and utilization of calcium requires the presence of vitamin D. Dietary sources of this vitamin include eggs, cereals, fish, leafy green vegetables and dairy products. Deficiency of calcium or vitamin D in children will lead to rickets. In this disorder there is deficient ossification of growing bones leading to softening and bending of the long weight bearing bones. Severe calcium deficiency may cause tetany which describes increased muscle excitability. In tetany even mild stimuli may cause skeletal muscles to spasm and generate cramps.

Phosphorus

Most of this is found in bones and teeth in the form of phosphate. Like calcium it is needed for bone formation, growth and maintenance. Phosphorus has several other vital physiological functions. It combines with lipids to form phospholipids which are the principle component of cell membranes.

Phosphorus is a component of the sugar-phosphate backbone of the DNA molecule, so plays a vital role in genetics. Phosphate ions are part of the ATP (adenosine triphosphate) and ADP (adenosine diphosphate) molecules which are vital to the way the body stores and utilizes energy. Dietary sources of phosphorus include nuts, fish, meat and dairy products.

Iron

Iron is essential for the formation of haemoglobin molecules in red blood cells and myoglobin in muscle. There are two forms of iron in the diet referred to as haem and nonhaem iron. Haem iron is readily absorbed from the gut into the blood and is derived from the haemoglobin and myoglobin found in fish, meat and offal, especially liver. This is why meat and offal are good for patients with iron deficiency. When the body is short of iron the gut is able to increase the proportion of absorbed haem iron. Conversely when less is required proportionally less is absorbed.

Nonhaem iron is derived from plant sources such as nuts, beans, peas, green vegetables and grains. It is also present in milk and eggs. This nonhaem form is not as well absorbed as haem iron. However, if nonhaem iron is eaten together with vitamin C much more is absorbed. Some iron may be stored in the liver, spleen and bone marrow in the form of a molecule called ferritin.

Deficiency of iron leads to iron deficiency anaemia. Patients may appear pale and complain of tiredness and shortness of breath. Globally iron deficiency anaemia is very common as a result of poor diets and hookworm infection.

Iodine

Iodine is found in seafood and sea salt. It is also present in vegetables, provided there are adequate amounts of iodine in the soil. Iodine is an essential component of the thyroid hormones. If there is not enough iodine in the diet the thyroid gland is not able to manufacture sufficient volumes of thyroid hormones leading to the clinical features of hypothyroidism. As thyroid hormones stimulate metabolism deficiency may lead to weight gain, feeling cold and constipation. Over time iodine deficiency will cause goitre to develop which describes a swelling of the thyroid gland.

Iodine deficiency in childhood will lead to defective bone formation, inhibition of normal growth and brain development will also be affected. If the deficiency is not corrected the outcome is a mentally retarded dwarf referred to as a cretin. Iodine deficiency in early pregnancy impairs normal fetal brain development. These deficiency problems present in many mountainous areas of the world where there is a lack of iodine in the soil. Women of reproductive age in these areas should receive iodine supplements. In developed countries iodine deficiency is no longer seen as it is added to salt.

Fluoride

Fluoride is necessary for healthy teeth. If there is no fluoride in the water supply to an area dental caries become much more likely. Sea fish and tea also contain fluoride. Children given adequate amounts of fluoride in early childhood, when their teeth are developing, enjoy significant resistance to tooth decay.

Other trace elements

Zinc is found in a wide variety of foods including meat, fish, eggs, milk, grains and legumes. It is a component of several intracellular enzymes, insulin and nucleic acids. Wound healing is impaired with even moderate zinc deficiency. Magnesium is used in many enzymes and is needed for normal bone development and neuromuscular function. As it is a component of chlorophyll (the green pigment in plants) deficiency is unlikely. Other essential trace elements include copper, cobalt, selenium and chromium.

Vitamins

Vitamins are organic nutrients essential for normal biochemical and physiological processes. Despite being vital for health the body is unable to chemically synthesise vitamins. This means they must be eaten in the diet already formed. Vitamins are not altered by the processes of digestion and are absorbed unchanged. Today, supplements of all vitamins are readily available. Many vitamins act as cofactors for enzymes. Cofactors are also referred to as coenzymes because they form chemical bonds with enzymes. In order for many enzymes to function they must also have a coenzyme (i.e. a vitamin cofactor) present. Together the enzyme and coenzyme facilitate and regulate biochemical reactions within a cell. These biochemical reactions are essential for normal cellular functions.

Water and fat soluble vitamins

Vitamins may be classified into fat and water soluble groups. Water soluble vitamins dissolve in body fluids and if taken in excess are readily excreted in the urine;

this means they are not stored in the body. Vitamin C, several of the B group, niacin and folic acid are water soluble. Vitamins A, D, E and K are fat soluble. These vitamins must be absorbed dissolved in lipids, which are themselves absorbed from the gut as chylomicrons. As these vitamins are fat soluble they may be stored in the body, the principle site being the liver hepatocytes. Storing vitamins is useful as they may be used by the body during periods when the diet is deficient. However, if an excess of fat soluble vitamins are eaten they will accumulate in the body causing a form of toxicity termed hypervitaminosis.

Vitamin A (retinol)

Vitamin A is present in foods such as liver and dairy products, but it may also be formed from the provitamin beta-carotene. A provitamin is a substance the body is capable of converting into a vitamin. Beta-carotene is found in orange or yellow fruits and vegetables, such as papaya, peaches, apricots and carrots and is also present in green vegetables. High vitamin A intake in pregnancy may lead to birth defects, which is why liver and vitamin A supplements are not recommended in the UK during pregnancy. Pregnant women and children should eat plenty of green vegetables as beta-carotene is not toxic.

Vitamin A is used in the formation of a retinal light sensitive pigment called rhodopsin which is essential for vision, especially in low light levels. This explains why deficiency leads to night blindness which can be rapidly reversed if vitamin A is given. Deficiency will also lead to a condition of the cornea of the eyes called xerophthalmia. In this disorder progressive deposition of keratin on the cornea leads to dryness and thickening. White plaques develop and eventually there is corneal softening, dissolution, infection and permanent blindness. In many poor parts of the world this disorder causes millions of cases of childhood blindness but can be completely prevented by giving vitamin A supplements twice per year.

Vitamin B_1 (thiamine)

B_1 is found in a wide variety of foods including, pork, duck, whole cereals and grains, nuts and pulses. Physiologically B_1 acts as a cofactor for enzymes which are involved in carbohydrate metabolism, generating energy from glucose. This means more is required with increasing intake of carbohydrates.

In some poor areas where the principle food eaten is polished rice, B_1 deficiency may lead to wet or dry beriberi. In dry beriberi there is a degeneration of nervous tissue called polyneuropathy. This causes feelings of heaviness and stiffness in the legs followed by pins and needles with numbness. Later the trunk, arms and brain are affected. In wet beriberi there is progressive oedema, starting in the legs but spreading to the whole body. The myocardium is eventually affected leading to cardiac failure. Young children are at particular risk where serious deficiency will lead to death.

Eating rice with the husks left on and adding legumes and pulses to the diet can prevent the deficiency. In severe cases supplements should be given. Deficiency of B_1 is also seen in chronic alcohol abuse where there is impaired absorption and metabolism, in addition to a reduced dietary intake.

Vitamin B₂ (riboflavin)

This vitamin is found in a wide variety of foods including dairy products, offal, fish, whole grain products, soybeans, green vegetables and bananas. Riboflavin acts as an enzymic cofactor for several oxidative, energy releasing, reactions within cells. Deficiency can lead to fissures at the corner of the mouth referred to as angular stomatitis, inflammation of the tongue and dermatitis of the face. Fortunately, as riboflavin is not broken down by cooking isolated deficiency is uncommon.

Vitamin B₆ (pyridoxine)

Vitamin B_6 includes several closely related compounds and is found in a wide variety of foods including whole grains, nuts, meat, fish and eggs. As vitamin B_6 acts as a cofactor for enzymes involved with amino acid metabolism the daily requirements increase with protein ingestion. While isolated deficiency is rare, B_6 is sometimes used therapeutically for drug induced polyneuropathy, sideroblastic anaemia and premenstrual tension, up to a maximum dose of 10mg per day.

Vitamin B₁₂ (cobalamin)

This vitamin is synthesised by various microorganisms and humans are dependent on animal sources. It is found in milk, eggs, offal, meat and fish, but it is not found in plants. This means vegetarians can meet their requirements from milk and eggs but vegans will eventually become deficient. Only small amounts are needed for normal physiology and the liver may store supplies for up to two years requirements. Synthesis of the nucleic acids, DNA and RNA, are dependent on vitamin B_{12}. As it is also essential for red blood cell maturation, deficiency will lead to macrocytic anaemia. In pernicious anaemia the ability to absorb B_{12} from the gut is lost and these patients depend on injections of the vitamin.

Folic acid (folate)

Found in green leafy vegetables, nuts, wholemeal bread, broccoli and offal such as liver and kidneys. As with vitamin B_{12}, deficiency of folate causes anaemia with the production of abnormally large red blood cells (macrocytic anaemia). An inflammation of the tongue called glossitis may also present. In addition to low levels of folate in the diet deficiency may be caused by excessive alcohol consumption which tends to reduce intake and also impairs utilization.

If mothers have a deficiency of folic acid around the time of conception and during the first 12 weeks of pregnancy there is an increased risk of neural tube defects such as spina bifida. About 5% of the population in the UK have a genetic deficiency of an enzyme involved in folate metabolism. This deficiency leads to high levels of an amino acid called homocysteine which may predispose to fetal neural tube defects and the development of circulatory diseases.

Folate, B vitamins and circulatory disease

High blood levels of homocysteine are an independent risk factor for ischaemic heart disease, stroke, heart failure and thrombosis (formation of abnormal blood clots in veins and arteries). In the UK perhaps 5-20% of the population have levels of homocysteine which are too high. Deficiency of vitamins B_1, B_6, B_{12} and folate will lead to an increase in homocysteine levels, especially in genetically prone individuals. Giving supplements of these vitamins, especially folate will reduce high levels of homocysteine in people who are genetically prone to the problem. Benefits to individuals not prone to high homocysteine levels will not be as significant.

Niacin

Niacin is a collective term for two related compounds called nicotinic acid and nicotinamide. It is found in a wide variety of foods including whole grains, offal and fish; however, it is lost when bran is removed from cereals. In the body niacin is used as a cofactor in many reactions involved in energy production. Deficiency presents in parts of Africa and Asia where maize is the staple food and causes a syndrome called pellagra which literally means rough skin. As metabolism of niacin depends on vitamins B_2 and B_6, deficiency of these can also lead to pellagra.

Pellagra presents with the 3 Ds. Dermatitis develops in areas of the skin exposed to sunlight with redness followed by cracking, thickening and dryness. Diarrhoea is often seen but constipation may also present. In chronic deficiency dementia will eventually develop but before this there may be depression and other psychotic features. As with most deficiencies, supplementation, with restoration of an adequate balanced diet results in dramatic improvement and resolution.

Vitamin C (ascorbic acid)

Vitamin C acts as a coenzyme and is also essential for formation of the structural protein collagen. It is present in all fresh fruit and vegetables such as broccoli, potatoes, oranges and tomatoes. Unfortunately the vitamin C content of foods is reduced by cooking and leaches out when vegetables are left in water. Deficiency of vitamin C is seen in babies who are fed on boiled milk and people with a diet low in fruit and vegetables. Smokers probably use up vitamin C more rapidly than non-smokers and so will be more prone to deficiencies.

Deficiency initially causes weakness and muscle pain. Continued deficiency leads to a syndrome called scurvy, which presents with features mostly caused by deficient collagen formation. Gums become swollen and tender and the teeth loosen. As wound healing depends on the synthesis of new collagen this process is inhibited. There may also be anaemia and bleeding caused by impaired blood coagulation.

Vitamin D

Most vitamin D is synthesised from a form of cholesterol when skin is exposed to sunlight. This is then converted by the liver and then the kidneys into the active form of the vitamin. Vitamin D may also be eaten in oily fish, eggs and liver. Vitamin D is needed for the absorption and normal metabolism of calcium and phosphorus. As these elements are essential for bone health, vitamin D deficiency will result in rickets in children and osteomalacia in adults. Both of these diseases are caused by inadequate bone mineralization.

Recent research has also shown that children who are given extra vitamin D in early life are partly protected from developing diabetes mellitus type 1. This indicates that even sub-clinical vitamin D deficiency in early childhood (which is not severe enough to cause rickets) may predispose to developing this form of diabetes. In adults lack of vitamin D is now considered a possible risk factor for the development of cardiovascular disease. Adults who have low blood levels of vitamin D (below 30 nanograms per ml) have been suggested to have a 60% increased risk for cardiovascular disease.

Vitamin E

Vitamin E is actually a collective name for eight related compounds. Plant sources provide vitamin E including green leafy vegetables, wheat germ, seed oils, soya, cereals and nuts. Most of the biological effects of vitamin E result from its antioxidant properties which aid in the maintenance of the health of all body cells. As vitamin E acts to stabilise cell membranes adequate amounts are needed to maintain the health of red blood cells. If there is a serious deficiency many red blood cells will become fragile and break up leading to haemolytic anaemia. Vitamin E also maintains the health of parts of the spinal cord and peripheral nerves explaining why deficiency may lead to neurological defects. The daily requirement for vitamin E will increase with the amount of polyunsaturated fatty acids eaten.

Vitamin K

This vitamin occurs in two forms. Vitamin K_1 is derived from food sources including green leafy vegetables, soya, rape seed and liver. Vitamin K_2 is synthesised by bacteria living in the colon. Vitamin K is used as a cofactor in the liver for the synthesis of several blood clotting factors. This means if there is a deficiency of vitamin K there will also be a deficiency of clotting factors potentially resulting in haemorrhagic complications. As a consequence there may be excessive bruising and blood will be slow to clot after an injury.

Newborn babies may be particularly prone to vitamin K deficiency as they do not yet possess the gut bacteria which synthesise the vitamin. Little vitamin K is transferred across the placenta from mother to fetus and breast milk only contains low concentrations. These factors may lead to a deficiency which can cause haemorrhagic disease of the newborn. In the UK all parents are advised to allow their neonates to be injected with some additional vitamin K to prevent this deficiency. Anticoagulant drugs, such as warfarin, inhibit vitamin K activity explaining why the vitamin may be used as an antidote. Three of the proteins present in bone forming osteoblasts are also dependent on vitamin K acting as a cofactor. Lack of vitamin K may therefore theoretically affect the development of rapidly growing bone in childhood.

Free radicals and dietary antioxidants

Some highly reactive oxygen radicals are generated as by-products of normal cellular metabolism. These include superoxide, hydrogen peroxide and other free radicals. A radical is part of a molecule which is very reactive, and will seek to oxidise or chemically react with other molecules in the area. For example, if part of a DNA molecule is oxidised by a free radical, it will become a different chemical compound; there will have been a change to the affected part of the DNA. A change in the genetic material (i.e. the DNA) of a cell is a mutation and may result in defective cell division, cell death or even malignant change. This means free radicals have the potential to disrupt the normal processes of cell physiology and division. Free radicals have been implicated as contributory factors in several disease processes including cancer, cardiovascular diseases and some degenerative disorders such as Alzheimer's disease. They may also contribute to the general ageing process. During many disease processes, inflammation and as a result of smoking the amount of free radicals generated increases.

Cells defend themselves against free radical damage by using antioxidant enzymes and antioxidants such as selenium, vitamins A, C and E, beta-carotene and flavonoids. Dietary sources of antioxidants are mostly from fruit and vegetables. While clinical trial data is currently lacking for the effectiveness of antioxidants, it is overwhelmingly likely that the following advice is beneficial. Maintain a high intake of fruit and vegetables; eat these as a meal, rather than with a meal. This is very likely to reduce the risk of cardio and cerebrovascular disease. Eat nuts as these are a good natural source of vitamin E. As flavanoids are natural free radical scavengers we should eat foods which are naturally rich in flavanoids. These foods include tomatoes, red grapes, apples, onions and carrots. Tea is a good source of flavanoids but coffee is not. Limit red meat consumption and eat less animal and saturated fats.

Metabolism

Cell physiology is generated and maintained by numerous biochemical reactions which are constantly occurring throughout the nucleus, cytoplasm and cell membrane. Some of these reactions generate energy or synthesise chemicals used within the cell, others produce substances which are exported to be used in the local tissues or other parts of the body. Metabolism describes all of the chemical reactions which occur within the body. It is the sum total of body chemical activity.

Energy units

One calorie is defined as the amount of heat needed to increase the temperature of 1 gram of water by 1°C. As a calorie is a relatively small unit it is more usual to discuss kilocalories, equal to 1000 calories. A kilocalorie (kcal) is sometimes written as a Calorie (using the upper case C). When a particular food item is described as containing 100 Calories, this is referring to 100 kilocalories.

Energy may also be measured in joules (J), a thousand being a kilojoule (kJ). One Calorie (i.e. one kcal) is equal to 4.186 kJ, and 1 kJ is equal to 0.239 Calories. When used in the body 1g of carbohydrate generates 4.1 calories (17.1kJ) of energy while 1g of protein will supply 4.3 Calories (18kJ). Fat is the most energy rich food type and on average yields 9.4 Calories (39 kJ) per gram. While alcohol is not a nutrient it does produce 7 Calories (29 kJ) per gram. One unit of alcohol is 10 mls of pure ethanol and contains about 8g of alcohol, producing 56 Calories (232 kJ). This means alcohol has the potential to cause obesity but is not nutritionally useful. Many alcoholic drinks contain additional carbohydrates which will further contribute to obesity.

Use of energy by the body

Basal metabolic rate (BMR) describes the amount of energy the body must use to maintain vital, life giving physiology, such as maintaining brain activity, liver biochemistry and heart beats. Most adults have a basal metabolic requirement of about 1800-2300 Calories per day. In addition to this basal metabolic requirement additional Calories will be needed for digesting food and activities such as moving. People who are sedentary may only need an additional 500 Calories per day. However, very physically active people may need an additional 2000 or even 3000 Calories per day.

Light exercise such as walking slowly will use less than 4 Calories (i.e. 4 Kcals) per minute whereas moderate exercise such as brisk walking or playing table tennis will use between 4 and 7 Calories per minute. Hard or vigorous exercise such as running, brisk cycling or walking quickly uphill will use more than 7 Calories per minute.

If the environment is cold the body will also need additional Calories to produce heat in order to maintain normal body temperature. In warm environments such as those around the tropics, heat loss from the body is less than in colder climates. This means more energy is required in colder environments compared to warmer ones. Oxygen consumption is a good guide to how much energy the body is using as oxidizing different fuel types yields similar amounts of energy per unit of oxygen consumed.

Catabolism and anabolism

Some chemical reactions break complex biological molecules down into simpler molecules. These reactions are described as catabolic and usually result in some energy being released from the chemical bonds which were present in the complex molecule. Other reactions are anabolic, these combine several smaller molecules to produce a larger molecule, for example, a group of amino acids may be combined to produce a protein. Anabolic reactions use some energy in order to form the new chemical bonds.

Metabolism during fasting

Provided adults are able to drink water they may survive without eating for over two months. However, if they exercise more energy stores will be used up and this time will be less. A few hours after the last meal blood glucose levels will drop; this will be detected in the alpha cells of the pancreatic islets which respond by releasing glucagon. This endocrine hormone converts stored supplies of glycogen into glucose. Once the supplies of glycogen have been used up, blood sugar levels will again fall. This results in less insulin being released from the beta cells and so blood insulin levels will be low.

Low levels of insulin in the blood allow stored fat to be broken down into fatty acids and glycerol. This increases the plasma concentration of these lipid molecules which may be used by many body tissues to produce energy.

Low levels of insulin also cause protein synthesis to be inhibited and protein catabolism to be increased. This will break down complex proteins into simple amino acids which may be used for energy production or converted into glucose in the liver by the process of gluconeogenesis. Clearly, the use of fat reserves and protein, largely from skeletal muscles, mean that weight will be progressively lost.

When fats are metabolised by body cells, in the absence of carbohydrates, ketone bodies are produced from fatty acids by the liver hepatocytes. The advantage of this is that ketone bodies may be used in the process of energy production by several types of tissues. Ketone bodies are actually two forms of organic acids and acetone. The acetone gives the breath a characteristic smell like 'pear drops'. Over time these ketone bodies will build up leading to ketosis. As ketones are not produced when fats are metabolised in the presence of carbohydrates it has been said that 'fats can only be burned in the fire of carbohydrates'.

Regulation of food intake

Body weight is determined by the balance between food intake and energy expenditure. This is consistent with the first law of thermodynamics which points out that energy can neither be created or destroyed. If a person consistently uses more Calories than are consumed they will lose weight. Conversely, consumption of more Calories than are used will cause the progressive development of obesity. This takes time to develop as a person must consume 9400 kcal more than they use in order to store one kg of fat.

Eating is controlled by two centres in the hypothalamus. Hunger comes from the hunger (or feeding) centre. In animal studies this can be electrically stimulated causing eating. However, if this area is destroyed an animal will stop eating altogether. The satiety centre generates a sensation of satisfaction to prevent further eating. If this is electrically stimulated an animal will stop eating.

Hypoglycaemia (low blood glucose) stimulates neurones in the hunger centre while inhibiting those in the satiety centre. This means a hypoglycaemic person will have the desire to eat. This explains why people often feel hungry after a period of exercise. Alcohol also lowers blood glucose levels and so stimulates appetite. Feedback from the stomach further modifies the desire for food. When the stomach is full and distended impulses from the vagus nerve reduce activity in the hunger centre and therefore suppress the desire to eat.

Longer term regulation of body weight is partly controlled by a hormone produced by adipocytes called leptin. When adipocytes contain adequate reserves of lipids they secrete leptin into the blood which stimulates the satiety centre. This could explain why many people are able to maintain a relatively constant weight over years and decades.

Early life nutrition, breast is best

Breast feeding should always be recommended to mothers as the best possible nutritional start in life for their children. There are also benefits to the mother such as reducing the possibility of developing breast cancer in later life. Breast milk is sterile so will not introduce any infection into the child. This is a vital point in areas where the water supply is not pure as infection can lead to vomiting and diarrhoea. Unfortunately such gastroenteritis remains the leading cause of death in young children in the world.

Newborns have small stomachs; they can only consume liquids but have a high nutrient requirement. Breast milk contains the ideal mix of water, fatty acids, amino acids, lactose, vitamins and minerals that the baby needs. As the child develops the composition of breast milk changes to give them precisely what they need, when they need it. If a child is hungry and takes more milk, more will be produced to meet the increased demand.

The first fluid secreted during breast feeding is colostrum. This yellowish fluid contains water, protein, minerals, vitamins and important immune proteins. These immune proteins include antibodies called immunoglobulin type A (IgA) which protects the child from gastrointestinal infections. The essential nutrients in colostrum are enough to meet all of the infant's nutritional needs until mature milk is produced. Breast milk is the only food and drink a baby needs for the first 6 months of life. Solid food should not be introduced into the diet before 4 to 6 months of age because the infants feeding abilities and digestive system are not mature enough to process it. Breast feeding can be continued as long as mother and baby would like it to. It is probably best to continue breast feeding for the first year of life with solid foods being progressively introduced after 6 months. In poorer countries breast feeding is probably desirable for the first 2 years of life.

Children who are breast fed are less likely to develop childhood atopic disease. This common disease has three possible manifestations; asthma, food allergy and a skin rash called atopic dermatitis. The risk of developing childhood atopic disease is increased if babies are fed cows milk during the first 6 months of life. It is therefore important that children under the age of 6 months are not given cow's milk, or milk formulas containing cow's milk. Much better to feed the mother on cow's milk and for her to feed the child with her own breast milk. Breast feeding also partly protects against several diseases of later life probably including obesity, diabetes, heart disease and even some cancers.

Final Thoughts

My congratulations if you have managed to work your way through the whole book. My hope and intention was that the book would be read as a whole, rather than dipped into, as would be the case with larger texts. The intention was to produce a 'learning' book, rather than a 'text' book. I hope this has worked and that you have been able to learn some of the principles of physiology, and ways of thinking, as well as some of the necessary facts.

As I was writing this book I had to constantly refrain myself from using the word 'amazing'. As I thought about the concepts, the beauty and intricacy of the body often hit me again in a fresh way. The vascular complexity of the liver is amazing, the overlapping triple fractal pattern of the lungs is amazing. How come all of the holes in the base of the skull are in just the right places to allow blood vessels and nerves to pass through?

Despite the complexity it seems to me that systems are as simple as they could be, in order to perform the functions required, there does not seem to be any unnecessary complexity.

Of course we should learn all of the science, anatomy and physiology we can, but as humans always leave space for wonder and admiration.

Three thousand years ago a man called David addressed his Creator with the following words;

I praise you because I am fearfully and wonderfully made;
your works are wonderful,
I know that full well.

Index